The Living Mirror

THE LIVING MIRROR

Images of Reality in Science and Mysticism

Paul Marshall

Samphire Press
1992

First published in 1992
by Samphire Press
BCM Samphire, London WC1N 3XX

British Library Cataloguing-in-Publication Data.
A catalogue record for this book
is available from the British Library.

ISBN 0 9519925 0 3

Printed by Antony Rowe Ltd.,
Chippenham, Wilts.

CONTENTS

ACKNOWLEDGMENTS

I would like to thank the many individuals who, directly or indirectly, have enabled this work to take shape. I am particularly indebted to family and friends for their support. Specific thanks go to Alan Hunter and Peter Annett, who commented on the first draft, and to Catherine James, who valiantly checked the final manuscript. All errors are, of course, my own.

INTRODUCTION

In *The Living Mirror,* I explore an idea that has been widespread in scientific thought, namely the belief that a *physical world* of particles and forces lies behind our experiences. The idea of a physical world has provided answers to age-old questions about the nature of reality, and has influenced the way we understand ourselves and our relationship with the world. As we shall see, however, an interpretation of reality based on physical theory alone proves to be unsatisfactory, for a preoccupation with the physical aspects of the world excludes much that is significant in experience and may lead to an impoverished account of human nature. This is not to say that physical theory must be abandoned or is in need of extensive modification—over the centuries, scientific endeavours have been extraordinarily successful in bringing to light the workings of nature, and research continues to yield theories of greater descriptive accuracy and predictive power. But as a comprehensive image of reality, physical theory is inadequate and needs re-casting into a form that can do greater justice to our rich, living experiences. The aim here, then, is to place the theories of physics within a more comprehensive understanding, to appreciate the value and relevance of physical theory but to integrate it into a broader picture.

The approach we follow calls upon two important ideas. The first is the belief that we should consider *experience* in its fullness and diversity, and avoid a narrow focus on just certain contents or types of experience. The second is the idea of an *external world,* a domain of existence that is credited with supporting our various experiences. According to the idea, familiar experiences make up only a small part of the total reach of existence—our colourful, buzzing, booming streams of consciousness show something of the world, but are like waves or surface currents on a great ocean of existence whose depths are hidden from us.

A major stimulus for the notion of an external world has been the recognition that sense-organs have a profound influence on the contents of experience. The recognition leads to theories of perception in which sense-organs act as channels from the external world to our experiences, feeding the latter with information collected from the external environment. The sensory content of experience is taken to *represent* or *reflect* some aspects of the external world, and may therefore be likened to the play of images in a reflecting surface: sense-experience acts as a *perceptual mirror* in which we meet *images* of the external world. In this mirror of sense-experience, we encounter the world partially and indirectly, for the range of information conveyed through the sense-organs is limited.

The idea of the external world is important to us here because it has assumed a special form in realist scientific conceptions of the world: it is often believed that our sensory experiences represent a real external world, conceived as a physical world of atoms, molecules, forces and fields, open to investigation through careful observation, theory-construction, and experiment. Scientific theory, like sensory experience, is then regarded as a mirror that reflects the physical world. In re-evaluating physical theory in the present work, I aim to regenerate this unsatisfactory *physical mirror* into a theory worthy of our living experiences, into a *living mirror* in which, perhaps, we may come to see ourselves more clearly.

Speculations about the existence of hidden forces or a hidden world behind experience have not been confined to the scientific enterprise. To cover the various notions of a hidden world in several areas of thought, I have chosen the word *substratum,* meaning a basis, foundation, bedrock. The substratum, whether philosophical, religious, scientific, or psychological, is commonly held to support or influence our experience, although at times its existence has become a matter of dispute.

In the long history of philosophical and religious thought, there have been numerous references to unseen influences and hidden realities. According to Plato, an eternal background of Forms lies behind the moving image of time, and sensory experience provides some knowledge of the background, albeit a shadowy knowledge. St Paul believed that we now see darkly and in part, as if with a looking-glass, but one day we shall see a *spiritual* reality directly, "face to face." In recent times *psychological* notions of a substratum have become prominent, expressed in concepts of an unconscious mind or unconscious mental processes. In Western thought, physical and psychological conceptions of unseen influences have tended to displace religious or supernatural accounts. The story of hypnotism, for instance, shows interpretations that shifted from the supernatural to the psychological, via a physical stage. At first regarded as a form of exorcism, then as a magnetic influence, hypnosis came to be viewed as a social-psychological phenomenon, an example of the power of suggestion, and provided evidence for the existence of a hidden psychological world underlying experience, the *unconscious.* It takes only a little introspection for us to gain the impression that our conscious mental life draws on a hidden reservoir of memories and unconscious thought processes. Sentences, images, memories and feelings appear in the stream of experience, yet their origins remain largely obscure to us. Our ability to recall events suggests that there is a store of memories feeding into experience. This vast store of memories is not present in our ordinary experience, but contributes to it, weaving a rich, temporal complexity into the moment.

The idea of hidden substrata raises several questions. Are there indeed such things, or is it presumptuous to go beyond experience and talk about unseen influences or substrata? If there are substrata, what might they be? How can we know about them? What role do they play in supporting our perceptions, feelings and thoughts? In what ways might the various substrata described in the physical sciences, in psychology and in religious thought be related to one another? Is there just one substratum, which the various disciplines have approached from different angles, highlighting different facets, or are the various conceptions of substrata irreconcilable with one another? If we hope to reach a satisfactory understanding of the world and ourselves, we shall have to address such questions.

In Part I of *The Living Mirror*, special attention is given to the relationship between our experiences and the physical world described in the quantitative sciences. This relationship, which has been discussed in philosophy and psychology under the title of *the mind-body problem,* has received much attention in the past, and continues to arouse interest. In recent times, the problem has intrigued neuroscientists who concern themselves with the relationship between physical brain-states and consciousness, and computer scientists who wonder whether their information-processing machines can truly simulate living beings. Another angle on the mind-body problem has arisen in modern physics, for some interpreters of quantum theory have argued that the 'consciousness' of the observer has a role in deciding the outcome of physical processes.

The mind-body problem, as I present it here, refers to the difficulty of linking our experience with an underlying physical world. I consider the physical world, as usually conceived in the sciences, to be much too limited to fulfil the role of substratum for our rich and varied experiences. A splash of scarlet, a taste of lemon, a feeling of love, a comprehension of meaning—how are these experiences to be related to a physical world totally devoid of colour, taste, feeling and meaning? In Chapter One, I outline my understanding of experience, and introduce the religious, psychological and physical concepts of a substratum. In Chapter Two, the influential notion of the physical world is discussed. It is helpful to consider the roots of the idea in ancient atomism and seventeenth-century mechanical philosophy, for we see how the substratum became a moving skeleton of matter through a theory of qualities that assigned only structure and motion to the external world.

After noting traditional approaches to the mind-body problem in Chapter Three, we address the problem through a form of idealism in which additional qualities are admitted into the substratum in order to supplement the qualities of structure and motion. In effect, the substratum is made *experiential,* and the idea of an experiential substratum encourages a broad study of the relationship between the substratum and our familiar experience. Several topics are raised that would not ordinarily occur side-by-side, for certain physical, psychological and religious areas of interest come together when we look at the substratum in a broad, experiential light. In Chapter Four I attempt to explore some of the farther reaches of experience in the hope that these may furnish clues about the nature of an experiential substratum. It is a problematic area to explore, and only a few steps are made towards its elucidation.

To proceed further, we concentrate on an issue that is perhaps most open to investigation given our current state of knowledge, namely the form that space and time might take in an underlying world. The topic brings out an important aspect of the mind-body problem, namely the connection between the *psychological time* of our familiar experiences and the nature of time in the substratum, whether considered to be the *physical time* of the sciences or the *eternity* of some philosophical and mystical strands of thought. Part I concludes with an outline of philosophical and psychological ideas related to the notion of an eternal substratum.

In Part II we settle down to an exploration of space, time and motion in the physical world. Chapter Six begins the investigation with a discussion of time as the fourth dimension of the four-dimensional space called *spacetime.* Here the problems of determinism and free will, as well as the relationship between transient time and static spacetime, call for some attention. To develop the subject further, we examine the implications of *the relativity of motion:* the motions of bodies are always observed relative to one another, not relative to an underlying substratum. In fact, an absolute physical substratum proves elusive. These considerations in Chapters Seven and Eight take us to the modern relativistic understanding of space and time.

Space, time and motion had long been fundamental in the physical sciences, but were largely taken for granted until the beginning of the twentieth century, when Einstein's theory of relativity brought about a fundamental re-evaluation. Relativistic theory, with its surprising results and its notion of an absolute spacetime, is highly pertinent to a discussion of the substratum, and Chapter Nine is devoted to Einstein's special theory of relativity and the absolute substratum of Hermann Minkowski . Chapter Ten presents Einstein's general theory and its application to the spatio-temporal structure of the universe. In Part II we look at the question of relative motion in considerable detail, including the special and general theories of relativity, so that the reader will be in a good position to understand the speculations that follow in the remainder of the book.

These speculations in Part III address a problem that arises when relativistic theory is accepted alongside the idea of a substratum with familiar spatio-temporal characteristics. To overcome the problem, the account assumes a highly speculative flavour, but takes us across ground that has been explored before in philosophical and religious thought. We arrive at a holistic view of the substratum, a substratum in which the constituent parts are intimately connected with one another. In Chapter Fifteen we conclude with a brief account of the second major surprise of twentieth-century physics, the quantum theory, in order to gauge whether our speculations in the preceding chapters may have any bearing on the apparently holistic behaviour of matter at the quantum level.

The Living Mirror will be of interest to the student and specialist in the disciplines of physical science, philosophy, history of ideas, religion and psychology, and to the general reader with a basic grounding in these areas. The subject-matter will be of particular concern to those intrigued by connections between modern science, psychology and religion, and to scientists and students of science who look for the *meaning* of physical theory. It should also appeal to those who find themselves involved in the restoration of fallen images, whether images of self, world or human nature.

The content is neither abstruse nor burdened with mathematics, but an elementary knowledge of physical science and psychology will assist the reader. The philosophical and scientific discussion is not technically rigorous, but I have aimed to present the subject-matter at a level that takes into account the many complexities and uncertainties. A glossary is provided for those unfamiliar with philosophical terminology, and certain words with specialised usages in the book are included here.

But now let us begin the renovation of the mirror, commencing with a look at *experience,* a starting-point that philosophers of diverse persuasions have considered the proper beginning for a study of the world.

PART I

The Scope of Experience

1. EXPERIENCE

All are familiar with experience. It may be a warm summer evening or a crisp winter morning, a gentle love or a rush of fear, a pang of hunger, a regret, a glow of excitement. To lose sight of the richness and diversity of experience leads to barren abstractions, and it is essential that we consider its nature and content in some depth.

EXPERIENCE

The word *experience* sometimes means familiarity with a person, thing or activity over a time, or the practical knowledge gained through such familiarity:

> "I have more life-*experience* than you, so do what I say and find yourself a job," chides the exasperated parent. The youngster's efforts, alas, are thwarted by a lack of job-*experience.*

Experience can also mean a special period or occurrence: "The trip to the seaside was a great experience." However, the meaning we are particularly concerned with here refers to the world of sights, sounds, tastes, emotions, thoughts. An attempt at a brief definition is likely to be a mere substitution of words. For instance, a definition might be worded: "experience is the apprehended." We then have to consider how 'the apprehended' is to be defined, and soon we find ourselves embroiled in difficulties.

An alternative to searching for a pithy definition is to point to a few instances of experience. I might suggest that you stroll through a forest, walk along a busy street, go for a swim, relax in a bath, taste various foods, plan an activity, and so forth, to gain fresh perspectives on experience. Or I might provide verbal descriptions of experience, covering typical varieties selected from the range of familiar waking and dreaming states, and from a host of less common states. The descriptions might include accounts of specific experiences or they might be lists of *categories.* In thinking about experience we categorise it, placing features with similarities into groups. Typical categories include colours, sounds, emotions, thoughts, actions, processes, materials, animals, people.

Sometimes the term *experience* has been used in a narrow sense, to cover only the sensory content of experience, excluding thoughts and emotions. Study is then confined to the sensory contents of experience and to the world of objects and processes that these are taken to represent. Experience as a whole may be unappreciated or devalued, viewed as a subjective mental domain of little importance, tied loosely to an objective, real physical world reflected in our sense-experiences. Several thinkers have opposed the narrow conception of experience and its tendency to encourage dualisms: notable among these have been the phenomenologists, following Edmund Husserl (1859–1938), and also the philosophers William James (1842–1910), John Dewey (1859–1952), and Alfred North Whitehead (1861–1947). For instance, Dewey expressed his dissatisfaction with the narrow focus on the sensory content of experience:

> ... "experience" has often been restricted, both by those who called themselves empiricists and by their opponents, to certain arbitrarily selected activities of the organism to which a privileged rôle is assigned. For experience has, notoriously, been limited to the activities of sense-organs—or rather to their products, called sensations, or, better, sensa. In the light of the history of culture, one can find reasons for this peculiar arbitrary selection. But, viewing the matter impartially, the limitation can only be regarded as one of the most extraordinary and uncalled for errors human belief has ever indulged in....[1]

The "error" restricts study to a few aspects of experience and encourages a problematic split between the *physical* and the *mental,* between *body* and *mind,* a "bifurcation of nature" as Whitehead called it.[2] The relationship between the mental and the physical will become the focus of attention in Chapter Three. There we shall approach the mental-physical divide by taking experience as primary, but not in the way Dewey advocated. He was not disposed towards the idea of a substratum, neither physical nor religious, for he viewed such ideas as escapist yearnings for a perfect world beyond our world of imperfection.

The task of describing experience is by no means straightforward. Some states of experience are poorly explored, and may be quite inaccessible, or difficult and dangerous to study. Even if we restrict ourselves to the range of experience we meet in fairly ordinary waking and dreaming states, we are still confronted by difficulties. The very act of focusing attention on some facets of an experience may alter the experience in significant ways.

EXPERIENCE AND TIME

A most elusive characteristic of experience is its *transience,* its fleeting quality. Vehicles speed along a road; a bird wings through the sky; dried leaves eddy in a gust; a song unwinds its melody.

One way of thinking about the temporal is to suppose that everyday experience is made up of a succession of momentary experiences, experiential 'nows'. Memories in the current experience tell us that there have been earlier experiences, and that objects have had earlier states, have continuities or histories stretching into the past. Time seems to involve a moment-by-moment change of experiential contents, one experience following another. Now, *time* is a word with many uses and implications, and it will be advisable to find terms that refer specifically to the experiential sense of momentary change. *Transience* and *Becoming* are possibilities, and there are several metaphorical expressions available, such as *flow* or *flux*. The river, ever-changing, sweeping everything along in its current, has often served as a symbol of time.

We do not distinguish individual moments: the succession of momentary experiences in our transient experience appears to be seamless. William James used the expressions *stream of thought* and *stream of consciousness* to indicate the unbroken continuity of experience, and the latter phrase has become the popular expression in literary contexts for the technique of depicting the flow of thoughts, memories and feelings.

In a world of calendars and clocks, there are conventional ways of thinking and talking about the temporal. Experiences or events are said to occur at certain times. A mathematical time of point-instants is constructed, with each successive experience assigned a position in the order of time-moments. There is an additional assumption that the content of each experience—of each moment of the 'stream'—is temporally distinct from the content of preceding and succeeding experiences. Is this conceptualised time, abstracted from experience and of undeniable value in the organisation of our lives, truly in agreement with our experience? Some have thought not, and we shall return to the question in Chapter Six.

CONTENTS OF EXPERIENCE

Experience is far from being a monotonous uniformity. It is exceedingly diverse in content, containing many parts or *sub-experiences*. Categorising the parts can be a dull exercise, and will detract from the living, integrated complexity of experience if the experiential parts are taken to be independent, elementary constituents from which the overall experience is constructed. However, the exercise can be valuable if it sharpens our understanding of experience, and brings across the variety and interrelations of experiential contents. An appreciation of the contents of familiar experience will prove to be particularly useful when we come to examine a special type of mystical experience in Chapter Four. The exercise also highlights the common ways in which classifications are made, and brings out some natural distinctions between contents. These natural distinctions have been amplified into the problematic dualisms opposed by Dewey, James and others, the dualisms of mind-body and spirit-matter. Because *experience* is a central concept in this work, it is important that it is discussed in some detail. However, the reader is advised to pass rapidly over the following sections on a first reading (resuming at the section entitled *Consciousness),* or leave them aside completely for the time being, to avoid immersion in too many details. The important points to appreciate at this stage are: (a) experience is not some 'shadowy nothing', but a complex, transforming unity of sensations, emotions, thoughts, notions of self and other; (b) in our experiences, various sensations are organised into a structured, spatial field of *extended* objects (flowers, trees, clouds, houses, people, and so forth), objects with shape, relative size and position.

1. *Sensations*

Some types of content appear to be quite basic, for they are not obviously divisible into further experiential constituents. There is, for instance, the category of *colour,* and the sub-category *blue,* with further distinctions into types of blue, such as *azure, ultramarine* and *cerulean.* Other common categories of basic experiential constituent include sound, odour, taste, warmth, cold, pain. The basic constituents have often been called *sensations,* because they are intimately linked with the sense-organs and sensory receptors. Traditionally, five senses and five corresponding types of sensation were described (sight, hearing, taste, smell, touch), but nowadays it is appreciated that the five-fold classification is limited. There are many skin and body sensations additional to the pressure sensation of touch, such as temperature, pain, muscular and visceral sensations. Furthermore, the classification was based on human experience and human sense-organs. Other organisms exhibit a great variety of sensory receptors, but the nature of the sense-experiences corresponding to these receptors is inaccessible to us. We may wonder, for instance, how electroreception (the sensitivity to electrical currents found in some aquatic species) is experienced.

Psychologists have pointed out that sensory experience involves many implicit interpretations. The term *perception,* contrasted with *sensation,* brings across the idea that much interpretation is involved. Ambiguous figures provide striking examples of the interpretation involved in visual perception, and one

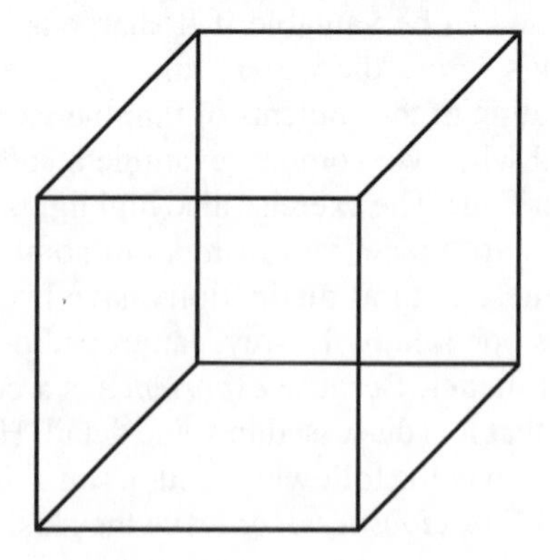

Figure 1.1. The Necker Cube.

of the best known of these is the *Necker Cube.* We interpret the lines of the two-dimensional figure drawn on the flat sheet of paper and see a three-dimensional cube. Furthermore, when the figure is looked at intently, the orientation of the cube may be found to reverse, the foreground becoming the background, and vice versa. A re-interpretation of the two dimensional figure has taken place.

2. *Emotions, Cognitions, Volitions*

Like sensation and perception, the contents placed in this category often come under the study of psychology. It is difficult to find a general name for the contents of this category, but for convenience we could refer to them as *personal psychological constituents,* because they are associated with the notion of a personal self that thinks and feels: "I am happy", "I am hungry", "I am thinking". As we shall see, these constituents are very closely implicated in the experiential self and its social world, and in the temporal span of the moment.

Dividing-lines between the sub-categories of personal psychological constituents can be very diffuse, for most constituents involve something of the others. *Emotion* or emotional feeling is one such category, and covers many kinds of experience including anger, fear, love, jealousy, sadness, joy, peace. Emotions very often have body-sensation components—feelings of warmth or cold, of muscular tension or relaxation, visceral sensations, skin sensations, sensations of facial and body posture, and so forth. William James is noted for his suggestion that emotions *are* patterns of body-sensation: "... we feel sorry because we cry, angry because we strike, afraid because we tremble ...."[3] Emotions also involve a behavioural component, being associated with actions and patterns of behaviour, and more recently the importance of *cognition* in emotional experience has been stressed.

Cognition is another complex facet of experience, and refers to the thinking, understanding, evaluating, representing aspects. It can be difficult to describe some of the cognitive constituents of experience, such as understanding and meaning. What does an experience of thinking involve? It might include a pattern of body sensations, muscular tension and body movements, emotions, the appearance of new thoughts, the connection of previously unconnected images. Thought in the form of *inner speech* or *inner images*, composed of sound and colour respectively, is a cognitive constituent of experience, and is used to *represent* other facets of experience. The differentiation of experience into parts is greatly aided by language. Words and pictures, which are themselves parts of experience, are used to represent other parts of experience. Thus, contents in experience can be represented by other contents in experience.

Another sub-category distinguished in the past was *conation,* which refers to the willing, seeking, decision-making facets of experience. Again, this is not a distinct category, but involves sensation, emotion, cognition and activity. Other sub-categories include hunger and thirst experiences, which again are not distinct from the other sub-categories.

Many of the personal psychological constituents have a temporal orientation. This is clear in our thoughts about past, present and future experiences, in our interpretations of current experience using memories and anticipatory ideas, and in many emotions and volitions that imply a concept of time, such as hope, boredom, expectation, desire, nostalgia, will, purpose. Many emotions and needs have a future-orientation that can motivate activity.

Attempts have sometimes been made to analyse the world into elementary, experiential building-blocks that are supposed to be the key to understanding complex, composite phenomena. These approaches are sometimes termed *elementarism* or *psychological atomism.* One variety, in Western philosophy and psychology, is *associationism:* complex psychological activity can be expressed as the linking or association of simple ideas or sensations, or complex behaviour can be regarded as the association of simple reflex actions. Another significant instance of psychological atomism in modern times was Wilhelm Wundt's (1832–1920) approach to psychology, which came to be called *structuralism.* Wundt hoped to isolate the elements of experience through a strictly defined, experimental method of inspection, termed *introspection.* The chemistry of the nineteenth century provided inspiration—matter had been described successfully in terms of elements and the combination of elements into compounds. By analogy, Wundt supposed that the elements of experience, the sensations and emotional feelings, combine into compounds of experience.

Psychological atomism has been criticised by a number of psychologists, including William James and the proponents of the *Gestalt* philosophy, a school of psychology founded by Max Wertheimer (1880–1943) that took a holistic attitude towards the psychology of perception and learning. In *The Principles of Psychology,* James argued:

> No one ever had a simple sensation by itself. Consciousness, from our natal day, is of a teeming multiplicity of objects and relations, and what we call simple sensations are results of discriminative attention, pushed often to a very high degree. It is astonishing what havoc is wrought in psychology by admitting at the outset apparently innocent suppositions, that nevertheless contain a flaw.[4]

Similarly, the Gestalt psychologists maintained that the analysis into elements is insufficient—the organisation of parts creates something more than a collection of isolated parts. The compound is more than its constituent elements, and "the whole is greater than the sum of the parts."

3. *Extended Objects*

Some contents of experience have the characteristic of *extension*—a tree, a house, a road, a mountain, for instance. In visual experience, patterns of colour make up a *spatial* field of such extended objects. Experiences of extension and spatiality are also supported by body sensations, including touch sensations, and involve the implicit perceptual interpretations we have noted above (see the discussion of Figure 1.1.).

Extended objects have characteristics of shape, relative size and relative position within the spatial field of extended objects. Extension and relative position occur in three spatial directions—the spatial field is said to be *three-dimensional.* It is also notable that the experience of spatial arrangement occurs *from* a central location: the extended objects in experience are arranged about a *centre-of-experience.* We see a world of objects extending into the distance from our central location.

Objects have some continuity through experience, continuing in approximately the same form over a series of experiences. Objects appear, undergo various changes to their shapes, positions, qualities of colour, textures and temperatures, disappear from experience, reappear, break up, transform into other objects.

As we have already noted, there has been a significant tendency to divide the world into at least two *distinct* domains. In modern times, a common form of the split has been the separation of sensations, emotions and cognitive features into one world, perhaps called *mind,* and the extended objects into another, conceived as representations of an underlying *physical world* of extended objects. Psychologists have generally studied the *mind* part, with further specialisations into schools, some focusing on emotions, others on perceptions or cognitions. Scientists are typically assigned the *physical* domain to study, the domain of extended objects. Psychologists who wish to be regarded as scientists in this narrow sense may be tempted to renounce any interest in the mental domain, and focus exclusively on the physical activities of animals, on their physiology and behaviour. This tendency was expressed in extreme form in the *philosophical behaviourism* of John Broadus Watson (1878–1958) and his followers.

4. *Self and Other*

A fundamental categorisation of experience is based on the concepts of self and other:

(a) The self: *Myself.* The experiential self, a highly complex, transforming integration of sensation, personal psychological constituents (emotion, cognition), extended object (body), and behavioural activity. *Myself* consists of my emotions, my thoughts, my thoughts about myself, my body, my actions.

(b) The other: *Yourself.* Other beings equivalent to 'myself', who are ascribed experiences, and are related to as experiencing beings. 'Yourself' appears in experience as an integration of 'your body', 'your voice', 'your communications', 'your actions', etc.

(c) The other: *It.* Extended objects or bodies that are not ascribed experiences. Typically, this category includes such things as stones, metals, chairs.

The infant develops the sense of being a self, distinct from other selves, and learns ways of relating to itself, other selves and inanimate objects. How this differentiation comes about in the cognitions, feelings and behaviour of the infant is an important subject of study for developmental psychologists. Psychologists of different schools have tended to focus on different contributing factors, but the process is likely to involve an interaction of several influences. These include relationships with established selves, such as parents, siblings, teachers, and peers, the unfolding of inborn psychological capacities and personality traits, the intellectual discovery of the experiential world, biological development, and so forth. There is no doubt that relationships with others, with the society of other selves, are of fundamental importance in the establishment of self. The point was made at the beginning of the twentieth century by Charles Horton Cooley (1864–1929), a student of John Dewey, in the theory of the *looking-glass self* or *reflected self.* We form impressions of ourselves and come to judge ourselves through the responses of others and the ways we interpret this feedback.

> Each to each a looking-glass
> Reflects the other that doth pass.[5]

The reactions of others act as mirrors: children come to see themselves as they imagine others to see them. The theory of the socially constructed self was developed further by George Herbert Mead (1863–1931) and the symbolic interactionists, a school of social psychology.

The extended object of *myself* is my body, and is located around the centre-of-experience. It contains the special parts called sense organs, which have a deep connection with the contents of experience. The *my body* at the centre-of-experience is unlike other extended objects in experience, including the bodies of others. The body of *myself* is not merely an extended object described in my visual and tactile experience—it is also associated with body sensations, emotions and cognitions, and responds to volitions. I feel pain or pleasure in my body, but not in yours, nor in the tree or stone. I experience my emotions in their fullness, but not yours, although I may be able to deduce what you are feeling from your expressions. I decide to move my arms and they move, but objects other than my body do not respond directly to my volitions.

Many thoughts and emotions organised into the experiential self involve a *concept* of self. William James made an important contribution to the study of self-psychology by distinguishing two facets of the self in experience, the subject and the object, both of which are parts of experience:

> ... personality implies the incessant presence of two elements, an objective person, known by a passing subjective Thought and recognized as continuing in time. *Hereafter let us use the words* ME *and* I *for the empirical person and the judging Thought.*[6]

The 'I' is the self as subject, the self *regarding* the self, consisting of self-reflexive cognitions and emotions, "the judging Thought" in which the 'I' occurs as subject: "I see ...", "I feel ...", "I think ...", "I experience ...". The 'Me' is the self as object, the empirical self. This is the self *regarded by* the self, comprising features taken to be part of self or very closely related to self: "My emotions, my body, my thoughts, my possessions." The self-as-object has received considerable attention in the self-concept theories of recent psychological thought. An individual's self-concept consists of thoughts and feelings held about self, including simple descriptive content, self-evaluations, and evaluations one supposes others hold. Positive, realistic self-evaluation or self-esteem has been recognised as an important condition for well-being.

William James's distinction between two facets of the experiential self—the object and subject contents—leads us to an important matter of terminology, namely the use of the word *consciousness.*

CONSCIOUSNESS

In this work, the term *experience* takes centre-stage, and I make efforts to avoid another term frequently employed in philosophical and psychological contexts. This is the word *consciousness,* which often turns up in discussions of the mind-body relation, being used as a substitute for the term *mind,* and contrasted with *body* or *matter.*

Consciousness has been used in several different ways. For example, it may refer solely to sense-experiences, or may be applied to experience in general, including inner speech and feelings, as well as to sense-experiences. *Consciousness* may also refer to experiences of self-reference or self-awareness, acts of *self-consciousness,* equivalent to James's "judging thought" described above. In this case, consciousness refers to those thoughts and feelings that acknowledge a self and its activities, ascribing to the self an existence, an identity, thoughts, feelings, volitions. Some have argued that all animals have consciousness, if consciousness means a stream of sense-experiences, but that only some kinds of animals have consciousness if the term refers to the cognitions and feelings of being a self.

There is one use of the term *consciousness* that requires our special attention: *consciousness* may be regarded as an observer existing *outside* its field of observation. William James developed his idea of the self as subject and object into a rejection of this supposed *consciousness* that observes or experiences the *contents of consciousness.*

> That entity is fictitious, while thoughts in the concrete are fully real. But thoughts in the concrete are made of the same stuff as things are.[7]

The placing of the self firmly in experience, both as subject and object, is a move towards bridging the conceptual split between self and the rest of experience. Of course, the conceptual distinction is a vital and proper differentiation of our ordinary experience, and disturbances to it can be extremely disruptive. However, the distinction between self and other may be exaggerated into a split in which the self is regarded as *outside* the experiential world. Consciousness is then regarded as an observer outside experience, an unexperienced observer who watches experience pass by. In psychological thought, this hypothesised observer may be equated with the I or self, or in religious thought with a personal soul or a transcendental Self. To avoid this implication, and the general confusion surrounding the word *consciousness,* I have preferred to base the discussion on the term *experience.* When I use such terms as *experiencer, experienced,* and *to experience,* I refer to parts of experience and conceptual relations between parts of experience, and do not mean to suggest that there is an observer beyond experience.

OTHER MINDS

We assume that others have experiences, that other human beings are experiencing beings. The philosophical uncertainty over this assumption has been called the *'other minds' problem.* Traditionally, an argument by analogy has been used to support the idea that some other bodies have experiences, are *conscious.* Your behaviour and your bodily structure, with its sense-organs, nervous system and brain, are so similar to mine that I assume you have experiences similar to mine. Through familiarity with my own experiences, I can have some idea of what you may be experiencing. I can try to imagine what experience may be like for you, perceptually, cognitively, and affectively. When bodies are not very similar to my body, it is less clear to me whether they are associated with a flux of experiences, and I have a poor idea of what the associated experience might be like. How am I to decide whether animals, plants, or minerals have experiences, are experiencing beings? The behaviour and structure of many animals suggest that they do have experiences, which include pleasure-pain sensations, emotional feelings and the self-other distinction. The situation is less clear with simpler life-forms, such as plants, bacteria and viruses, or with objects that would normally be regarded as lifeless or inanimate, such as rocks and metals. The commonly-held, mixed view—that some *not-myself* bodies have experiences, whilst others do not—lies between the extreme positions of *panpsychism* (all objects are associated with experience) and *solipsism* (there is only my stream of experience). Few philosophers would be inclined to the latter position, with its unattractive ethical implications. Not quite as extreme as solipsism, but approaching it, is the view that only human beings are experiencing beings.

The other minds problem follows from the *privacy* of experience—each experiences a single stream, not many streams together. Existential thinkers describe the isolation or aloneness of the individual. Experiences are unique and cannot be fully shared. We can discuss our experiences and form representations of the other's experience in our imagination and feelings, but we are barred from the actual experiences.

There is, however, a good deal of overlap in experience. We might, for instance, discuss an apple that appears in our separate experiences and agree that it is coloured red. If we disagree, we may be able to account for the differences in terms of our particular perspectives and other circumstances of observation. The experiential objects will not be exactly the same, but will be fairly similar. In contrast, the emotional and cognitive facets of experience—parts of the experiential self—are confined to each flux. We do not share a feeling in the same way that we share the visual experience of the red apple. The shared facets—sensations organised in patterns of extended objects—are called *outer, external* or *public,* in contrast to the *inner, internal* or *private* facets of experience. Strictly speaking, however, both the private and the public facets of our experiences are private, and we may wonder whether there is anything outside our private experiences that is truly public, something common to all that enables each one to have similar experiences.

BEYOND SENSE-EXPERIENCE: THE SUBSTRATUM

The experiences of others are outside one's own experience. Are there other aspects of existence that are not *directly* encountered in one's own experience? It has often been claimed that there are such aspects. These hidden existences are held to influence our experience or support it in some way, enabling our experiences to occur and contributing to their content.

In the introduction, we noted that the study of sense-perception can lead to the idea of a hidden world behind experience. Other considerations have also encouraged the idea. For instance, a natural phenomenon might defy simple explanation and initiate a search for hidden processes and causes. Consider the enigma of the magnet. Magnetic interactions are sufficiently uncommon and striking to catch the attention and arouse puzzlement. A magnet and an iron nail draw together. Two magnets attract or repel each other, depending on their relative orientation. Yet there is no visible contact between the bodies: it seems that an invisible influence operates across the intervening space. We cannot see or touch the influence, but the attraction between the magnet and the iron hints that there is one. Magnetism suggests to us that the workings of nature are not fully revealed in our sense-experiences.

In the infancy of Western science, Thales of Miletus observed the power of a magnetic mineral to move a piece of iron, and according to later accounts, he concluded that all things are full of gods. Two and a half thousand years later, the puzzle of magnetism inspired another major contributor to the development of science. Albert Einstein (1879–1955) recounted that, as a child of four or five, he was shown a compass by his father. The behaviour of the needle impressed him greatly, for it suggested to him that "something deeply hidden had to be behind things."[8] As we shall see, Einstein's insights into electromagnetic phenomena were to revolutionise twentieth-century scientific understanding.

Between Thales and Einstein, the understanding of hidden influences at work behind experience had changed considerably. From the seventeenth century, the idea of the material or physical world came into prominence, a world of particles, forces and fields that underlies our familiar experience. The magnet exerts its influence through a magnetic field, or through particles that 'carry' the magnetic force. In a physical interpretation of the external world, we would suppose that the book we see and read now is a sense-representation of a material or physical book, a sensory image of the book in the perceptual mirror of our experience. The external, physical book, made of atoms and molecules bound together by physical forces, is not known to us directly, but we meet it indirectly through its perceptual image.

RELIGIOUS SUBSTRATA: HIDDEN REALMS AND BEINGS

Aspects of existence outside familiar experience have been conceived in many different ways and have been given a variety of functions in the scheme of things. In religious thought, the unseen aspects have been viewed as spiritual realities, substances, beings and realms, and have assumed a great variety of forms over the millennia of religious speculation: magical forces, nature-spirits and powers, souls, heavens and hells, the many gods of polytheistic religion, the One God of monotheistic religion, the *logos,* the Absolute of religious monism, the Godhead. I shall refer to such hidden aspects as *religious substrata,* meaning to indicate that the substrata have been entertained in thought of a religious nature. It is difficult to find appropriate terms with which to discuss these issues, for such words as *religious, spiritual, mystical,* are often vaguely applied, or tend to stir up antagonistic and defensive reactions that obstruct discussion.

The idea of a religious substratum has often fulfilled an explanatory role, providing a means of comprehending the world of experience. The religious substratum has been viewed as the creative source of the material world, a provider of organisation and harmony, a web of unseen forces acting in nature and man, a resource to be utilised in the control of nature, a giver of meaning or purpose to life, a source of consolation, a basis for codes of behaviour. It has also provided a framework for interpreting experiences outside the familiar range, including unusual dream states, meditative and mystical states, trances, and disturbed states. Conceptions differ in the level of involvement attributed to the religious substratum in guiding, sustaining or influencing the course of events. For instance, God might be placed completely beyond the world, fully transcendent, having no involvement, except perhaps by way of being the creator. Alternatively, God may be regarded as separate from the world, yet also continuing to support it. Or God may be viewed as immanent in the world, perhaps through an identity between the world and God *(pantheism)* or through the world constituting a part of God *(panentheism).* The relationship between the religious substratum and humankind is a similar matter. Again, God may be envisaged as distant, an external God separate from its creatures, or as indwelling within the constitution of the soul, psyche or personality. The understanding of the relationship between the religious substratum, man and nature is bound up with questions of good and evil, the existence of suffering in the world, and man's free will and independence. There is the problem of explaining why a God, conceived as an ultimate good or source of good, has engaged in creating and supporting a world rife with suffering and cruelty. There are, of course, many ways of approaching the question. Beings opposed to the benevolent God may be held responsible for the undesirable features of the world, or it may be argued that the darker facets of experience are inevitable if creatures are to have any real self-identity, free will or the capacity to develop.

A PSYCHOLOGICAL SUBSTRATUM: THE UNCONSCIOUS

Two specialised conceptions of the substratum have undergone significant development in recent times and have absorbed some of the functions previously ascribed to the religious substratum. One is the concept of an underlying *physical world,* which shall be examined in detail in the next chapter. The other is the notion of the *unconscious,* or of *unconscious processes,* discussed in some psychological theories. Experience, we have noted, can be divided into various categories and these tend to become the subject of specialised study. The notion of a physical world has emerged primarily as an underlying basis for the extended objects and their transformations, whilst the unconscious has provided a substratum for perceptions and the personal psychological constituents, our thoughts and emotions.

The idea of a psychological substratum—unexperienced processes and contents that underlie the psychological constituents of experience—has become a commonplace in twentieth-century thought, but the essential notion has been around for a very long time, frequently as part of philosophical speculations on the nature of the religious substratum. An example is Plato's (427–347 B.C.) Theory of Forms: the Forms or Ideas are eternal universals that participate in the world of transitory sense-experience. The acquisition of knowledge involves the recollection *(anamnesis)* of ideas that the soul has forgotten—the unconscious is made conscious.[9] A notable instance in Eastern thought is the concept of the *alaya-vijnana* in the idealist *Yogacara* or "mind-only" school of Mahayana Buddhism, which flourished in the sixth century A.D. The *alaya-vijnana* is a "storehouse consciousness" from which everything derives, including the personal psychological contents.

In Western thought, the idea of the unconscious has undergone major developments over the last four hundred years, with the existence of unconscious processes and contents increasingly recognised.[10] The concepts of mind and self have thus come to embrace two areas, the conscious and the unconscious. The conscious experience of each individual is supported by an unconscious or a system of unconscious processes, and beneath the experiential self, we can infer that complex processes are at work. Accordingly, we can imagine that there is a self-system spanning conscious and unconscious existence.[11] In line with the earlier comments on consciousness, the unconscious aspects of self are not to be regarded as an observer who watches experiences, an external consciousness. The presence of unconscious activities influencing and perhaps interacting with conscious experience leads easily to the idea of a self outside our familiar experience. This self, however, is not a contentless observer, completely separate from experience, but is part of the self-system, with definite content. We shall return to the substratal aspects of *self* in Chapter Four.

Various notions of an unconscious have arisen to address specific aspects of our experience, and have in consequence tended to be partial. The unconscious substrata of perception and cognition were some of the first to be discussed in modern Western thought, and are receiving a great deal of attention now that information-processing ideas have come into fashion, stimulated by the emergence of computer science. The perceptual and cognitive unconscious covers a number of processes, such as the implicit interpretation occurring in perception, the storage and retrieval of memories, language acquisition, learning, and processes involved in thinking, such as the representation of experiences as concepts and the organisation of these into patterns of concepts, or *schemas*. It seems that we have unconscious maps or schemas of the experiential world, built up over many experiences. These include schemas of:

ourselves, including our bodies,

others we know, including our relationships with others,

stereotypes (the politician, the male, the English, the extravert type),

spatial and temporal maps (the route to work, plans for the future),

procedures (cooking a meal), actions (typing, playing the piano),

stories and scenes (typical situations or patterns of events).

The unconscious patternings of information are complex, inner images of the world that we draw upon for the interpretation of current experiences. They enable thought to go beyond the content of current sensory input, to work independently and creatively, to plan, to explore possibilities and impossibilities, to imagine, to fantasise. The creative activity of the unconscious is shown to great effect in dreaming—whole streams of experience are generated which are largely independent of the current sensory input. The processes whereby experiences are stored, conceptualised, schematised into patterns, and worked upon in thought processes, are unconscious, as are the forms in which the experiences are stored. The cognitive unconscious is replete with vast amounts of cross-referenced information and teems with unconscious thought processes that are connected in some way with conscious thinking—inner and outer speech, trains of visual images, body language, play.

The existence of unconscious contents and processes has also been inferred from aspects of experience that are not exclusively or mainly cognitive. In the eighteenth and nineteenth centuries there was some interest in the unconscious aspects of emotion, instinct, will, motivation, creative imagination, dreaming, hypnosis, mental and physical illness. In the atmosphere of nineteenth-century German idealism, romanticism and nature philosophy, the unconscious took on a universal flavour, with the personal rooted in both the unconscious organic processes of Nature and the spiritual ground of the Absolute.[12] This development prepared the way for a wide-ranging presentation of philosophical, religious and psychological aspects of the unconscious, in Edmund von

Hartmann's (1842–1906) *Philosophy of the Unconscious* (1868). In the early decades of the twentieth century the fortunes of the idea were mixed. On the one hand, the unconscious was banished from academic psychology in the behaviourist purge of anything deemed 'private' or 'unscientific'. On the other hand, a highly specialised concept of the unconscious became extremely influential: Sigmund Freud's (1856–1939) theory and treatment of psychological disturbance. Freud distinguished between the *preconscious,* consisting of temporarily unconscious contents that are easily made conscious, and the *unconscious,* in which contents are actively withheld from experience by processes that are themselves unconscious. He painted a picture of the unconscious as a battleground where primitive sensual and aggressive instincts are in conflict with controls internalised by the infant from parental and social expressions of authority. Unacceptable urges and memories of unpleasant experiences are repressed, banished to the unconscious as a defence against intolerable tension and anxiety. From here they exert a powerful and potentially disturbing influence on the personality and on social relationships. Freud saw evidence for repressed material in hypnotic phenomena, slips-of-the-tongue and dreams, and the original aim of the therapeutic process of psychoanalysis was to make the unconscious conscious, to bring insight into, and respite from, psychological conflict.

Since Freud's first steps to map out in detail the structure and processes of the unconscious, theories of the unconscious in the therapeutic context have developed in a variety of ways. For instance, in Carl Gustav Jung's (1875–1961) analytical psychology, the psychopathology of the unconscious is only part of the story. Harking back to broader notions of the role of the unconscious and the nature of man, Jung maintained that Freud's conceptions were much too limited: the unconscious is also a source of personal growth, creativity and religious experience, and is capable of autonomous functioning behind the scenes to promote the development of personality, the process of *individuation.* According to Jung, the unconscious loses its personal aspect at deeper levels, where it becomes universal or collective, a repository of inherited qualities, instincts and archetypal patterns built up over a long history of biological evolution and cultural development.

The psychological substratum is clearly very complex, for the activity of unconscious processes can be inferred from many of the 'psychological' facets of experience, and attempts to map unconscious structures and processes will have to take the range and complexity into account. If we go along with the notion of a psychological substratum, we are faced with a number of difficult questions. What is its nature? How does it interact with our experience? In what ways is information stored and worked upon in the unconscious? In the present climate of thought, the unconscious is most likely to be interpreted as a collection of structures and processes existing in a purely physical substrate—

biochemical and neuronal processes, or information-processing routines performed on the hardware of physical brain-structures. In other words, the psychological substratum is viewed as a special region of the physical world, and constitutes a physical interface between the rest of the physical world and our experience. The unconscious is then identical to structures and processes in the physical brain. On the other hand, theories that postulate unconscious fears and desires, or unconscious *meaningful* activity, might be taken to imply that the unconscious also has experiential elements, experiences of feeling and understanding that accompany our ordinary experiences but are not directly a part of them, and are therefore unconscious with respect to our ordinary experience. We shall return to the subject of unconscious experience in Chapter Three.

THE PROBLEM OF KNOWLEDGE

Questions about the nature of the substratum, whether considered in religious, psychological or physical contexts, are *metaphysical* and *ontological* questions. They are difficult to answer because the substratum is not directly presented to us. The existence of a substratum is inferred, and not known for certain. Thus, another type of question arises, an *epistemological* question: can we have knowledge of the substratum and can we even be sure that there is one? We shall take a brief look at the problem of knowledge, before proceeding to one highly influential answer to the ontological question: the physical world of scientific realism.

There may be good reasons for positing an underlying basis, but it is difficult to prove that there is in fact a basis. Indeed, it could be argued that there is no such basis. Perhaps the Sophist Protagoras (*c.*480–*c.*410 B.C.) intended such a view in his well-known saying: "Man is the measure of all things." This phrase can be interpreted to mean that each man's experience defines a personal truth, and personal truth is the *only* truth: "truth is what appears to each one." There may be no substratum, just various partial experiences. Even if there is a substratum, we may not be able to know anything about it. Perhaps the substratum is so different from familiar experiences that we shall never be able to understand it. It may be utterly beyond our comprehension. We seem to be tied to the experiences of which we are a part, and the ideas that we form about any substratum have to be expressed in the images, symbols and analogies collected from our experiences. While admitting the existence of external objects, the Scottish philosopher David Hume (1711–76) argued that all our ideas, including abstract ideas, have their origin in perceptions. Our ideas and imaginings are ultimately reworkings of things that have been encountered in sense-experience, and we cannot go beyond to the external world.

> Let us chace our imagination to the heavens, or to the utmost limits of the universe; we never really advance a step beyond ourselves, nor can conceive any kind of existence, but those perceptions, which have appear'd in that narrow compass. This is the universe of the imagination, nor have we any idea but what is there produc'd.[13]

Stimulated by Hume's philosophy, Immanuel Kant (1724–1804) drew attention to the *constructed* nature of our experiences. Kant disagreed with Hume's assertion that everything derives from sense-experience, and argued that the perceiving subject has innate concepts, prior to experience, that process or synthesise the information provided by the senses and thereby construct our perceptions. Experience is then a product of the interaction between information transmitted to the senses and the innate, constructive processes of an organism. In Kant's terminology, our experience consists of *phenomena,* or appearances, in contrast to *noumena,* the things-in-themselves *(Ding-an-sich,* thing-in-itself), which lie behind the phenomena. We cannot imagine the noumenal world: it is transcendental, beyond experience. We cannot escape the structuring we contribute to experience. Even the ordering of phenomena in temporal and three-dimensional relations is to be viewed as the product of our synthesising minds, and not reflective of the underlying noumena. Time and space are subjective forms of perception that do not characterise the things-in-themselves.

For both Hume and Kant, the underlying world is unknowable. This conclusion is elaborated by tough-minded empiricist or positivist philosophers who urge us to stay with experience and desist from metaphysical speculation on substrata underlying sense-experience. We are told that we should restrict ourselves to discussions of phenomena, for we cannot talk meaningfully about the nature of the underlying world. Metaphysics and ontology become dirty words. Although we might not agree with the extreme position of the positivists, it has to be conceded that any knowledge of the underlying world we deduce from studies of phenomena will be open to considerable doubt.

The approach of philosophical *scepticism* is to maintain that although we might search for a certain knowledge of the underlying basis, we shall never find it. Often a distinction between *appearance* and *reality* is emphasised by sceptical thinkers—we have knowledge of the appearances in our experience but no reliable knowledge of the underlying world, which is taken to be *the real.* A *veil of appearance* obscures our knowledge of *reality.* The outstanding proponent of scepticism in the ancient world was Pyrrho (*c.*360–*c.*270 B.C.), who is said to have taught that we can know only things as they seem, not as they are, and that we should suspend our judgement if we wish to attain a state of tranquillity.

To summarise the various attitudes noted above, we can elaborate the veil-of-appearance metaphor. The sceptics regard the tapestry of experience, with its multi-coloured, sonorous forms, as a curtain that largely obscures a world beyond. They admit that knowledge of the curtain is available, and that the patterns may give some indication of what lies behind it, but they suppose that the obscuration is such that no reliable knowledge of the world behind the curtain is available. The curtain may be dismissed as 'appearance', and the 'real' world given up as inaccessible, for the curtain cannot be opened. Hume suggested that all we can do is rework the curtain patterns, and the world behind remains inaccessible. Kant argued that the phenomenal curtain is weaved according to pre-existing instructions supplied by ourselves, which introduce forms that are not characteristics of the things-in-themselves behind the curtain. Spatial extension and temporal relations are solely characteristics of the curtains we weave, and do not apply to the world beyond.

The empiricists study the curtain designs to gain knowledge of the curtain, and may be dismissive of attempts to infer what lies behind. They are likely to reject the notion of innate instructions responsible for structuring the curtain and its patterns (Kant's constructivism) or of innate ideas that make the curtain knowable or comprehensible (rationalism, idealism). Similarly, the positivists are dismissive of attempts to speculate on what lies behind the curtain. Because the curtain seems to be permanently closed, the positivist argues that it is useless or meaningless to talk about what may lie behind it. Indeed, the very conception of something behind the phenomenal curtain may be a fiction, and ontology is completely rejected. The tapestry is not a curtain because it cannot be opened and does not cover anything. The tapestry is all that we experience and is the only actuality.

The curtain metaphor may be a graphic way of illustrating various philosophical positions, but is in danger of leading us to the sharp separation between the experiencer and the experienced, a dualism that we have sought to avoid here. The metaphor tends to conjure up the image of a person, self or *consciousness* gazing at the phenomenal tapestry behind which lies the substratal world. However, I wish to avoid this dubious separation between observer, phenomena and noumena. The experiential self is part of the tapestry, the conscious aspect of a self-system that reaches deeply into the substratal regions of the world. The same reservations apply to the mirror metaphor, in which the mirror and its images correspond respectively to the curtain and its patterns. The experiential self is contained within the mirror of experience, an experiential mirror that we suppose reflects the substratum. The experiential self is not an external observer or 'consciousness'.

2. THE PHYSICAL WORLD

In this chapter we focus on an extraordinarily influential notion of the substratum—the *material* or *physical world* described in the sciences. The material world, governed by mechanical laws, seized the imagination of natural philosophers in the seventeenth century, and continues to exert a powerful hold. It is important that we grasp the essential features of the mechanical world-view, for the philosophy has encouraged major advances in our comprehension of the world and cannot be dismissed lightly. We shall first consider the idea that objects in our sensory experience are perceptual representations of objects in an underlying world, and then consider the central feature of the mechanical philosophy, the idea of a substratum filled with material objects in motion and lacking qualities of colour, sound, taste, and so forth.

The atomists of ancient Greece imagined that behind the veil of sense-experience there existed a world of matter in motion, a substratum completely devoid of colour, sound, taste, smell, pain, warmth and cold. In the seventeenth century, philosophers again came to believe in a material world behind the flowing drapery. If Nature were to drop her flowery robe of appearances, adorned with its multitude of colours, sounds and tastes, we would find a skeletal anatomy dancing in a void. The philosophers of the seventeenth century went further than their ancient predecessors: they created an enormously successful *mathematical* account of matter in motion. Mathematics provided the means of investigating and describing the regular steps and turns of the skeletal dance. However, the power of mathematization soon undermined the idea of a purely material substratum, and led to the theory of a physical world. The *mechanical* or *material mirror* of the natural philosophers became a *physical mirror*.

Not all have believed that scientific theories mirror a world behind perceptions. Some have been impressed by the philosophical uncertainties that we noted at the end of the last chapter. These uncertainties have been expressed in the scientific context as a debate between realists and anti-realists.

THE STATUS OF SCIENTIFIC CONCEPTS

Scientific theories have often described objects, processes and quantities that are not directly presented to us in sense-experience. In modern times, these have included molecules, atoms, sub-atomic particles, electromagnetic radiation, energy, forces, fields, the curved spacetime of relativistic theory and the wavefuntion of quantum theory. What are we to make of such concepts? Do they refer to actually-existing features of the underlying world? The reality of physical entities is a question we shall encounter again in later chapters, when we consider spacetime and the quantum theory. The latter, in particular, has stimulated a number of interpretations embodying different attitudes to the reality of scientific entities. Views on the ontological status of scientific concepts can be divided into two main schools:

1. *Anti-realism:* The philosophical doubt that knowledge of the things-in-themselves is possible leads to the view that science is merely the study of phenomena, and reveals nothing about a substratum, if indeed there is such a thing. It is fruitless to speculate on what lies behind the curtain, and the curtain may be all that exists. *Instrumentalist* anti-realism views scientific theories as instruments for predicting phenomena from observations of previous phenomena, rather than actual descriptions of an underlying world. Scientific theories have no explanatory function—their value depends on their predictive accuracy, not on the descriptions they provide of a hypothetical physical substratum. One view supposes that scientific theories are complete fictions, albeit useful ones, whilst another accepts that a scientific theory might give a true account of the world but we shall never know for sure if it does. Two theories may yield accurate predictions yet present different pictures of the world. This is no problem for the instrumentalist, who denies that the pictures have any ontological value. Thus, in quantum physics the instrumentalist will not be troubled by *wave-particle duality,* to be described in Chapter Fifteen—an apparently contradictory particle description and wave description can be embraced by an instrumentalist because the use of the two descriptions yields good predictions, and the question of the nature of the substratum is of no interest. In the late nineteenth century, positivism inspired anti-realist attitudes to scientific theory and influenced early twentieth-century scientific thought, including relativistic and quantum theories. Positivist philosophers of science warned against going beyond the senses into realms of metaphysical speculation. Ernst Mach (1838–1916), an early exponent of the positivist view in the philosophy of science, maintained that scientific theories describe the co-ordination or correlation of sensations, and that we have no power to venture beyond sensation to an underlying world. Another expression of positivism in the philosophy of science was P. W. Bridgman's (1882–1961) *operationalism,* according to which scientific theories and entities should be defined in terms of the operations conducted by the scientist. Thus, *length* refers to the experiential measuring-operation performed with a ruler or another measuring instrument. The anti-realist or tough-minded empiricist is likely to dismiss talk of a substratum as "mere metaphysics."

2. *Scientific Realism:* In the realist view, scientific theories do provide knowledge of an actually-existing physical substratum. This substratum may be called

physical reality, the *physical world, external reality,* the *external world, external existence,* or *objective reality.* Some of the objects and processes of physical theory are held to represent accurately the structures and processes in the physical substratum. The realist, for instance, is likely to hold that atoms have an actual existence beyond scientific theory and measurement. However, the prudent realist, who is familiar with the history of science, accepts that scientific theories are provisional accounts, approximations that may not provide particularly good pictures of the world, yet correspond to some extent with the actual structures and processes of the substratum. Scientific accounts may be in need of considerable revision—the physical mirror may yet require drastic regrinding and polishing before it reflects truly—but there is the hope that scientific theory progresses towards more accurate and truthful representations of the physical substratum.

Unlike the instrumentalist, the scientific realist is not content with the simultaneous use of descriptions that paint different pictures of the physical world. Unhappiness with disparate descriptions may show in a desire to find a unified theory that is able to bring together all phenomena within the compass of a single, coherent system. A related problem for the realist may be the existence of several equivalent mathematical approaches to a single area of physics. The approaches all yield the same results, but utilise different physical quantities and mathematical treatments. The physicist switches between approaches to find a simple way of tackling a particular problem, or, if a science teacher, chooses the approach to suit the level of training of the student. But the realist wishes to describe the world as it actually is, and a multiplicity of equally applicable descriptions provides a disconcerting abundance of choices. Which physical description is to be regarded as ontologically primary, closest to the physical world as it actually is—a force, momentum, energy, field, or spacetime-metric description?

The remoteness of many scientific terms contributes to the realist's problems. In the development of scientific theories over the last few hundred years, concrete, qualitative models have given way to highly mathematical descriptions: much modern physical theory resides in equations that describe relations between numerical quantities derived from measurements of phenomena. These quantities include energy, momentum and force. The realist supposes that the equations say something about the external world, but the picture is not readily comprehensible and the explanatory content of mathematical theory may not be found satisfying if the theory is not expressible in terms close to our everyday experience. One form of scientific realism maintains that scientific theories tell us something about the external world, by bringing out *mathematical* patterns in the structures and process of the external world, but denies that the theories reveal the things-in-themselves as they actually are.

PERCEPTION OF THE SUBSTRATUM

Scientific realism, like realist theories in general, finds support for the idea of a substratum in the study of sense-perception. Clearly, the sensory constituents of experience have a special relationship with the sense-organs or sense receptors. Suppose I hold an apple in my hand. I look at the apple and see that it is red and round. When I close my eyelids, I no longer have the visual experience of a red, round shape, but continue to have a touch-experience of roundness. Parts of my body, the sense-organs, are linked specifically with particular contents of experience, eyes with visual content, ears with auditory content, and so forth.

In the normal course of describing our sensory experiences, we do not refer to the involvement of our sense-organs and nervous system. We use such phrases as "I see the red apple" or "I taste the sour apple", without reference to the role of the eyes or tongue in the perceptual process. We often speak as if objects have certain properties independent of ourselves, such as the redness or rotundity of the apple. The apple exists, red in colour, round in shape, with a certain taste, whether or not I look at it, touch it or taste it. When such everyday assumptions are classed as a philosophical position, they constitute *naive realism,* and it is common for arguments to be invoked to demonstrate the inadequacy of the position.

Philosophers have long argued that there is something *relative* about our sensory experiences. Many characteristics of objects in sense-experience are *not* independent of the experiencing organism. The sensory experience of an object depends on such features as the spatial relationship of the sense-organs with the object, and the state of the sense-organs. We have also noted that implicit interpretation is involved in the perceptual processing of sensory stimuli. The interpretation depends on the so-called *perceptual set* of the organism, which includes such factors as previous experience, expectations, understanding of the context, emotional state.

Some typical instances cited in philosophical discussions of the relativity of sense-experience include:

> Objects look different from different perspectives, change shape as they rotate, become larger as they move towards us and smaller as they recede.
>
> The taste of a food may be affected by the recent tasting of another food.
>
> A person who is colour-blind may experience an object as single-coloured, whilst another with normal sight is able to distinguish both red and green colours.

When a straight rod is dipped into water, the rod is seen to bend at the surface of the water, but still feels straight to the hand. There is a conflict between visual and touch perceptions.

It is also argued that if we had different kinds of sense-receptors, the contents of our experience would be rather different. Certainly, there are many instances of organisms capable of sensing beyond our range and in sense-modalities that we do not share. Many animals, for instance, are capable of hearing ultrasonic frequencies above the upper limit of human audition.

Such considerations may suggest that sense-organs and perceptual processes act as intermediaries between our sense-experiences and an underlying world, and make contributions of their own to the experience. The qualities of objects in sense-experience are not independent of us. The redness of the experienced apple is dependent on the apple-eye-brain relationship, and cannot be assumed to be an attribute of the apple in the substratum.

In scientific thought, objects in sensory experience have commonly been viewed as *representations* of objects in the underlying material or physical basis. The view is sometimes called *representative realism,* and in the history of Western philosophy it is often linked with John Locke (1632–1704), who held that the underlying objects are different in some significant respects from the objects in experience. We shall consider these differences in the next section, under the heading *Distinctions between Qualities.*

In the representative theory, the sense organs and nervous system act as intermediaries between the substratum and its representations in our experiences. A typical sketch of the perceptual process would describe the stimulation of sense-organs, followed by transmissions along nerves to the brain, where signals are constructed in some unknown way into the sensory content of experience. Let us refer to objects in sense-experience as *sense objects,* and objects in the substratum as *substratal objects.* The scientist might refer to these substratal objects as *physical objects.* The red apple in sense-experience is a sense apple and represents a substratal apple. An explanation of the perceptual process would begin at the substratal apple, which emits a substratal light-radiation. This reaches the substratal eye, where it is focused onto the substratal retina to produce a two-dimensional image of the substratal apple. Substratal retinal nerves are stimulated by the light and transmit signals to regions of the substratal brain. From these signals the sense apple of our experience is created in some mysterious way. The sensory process is summarised in Figure 2.1. The notion of substratal objects helps us to interpret various features of experience. The substratum:

1. *Unites experiential perspectives.* The different perspectives contained in our separate experiences follow from the different positions occupied

by our senses in the substratal world of objects. We suppose that there is one common substratal apple behind our diverse perceptions of the apple.

2. *Provides continuity of existence to objects.* Objects disappear from experience and may later reappear in experience. Are we to suppose that an object ceases to exist when it is placed in an opaque box and disappears from our transient experiences? The substratal world of objects allows for the continued existence of objects at the substratal level when they are no longer in our experience. Substratal objects continue to exist, whether or not they are represented in our sense-experiences.

3. *Provides structural completeness.* The scope of sensory experience is limited, being dependent on perceptual processes. We do not see inside opaque objects, but suppose that they have internal structures. Nor do we see the full extent of large or small structures, but these can be revealed in our experience with the help of optical instruments, such as telescopes and microscopes. The substratum provides structural completeness, contains all objects and their parts, whether or not we meet them in our experiences.

4. *Provides causal completeness:* When we attempt to trace the sequences of events in our experience, we may find that many links are missing. We deduce that processes are at work that are hidden from us. Sometimes the processes are revealed by shifting the perceptual perspective or by removing opaque surfaces that obstruct vision. Remove the back of a clock, and the inner workings are revealed. Again, instruments may be helpful in revealing hidden processes. The substratum, we suppose, contains all the hidden steps and causal links in processes.

Thus, the substratum provides a complete basis for all our partial experiences through its completeness of content, structure and process.

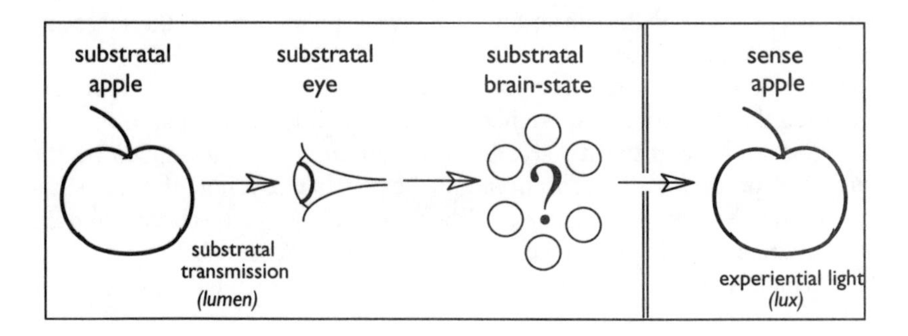

Figure 2.1. Outline of the perceptual process: substratal apple to sense apple.

Finally, we should note that representation does not necessarily mean *resemblance.* Consider various kinds of representation in experience. A photograph is similar to the scene it represents. In this example, the representation resembles the represented—there is a similarity of form. However, representation does not necessarily involve resemblance: consider the relationship between the music generated by a record player and the structure of the groove in the gramophone record. Variations along the groove cause the pick-up needle (stylus) to vibrate. The vibrations are converted into electrical signals, which are amplified and fed into a speaker, producing the air vibrations that stimulate our sense of sound. We hear music, but the music cannot be said to resemble its groove representation on the gramophone record. More recent technologies provide similar examples: consider, for instance, the relationship between the images we see on a computer screen and the encoding of the images on the computer's magnetic or optical storage devices.

In a resemblance type of representational theory, there are resemblances between sensory contents and the substratal objects. By studying our experiences we may be able to gain some idea of the nature of the substratum, since a relationship of resemblance holds. The substratum need not be a total mystery if it is similar in some respects to our familiar experiences. But resemblance need not imply a close copy. Sense objects could resemble substratal objects without being exact replicas. A painting may not resemble its subject accurately.

DISTINCTIONS BETWEEN QUALITIES

Some qualities of sensory objects may have no resemblance at all with anything in the underlying world. This idea played a crucial role in the development of scientific thought, and is central to the notion of the material world. It has been common for shape, size and motion to be ascribed to *both* sense objects and substratal objects, but colour, taste, sound, smell, heat, pain, and so forth, have been regarded as qualities existing *only* in our experiences, with no occurrence in the substratum. The sense apple resembles the substratal apple in its round shape, but the red colour belongs only to the sense apple. The substratal apple has no red coloration, or any colour qualities at all. It is supposed that in sensory experience there are qualities additional to those in the substratum, and that these additional qualities are introduced by the perceptual processes. The sensations and the personal psychological constituents, such as emotions, meanings, volitions, are thought to be absent from the substratum, but dependent on the substratal qualities. These substratal qualities have typically been regarded as the size, shape and arrangement of objects, and the motions of objects.

The spatial qualities of size, shape and arrangement can be called *geometric.* Qualities of motion, such as rest, velocity and acceleration, are called *kinematic,* and introduce the temporal feature of change to the spatial qualities. In addition, there are the visual, auditory, olfactory, tactile and gustatory qualities. These are associated with sense-organs: colour with the eye, sound with the ear, smell with the nose, and so forth, and are sometimes called *sensible qualities.* There are also the various personal psychological constituents, which in psychological atomistic theories are viewed as compounds of sensible qualities. Now, the term *sensible quality* assumes that the qualities occur only in sense-experience, and it fails to recognise that the geometric-kinematic qualities also occur in sense-experiences and could equally be called *sensible.* It would therefore be useful to find a different expression for qualities that are not geometric-kinematic. It is not easy to find a satisfactory alternative, and I shall make do with the term *astructural quality* for those qualities, such as colour, smell, and taste, which are commonly regarded as distinct from the *structural qualities,* the geometric and kinematic qualities of structure and change of structure.

The traditional distinction between qualities has had many variations, too many to consider here, but we can isolate three major components of the distinction:

1. *The occurrence of qualities:* Structural qualities are *common* to the objects of experience and the substratum, and a relationship of resemblance is thought to exist. The extended sense apple resembles the extended substratal apple. The astructural qualities, such as colours and tastes, exist only in experience, not in the substratum. In experience, the astructural qualities flesh out the bare structural bones.

2. *The causal power of qualities:* The second distinction involves the causal or explanatory power of qualities. In the material conception of the world, it is hoped that a consideration of only structure and motion will suffice to explain processes in both the substratum and in our experience. Astructural qualities have no causal or explanatory role.

3. *The ease of quantification of qualities:* The structural qualities are amenable to mathematical description, whereas the astructural qualities are not so easily expressed in numbers. The structural qualities are viewed as quantitative, and the astructural qualities as qualitative. The tendency to exalt the quantitative will be noted shortly.

In the material interpretation of the apple, the important features are the geometric and kinematic qualities of the substratal apple. It is supposed that these act as causes and are readily quantified, unlike, say, the red colour of the sense apple.

ANCIENT ATOMISM AND THE MECHANICAL PHILOSOPHY

The distinction between the qualities of experience and the substratum made its first appearance in the atomic theory of the Greek philosopher Democritus (*c.*460–370 B.C.). Democritean atoms were elementary building-blocks, very small, physically indivisible, and possessing only the qualities of extension and motion. The substratum consisted of two distinct entities, the atoms and the void through which the atoms move. This was the atomic theory of Leucippus and Democritus—the world consists of atom ("what is") and void ("what is not"). Democritus was sceptical about the knowledge of sensory experience, and instead found reality in a world of solid, indivisible atoms, infinite in number, and having shapes and sizes, and perhaps weights. The atomic theory of Democritus influenced Epicurus (*c.*341–270 B.C.), whose version of atomism passed to later generations through the poem *De Rerum Natura (On the Nature of Things),* composed by Lucretius (*c.*98–55 B.C.).

Some of the attraction of atomic theory lies in its explanation of change, and the ancient atomic theory can be interpreted as an attempt to reach a compromise between a theory of total permanence and a theory of total flux. Objects consist of arrangements of atoms in a void, and the void enables changes to the objects to occur through the rearrangement of the constituent atoms. The patterns change, but the atoms are everlasting. Atomic theories also have the attraction of being able to account for a great variety of objects with only a limited number of basic building-blocks, just as a few letters may be placed together to generate a vast number of words and sentences. The letter analogy was made popular by Lucretius. To extend the analogy even further, identical dots can be arranged into patterns to build up pictures and the letters of the alphabet. Only when the pictures and letters are examined very closely are the 'dot-atoms' noticed. Democritean and Epicurean atomic theories attempted to derive complex structure, diversity, and change of structure from the simple, the few and the unchanging.

The atomic theory of the Ancient Greeks underwent a gradual revival in the early days of modern experimental science, along with the distinction between geometric-kinematic and astructural qualities. Atomic theory had a great impact on seventeenth-century Western thought, and provided the basis of the *mechanical* or *corpuscular* ('corpuscle', a little body) philosophy that has had such a lasting effect on later scientific theory. The Democritean theory impressed Francis Bacon (1561–1626), and Pierre Gassendi (1592–1655) revived the atomism of Epicurus. Galilei Galileo (1564–1642) was another major figure attracted by atomism and the distinction between qualities. Galileo supposed that the aim of the scientist was to reach behind the fallible, relative world of the senses to the underlying geometrical figures in motion, amenable to mathematical treatment. In a widely read work, *Il Saggiatore* (1623), he argued that heat is a purely subjective sensory phenomenon, caused by the rapid motion of tiny particles impinging on the body. Like colours, tastes, sounds and odours, heat is not a quality of the substratal objects:

> To excite in us tastes, odors, and sounds I believe that nothing is required in external bodies except shapes, numbers, and slow or rapid movements. I think that if ears, tongues, and noses were removed, shapes and numbers and motions would remain, but not odors or tastes or sounds.[1]

In the influential philosophy of René Descartes (1596–1650), the distinction between qualities took on a central role through the identification of matter with extension. Descartes' *modern philosophy* differed in an important respect from the ancient atomism revived by others, for he denied the existence of the void or vacuum, of empty space, and took the corpuscles of extended matter to be physically divisible. Yet the explanatory intention was the same: to provide an account of the world solely in terms of matter in motion. We need only consider the sizes, shapes, and arrangements of matter in motion to explain everything in the world, and the only conceivable interaction is through the impact of particles in collision. This was the early mechanical philosophy, the philosophy of matter in motion. The idea of forces or influences acting at a distance, without any intermediary mechanisms of colliding material bodies, was not admissible. Everything, save the activities of God, had to be explained in terms of solid particles in collision.

The appeal of the mechanical type of explanation presumably derives from our everyday familiarity with 'mechanical' causes and effects, with objects colliding and recoiling, or pushing and pulling one another in mechanisms. Some interactions, like gravitational attraction and the attraction and repulsion of magnets, are not obviously mechanical, as the effects occur without any visible contact, but the mechanical philosophers supposed that even these could be explained in terms of the geometric properties of matter in motion. Descartes attempted to give qualitative mechanical explanations of various phenomena, such as heat and light, and supposed that gravitational effects arise from the flow of subtle forms of matter in vortices. Scientific explanation was to invoke the motions of extended matter, without recourse to non-material influences.

The corpuscular philosophy was allied with the growing experimental work of the time. For instance, Torricelli's demonstration of a vacuum in 1644 made the Cartesian and Aristotelian rejection of the void ("nature abhors a vacuum") much less acceptable. Robert Boyle (1627–1691), a leading exponent of the corpuscular philosophy, was deeply involved in experimental research, and found his results were in harmony with a corpuscular philosophy. Boyle is remembered for his application of the corpuscular philosophy to chemistry. He was dissatisfied with the entities that some contemporaries took as basic, such as the elementary fire, earth, air and water, or the three principles of the Paracelsian alchemists, the *tria prima* of sulphur, mercury, and salt. These were not the familiar substances, but special essences. The presence of the salt-principle, for instance, would give a substance the quality of solidity. Boyle hoped that a corpuscular approach would provide more effective explanations. Instead of using circular explanations—for, instance, a stone is solid because it contains much elemental earth or salt-principle—the corpuscular philosophy aimed to explain all qualities in terms of a few basic qualities, the extensions, patterns and motions of the corpuscles. The emphasis was placed on structure, or *texture* in Boyle's terminology, as the basis of qualities. The arrangement of corpuscles gave a substance its qualities, rather than elementary principles that confer qualities, but are endowed themselves with these qualities in some unknown way. The denunciation of hidden or 'occult' causes was a prominent theme in seventeenth-century science, and was related to earlier dissatisfactions *(nominalism)* with the idea of universals independent of particulars (for instance, 'solidity' regarded as an actuality distinct from solid objects).

Boyle introduced the terminology of *primary qualities* and *secondary qualities,* which has been much used in discussions of the qualities and their differences. These terms were not used consistently or clearly by Boyle, nor by others who adopted the terminology, including Locke, in the influential *Essay concerning Human Understanding* (1690). Much confusion has resulted over the application of the terms. But as a general guide to Boyle's usage, we can note the following distinctions.[2] The *essential* or *primary* qualities refer to the geometric and kinematic qualities of corpuscles: shape, size, mobility. What we have termed the astructural qualities (colours, sounds, tastes, pain, and so forth) are called *sensible qualities,* and characterise the objects in experience but not the corpuscles. The *secondary qualities* of underlying bodies seem to be those properties that give rise to the sensible qualities in experience. These secondary qualities are particular arrangements and motions of corpuscles in objects. It is, however, very common to find the term *secondary quality* used to denote the astructural or sensible qualities, the colours, sounds, tastes, and so forth.

Let us consider colour perception in the framework of the corpuscular philosophy. Colour qualities belong only to the objects in experience. The objects in the material substratum are built up of corpuscles that have the primary qualities of shape, size and motion. The particular arrangements and motions on the surfaces of substratal objects interact mechanically with the matter between the objects and the eye. For Isaac Newton (1642–1747) and Boyle, this involved the reflection of light corpuscles from the surface to the eye, and for Descartes it involved a pressure transmitted through the intervening matter, like a sound wave though air. The reflected corpuscles interact with the corpuscular patterns in the eyes. Further mechanical interactions occur in the nerves and converge on the material brain, giving rise to the luminous experience of geometric objects fleshed out with colour/light qualities.

It will be useful to have terms that highlight the two very different meanings of the word *light* in the above description—light as a transmission from object to eye, and light as an experience. The mechanical philosophers took the latter to be subjective personal experiences, and interpreted the former as matter in motion in an objective material world. *Lux* and *lumen,* terms from mediaeval light theory, are useful words for distinguishing between the two meanings of light, although the terms do not correspond exactly to our modern notions, and medieval authors used them in various ways.[3] Disregarding the historical complexities, we can take *lux* to be light-experience, our experiences of colour, shade, brightness, and so forth, whilst *lumen* shall refer to the means by which information is transmitted from an object to the eye. Nowadays we would commonly regard the means of transmission, the *lumen,* as electromagnetic waves, or as photon particles. Like the corpuscularists, a modern scientist would not ascribe colours to the *lumen,* but would suppose instead that various frequencies and combinations of frequencies of light radiation stimulate the network of visual receptors in the eye, to produce patterns of nerve impulses that are constructed in the brain and somehow yield an experience of colour. In the *Opticks,* Newton is clear that light rays are not themselves coloured, but stir up the sensations of colour. Light rays that make objects appear red are termed "Rubrifick or Red-making", and the reader is warned:

> And if at any time I speak of Light and Rays as coloured or endued with Colours, I would be understood to speak not philosophically and properly, but grossly, and accordingly to such Conceptions as vulgar People in seeing all these Experiments would be apt to frame. For the Rays to speak properly are not coloured. In them there is nothing else than a certain Power and Disposition to stir up a Sensation of this or that Colour.[4]

It is not at all obvious how *lumen* stirs up *lux*—we shall return to this difficulty when we consider the mind-body problem in the next chapter. Science concerned itself with the *lumen,* while *lux* receded from interest, dismissed as a quality peculiar to subjective experience, and of no importance in the mechanical understanding of the world.[5]

THE MECHANICAL PHILOSOPHY UNDER ATTACK

The corpuscular philosophy met with opposition. Rooted in the ideas of Democritus and Epicurus, atomism was open to the charge of atheism, and many of its exponents strove to show that atomism could be reconciled with religious beliefs. Perhaps it was feared that a doctrine of corpuscular matter would explain nature in its entirety, and the material substratum would displace the religious substratum—there would be no place left for God or spiritual activity in the new conception of the world. Thus, some seventeenth-century mechanical philosophers stressed that the new philosophy was not intended to exclude the divine, that matter in motion was not the sole agent behind the world of the senses. Thus Gassendi attempted to present Epicurean atomism in a form compatible with the Christian world-view. Boyle doubted that matter and motion were sufficient to explain all things, and Newton suggested that God originally set the matter in motion and steps in periodically to keep the planets in their orbits. The mathematical order enshrined in Newton's account of planetary gravitation could be interpreted as a sign of divine activity in the cosmos. Newton's view of corpuscles also called on the divine—God created matter with properties to suit the divine purpose:

> All these things being consider'd, it seems probable to me, that God in the Beginning form'd Matter in solid, massy, hard, impenetrable, moveable Particles, of such Sizes and Figures, and with such other Properties, and in such Proportion to Space, as most conduced to the End for which he form'd them; and that these primitive Particles being Solids, are incomparably harder than any porous Bodies compounded of them; even so very hard, as never to wear or break in pieces; no ordinary Power being able to divide what God himself made one in the first Creation.[6]

Some felt uneasy with the new philosophy, and attacked it for the atheistic materialism into which it could slip. The most famous attack on the mechanical philosophy from a philosophical standpoint was launched by Bishop George Berkeley (1685–1753), who concentrated his efforts on exposing Locke's presentation. Another famous attack was made by William Blake (1757–1827), who strenuously rejected the mechanical philosophy and its 'false trinity' of Bacon, Newton and Locke.[7] We shall consider Blake's understanding of matter in Chapter Fourteen.

Berkeley's response was to reject completely the existence of an underlying material world. He put forward a philosophy of *immaterialism,* denying that there was a substratum of material objects supporting experience and endowed with geometric-kinematic qualities. According to Berkeley, only ideas have existence, and objects are ideas. The term *idea* is used in a special sense, common among seventeenth-century philosophers, including Descartes and Locke, to denote the whole range of experience—sensations, emotions, memories, thoughts. Berkeley therefore makes the important point that both extended objects and personal psychological constituents are parts of our experience, but goes further and says that there are no underlying extended objects. Berkeley's rejection of corpuscular matter does not mean that he also rejected experimental science or the notion of an underlying basis. It was the supposition of an imperceptible and unimaginable *material* substratum that he challenged. Yet Berkeley retained the concept of an underlying basis: this was not a material substratum, but the regulating activity of an immaterial God. It is God's full perception that maintains the continuity of objects across gaps in our experience.

Berkeley makes an interesting point in his attack on geometric-kinematic matter. Geometric qualities and some of the supposedly astructural qualities cannot be separated from one another in our experience. Can there be extended objects with no colour or touch qualities? In experience, objects with size and shape always have colours[8] filling them in, or touch sensations defining their boundaries. We never encounter extension without at least one astructural quality, as it is the astructural qualities of colour and touch sensation that build up the spatial qualities of objects in our experience. Is it meaningful, then, to suppose that there are extended substratal objects that have no visual or tactile qualities? Berkeley supposed not, and took this to be an argument against the mechanist's distinction between qualities. It is an attractive point to make but is not a conclusive argument against the distinction, for it relies on our inability to separate geometric from visual or tactile qualities. It does not necessarily tell us anything about the substratum. Berkeley's point, however, alerts us to the fallacy of imagining that we can picture the substratum in our experiences if we have ascribed it only geometric-kinematic qualities.

Suppose we try to imagine the material substratum, consisting of a space in which solid, extended, minute particles move about, joining temporarily into patterns, then moving apart to form new patterns. We can imagine these atoms only if we endow them with some astructural qualities, since it is not possible to imagine extension without some contrast of light and shade, or an experience of touch. The tendency, then, is to imagine extended atoms as shapes filled with some visual qualities, perhaps shaded grey, or transparent with outlines. We then imagine the underlying world to be made of these extended particles, a hybrid of geometric qualities with some visual qualities to aid our imagination. We envisage the substratum as a world of grey 'billiard balls' in motion through a void of space. These considerations also apply to attempts to imagine or illustrate the more sophisticated atoms and sub-atomic particles of modern physics.

Berkeley's point also complicates our understanding of what we mean by a resemblance between the geometric-kinematic qualities in sense-objects and the corresponding geometric-kinematic qualities of substratal objects. It is an unimaginable resemblance, because we cannot picture the underlying world without astructural qualities. Normally, when we talk of resemblance, we mean that qualities or combinations of qualities look like, sound like, taste like or feel like one another. But we do not experience the geometric-kinematic qualities of the substratum and cannot conceive of doing so without some of the astructural qualities of our familiar experience. Hence, we cannot apply *resemblance* in the usual experiential sense. Instead, it is an unimaginable structural correspondence.

THE QUANTIFICATION OF QUALITIES

What justification is there for making the kinds of distinction between qualities we have just considered? We saw that a powerful impetus for adopting a distinction was the speculative scientific theory of atoms, and it is sometimes stated that the strongest justification for making the distinction comes from the success of scientific theories. The scientific enterprise has had considerable success in tracing the causal interactions between objects by confining its efforts to a treatment of essentially geometric-kinematic qualities, with no explanatory role given to astructural qualities. It is true that scientific theory has moved on considerably from the corpuscular philosophy, and it is no longer suggested that there are such things as extended, solid atoms, but the emphasis on structural features remains. There is no role for colours, tastes, and so forth, in scientific accounts of the underlying world. It is supposed that we can account perfectly well for all that happens in the world by considering only physical properties.

It is doubtful whether the revival of atomism would have had much long-term impact if it had not been for the effective exploitation of the quantitative/qualitative distinction between qualities. Geometric-kinematic qualities are attractive candidates for the explanatory terms of a science because they are particularly amenable to measurement, to representation as relative numerical magnitudes that remain the same, whatever relative perspective or sequence of perspectives is used to take the measurements.[9]

The mathematical justification for distinguishing between qualities points to another stream of ancient Greek philosophical thought behind the emergence of modern science, an influence that transformed the qualitative atomism of Democritus into a modern quantitative science of motion. This influence is the Pythagorean-Platonic elevation of number, ratio and geometry. Here the distinction between structural and astructural qualities is based not on a mechanical atomic theory of matter, but on a mathematical world-view in which the mathematical and quantitative is ascribed a higher order of reality than the qualitative. The Pythagoreans were inspired by the order they observed in the world, a harmony to be found in the regular motions of the heavenly bodies and in the ratios of musical intervals. The numerical harmonies in the world were taken to reveal an underlying mathematical order. Number pointed to the hidden order, beauty, proportion in the world, the *kosmos* ('order', 'ornament'). Number and ratio were not merely confined to the motion of planets but also had close links with the human sphere, as the harmonies of musical notes seemed to show. In Pythagorean thought, the study of numerical relationships became a way towards a deeper level of truth than is apparent in sense-experience.

The importance of mathematics in the pursuit of knowledge was presented to a wide audience through the philosophy of Plato, whose epistemology distinguished various levels of knowledge that have increasing reality. In the *Republic,* Plato gave a four-level scheme. Logical and mathematical-scientific reasoning was placed under the knowledge of the Forms, but was regarded as superior to belief, and to sensory experience and its images.

The mathematical criterion for distinguishing between qualities was stressed in the early days of modern science by Johannes Kepler (1571–1630), who was much taken by the Pythagorean-Platonic philosophy of number. Kepler's search for explanations of the numerical attributes of the solar system—such as the diameter of planetary orbits—proved to be an enormous stimulus for the mathematical search for an accurate account of the world. After a fruitless attempt to interpret the distances between the six heliocentric planetary spheres in terms of the five Platonic solids, Kepler discovered the laws of heliocentric planetary motion. Kepler's successful mathematical treatment of celestial motion combined with Galileo's advances in the quantification of terrestrial motion to lay the groundwork for Newton's science of motion.

The measurement of extension, size, position and motion has come to be a fundamental aspect of scientific investigation. Measurement of geometric and kinematic qualities can be used to build a detailed mathematical representation of a geometric-kinematic substratum. Theories are based on a collection of numerical explanatory elements: extension, position, velocity, acceleration, and various quantities related to these, such as mass, force, momentum and energy. The scientific realist looks for a mathematical description of geometry and motion in the substratum. The geometric-kinematic qualities stand out as easily quantifiable, and it is supposed that nothing more is required for us to produce satisfactory explanations.

This is not to say that we cannot attempt to measure the astructural qualities. We could, for instance, devise a system of standard, graded colour or odour samples to be used for comparison with the colours or odours of sense-objects, just as we compare the extensions of sense-objects with standard lengths. But this is a much more difficult task than measuring extensions with a ruler, and it is not clear how we could associate numbers with the astructural standards in the same way that we can produce continuous number-lines to quantify spatial and temporal characteristics. And it is unlikely that we would get very far if we attempted to devise a science whose causal explanations were based solely on comparisons of astructural qualities and their transformations.

There are valid distinctions to be made between qualities, and some concern the way in which qualities can be quantified and incorporated into mathematical descriptions. However, the claim that physical properties are *all* that we need to produce a satisfactory account of the world remains to be proved. Problems arise when we look at our own activities and those of other experiencing beings. Here the astructural qualities seem to have important explanatory roles—"I liked the taste of the apple so I ate another one." Perhaps a science of physical qualities is only part of the story, and other qualities need to be taken into account.

THE EXTERNAL WORLD: MATERIAL TO PHYSICAL

The mechanical philosophy has been immensely influential in the development of physical ideas. Mechanics became the exemplary mode of explanation: other branches of physics strove to incorporate and emulate the mechanical explanations of phenomena. However, the mechanical philosophy in its original form was short-lived. The geometric and kinematic qualities alone soon proved to be insufficient to construct satisfactory scientific theories, and the corpuscular philosophy was replaced by a broader physics that entertained additional concepts, such as force and energy. Exponents of the corpuscular philosophy, such as Galileo, had been unduly optimistic about the explanatory power of mobile, solid, extended atoms, which interact with one another by impact. They had hoped to sweep away the circular explanations, and to rid natural philosophy of hidden powers that add nothing to the understanding. Matter, motion and collision were to be the sole explanatory principles.

But the early mechanical models, typified by Descartes' qualitative explanations, proved to be sterile in comparison with the mathematical description of nature introduced in Newton's dynamics and his universal law of gravitation. Newton's contribution advanced the scientific theory of motion beyond the conceptual parsimony of the early mechanical philosophy, which had focused exclusively on size, shape, and interactions through bodily impact. Each material body was now to be associated with a quantity called *mass,* a measure of the body's resistance to changes to its state of motion. Mass, not size or shape, was the important attribute of matter in motion. Furthermore, the universal law of gravitation provided a mathematical description of gravitational *forces* acting between material bodies. Newton's mathematization of gravitation threatened the early mechanical philosophy because it seemed to imply that a mysterious factor was at work in the material world, namely a gravitational force. It was feared that the introduction of the idea of forces acting between bodies over distances was a regression to the benighted philosophy of earlier times, which the mechanical ideal of interaction through contact was intended to overthrow. Physical forces of gravity guiding the planetary motions had been considered before, notably by Kepler and Giovanni Alfonso Borelli (1608–79), but Newton's mathematical gravitational theory could not be neglected because it worked so well, and was integrated with Newton's successful general treatment of motion. A number of contemporaries, including Christiaan Huygens (1629–95) and Gottfried Wilhelm Leibniz (1646–1716), accused Newton of reintroducing hidden causal powers, although they recognised the value of the mathematical treatment. How were these forces to be interpreted? Newton was reluctant to commit himself to an explanation of the nature of the forces described in his mathematical theory. In the second edition (1713) of his *Principia,* the famous phrase "I frame no hypotheses" *(hypotheses non fingo)* appears:

> But hitherto I have not been able to discover the cause of those properties of gravity from phenomena, and I frame no hypotheses; for whatever is not deduced from the phenomena is to be called an hypothesis; and hypotheses, whether metaphysical or physical, whether of occult qualities or mechanical, have no place in experimental philosophy. ... And to us it is enough that gravity does really exist, and act according to the laws which we have explained, and abundantly serves to account for all the motions of the celestial bodies, and of our sea.[10]

In spite of his resolution to frame no hypotheses, Newton ends the scholium with a suggestion that a "subtle spirit" is responsible for cohesion, electric attraction and repulsion, light propagation, and nervous transmission in animals. In his later thought, he considered an aether theory: the aether, he suggested, might consist of an all-pervading medium, possibly corpuscular, which supports gravitational attraction as well as other physical processes. In the seventeenth-century climate of antipathy towards the Aristotelian occult qualities, it was politic to avoid commitment to an explanation of gravity, and Newton insisted that gravitation was not an occult quality, but an empirical fact, the causes of which would eventually be discovered. Later generations, for whom force-calculations became a routine exercise, were less sensitive to the philosophical issues. The unthinking acceptance of forces into physics as causal agents behind motion could then lead to the facile type of explanation that the corpuscular philosophy had vigorously opposed: "Why do bodies move together?"—"As a result of gravitational attraction." It was this circular kind of explanation—which pretends to an explanation but merely restates the question in the form of an answer—that induced positivist philosophers of science in the late nineteenth century to rid physics of the unobserved, such as force interpreted as a causal agent. To the positivist or anti-realist, force is not a hidden causal agent, but an acceleration of a body that is observed and measured. In spite of the strong positivist influence in recent science, it remains quite common to talk about forces as if they are actually existing causal powers.

There has also been another strand of thought having a bearing on the status of forces. Albert Einstein interpreted gravitational force as the curvature of spacetime in the presence of matter, a move that eliminates gravitational force acting over three-dimensional space as a fundamental entity, and replaces it with the curvature of a higher-dimensional space. Geometric qualities attributed to a four-dimensional substratum can be interpreted as absorbing the qualities of motion. Attempts have since been made to extend the approach to the other known forces of nature, as we shall note in Chapter Thirteen.

The introduction of mass and force in a mathematical theory of phenomena transformed the corpuscular philosophy into a broader mechanical science, in which mechanism was not restricted to impact forces between material particles but also embraced forces acting across space without clear reference to material intermediaries. For the realist, the material substratum became a physical substratum. The idea of solid atoms eventually faded from the forefront of scientific speculation, if not from the popular imagination and the deeper recesses of the scientific mind, and it could still be applied with success in the nineteenth-century kinetic theory of heat. In general, however, there was a significant move to concepts of force-centres and mathematical field theories. The idea of solid, extended particles had never been satisfactory, for it raised several difficult questions. What holds a group of atoms together? It is no good supposing that atoms have hooks and can interlock with one another, for there is still the problem of how a single extended atom or its hook holds together. What prevents a corpuscle from disintegrating into smaller parts, and these parts into smaller parts? What gives an atom its cohesiveness, its resistance to penetration? The mathematical descriptions of forces were sufficient—the extended bodies added little if anything to the picture.

Newton's successful mathematical treatment of force paved the way for later developments. Newton himself considered non-gravitational forces of attraction and repulsion acting between atoms of matter and responsible for all physical, chemical and physiological processes. Newton could explain the cohesion of corpuscles as a result of inter-atomic forces, but he did not go on to question the inner cohesiveness of his solid, immutable particles. Leibniz, Newton's arch-rival, stimulated another line of thought that led away from the solid, extended atoms of corpuscular philosophy. Leibniz had developed a metaphysics of *monads,* extensionless simple substances that are centres of force. In 1710 the Italian philosopher Giambattista Vico (1668–1744) posited a theory of point-centres, and this was followed by Rudjer Boscovich's (1711–87) mathematical atomism, presented in *A Theory of Natural Philosophy* (1763), in which Newton's inter-atomic forces were combined with Leibniz's extensionless points. The Boscovichian point-centres exert forces on one another, attractive when widely separated, repulsive when close together. Extended objects are patterns of these unextended points. John Michell (1724–1793) and Immanuel Kant also considered the possibility that matter consists of point-centres of force, and in the nineteenth century, Humphrey Davy (1778–1829) and Michael Faraday (1791–1867) entertained the idea of point-atoms as centres of force.

The *field theory* of Faraday turned attention away from the central particle to the surrounding medium, the *field,* through which electromagnetic forces could act between centres. During the nineteenth century, attempts were made to interpret the field mechanically, in terms of the motions of material parts or a fluid aether, but again the mathematical treatment took precedence, through the work of James Clerk Maxwell (1831–79), and the mechanical analogies were eventually abandoned. Solid atoms and the material aether have been dematerialised through mathematization, and the underlying world has come to be viewed as an arena of point-particles, fields and forces. It is common to imagine that these mathematical entities, described by equations, actually exist in the underlying world, but it is not at all clear how we are supposed to conceive of them. To add to the confusion, the quantum theory has received a prominent anti-realist interpretation.

The developments in physics since the seventeenth century have meant that the underlying world of realist science can no longer be called material. Instead, the various entities that populate the modern scientific imagination—atoms, protons, electrons, anti-matter, quarks, strings, fields, forces, wavefunctions, curved spacetime—refer to things in a *physical* world, at least for the uncomplicated realist. However, the legacy of the corpuscular philosophy and its distinction between qualities lives on. The physical world, whether viewed as a complex ocean of vibrating fields or as a spacetime structure, is regarded as devoid of astructural qualities, of sensations such as colour and sound, and psychological constituents such as emotion and meaning.

3. THE MIND-BODY PROBLEM

The idea of a material or physical substratum leads to a major perplexity. How is our transient experience, with its colours, sounds, odours, tastes, emotions, meanings, to be related to a physical world that lacks such features? The difficulty has been called *the mind-body problem.*

THE MIND-BODY PROBLEM

We have seen that in the early days of modern science, there was the expectation that an account of structure and motion would suffice to explain everything in nature. The profusion of explanatory entities weighing down earlier philosophy was abandoned for a scheme of matter and motion. Many qualities in experience—the astructural or 'sensible' qualities such as colour, sound and taste—were to be viewed as derivatives of matter in motion (matter, motion and force in the later mechanical philosophy).

The approach, however, runs into difficulties when attempts are made to trace the causal chain between a material or physical object and its representation in experience. A gap appears in the account, a divide between the physical state of the experiencing organism's body and the experience itself. In the case of vision, the transmission of changes in the physical world can be traced from the surface of an object to the eye, via an intermediary process in the physical world, a *lumen* consisting of corpuscles or aether waves in some of the older theories, and photons or electromagnetic waves in modern descriptions. The account continues with an image projected onto the retina of the eye and the stimulation of light-sensitive photoreceptor nerve cells in the retina. Signals, consisting of changes in electrical states along nerves, are first processed in the layers of retinal nerve cells, and are then transmitted to parts of the brain, where further processing takes place. It is not clear what follows, but we might speculate that a physical representation is generated in the brain or in parts of the brain, which structurally represents or even resembles features of the original object in the physical world outside the body. The nature of the physical representation within the brain is not at all clear, but suggestions might include patterns of:

1. electrical changes along certain nerve cells,
2. biochemicals, such as neurotransmitters at nerve-cell connections,
3. electrically charged ion concentrations in brain matter,
4. electrical fields in the brain.[1]

Whichever physical entity we choose, a gap appears in the physical explanation of perception. How do we proceed from the physical brain-state, devoid of colour and sound, to experience with its diversity of astructural qualities, emotion and meaning? Has the endeavour to explain all qualities by admitting just a few into the substratum turned out to be unworkable? How justifiable was Galileo's belief that in external bodies there is nothing other than size, shape, or motion? In following the mechanistic path, we find that the physical underlying world meets experience at a divide, across which we find no obvious bridge. On one side is an unimaginable world of physical entities lacking astructural qualities, whilst on the other is our colourful, sonorous world of experience, with its feeling and meaning.

The mind-body problem is complicated by different interpretations of the principal terms, particularly *mind. Mind* has been understood in several ways. For instance, it may be identified with soul or spirit, viewed as something utterly distinct from matter, having no extension, and unconnected with the laws of the physical world. Alternatively, *mind* can refer to the world of our experiences, or to our experiences *plus* the unconscious physical processes that support them—*mind* is then a system spanning the divide. Or *mind* might be regarded as *consciousness,* interpreted as an independent observer viewing the contents of experience. This position has been avoided here. Instead, our familiar experiences make up the *mind* half of the problem. The other half is the material or physical substratum, including the physical bodies of organisms, the substratal bodies of experiencing beings. How are substratal brain-states and body-states to be linked with experiences, with our sensations and personal psychological contents?

There is plenty of evidence to suggest that there is a link between the contents of experience and specific physical structures and processes in the body. For example:

1. We have already noted the role of the nervous system in the perceptual process, which involves the transmission of signals from sense-receptors to the brain. The nervous system also acts in the other direction: signals are transmitted from the central nervous system to the muscles, initiating and controlling movements. I decide to open my hand, and my hand opens. What is the connection between my experiential decision and the physical processes involved in opening my hand?

2. Aspects of experience have been correlated with specific regions of the brain *(localisation).* For example, various structures in the limbic system have been implicated in emotional experience. Another well-known instance of localisation is the lateralization of brain functions between the right and left cerebral hemispheres.

3. Certain substances, termed *psychoactive,* affect mood and perception. Stimulants, tranquillisers, hallucinogens, anti-depressants fall into this category. How is experience altered by the drug-induced changes to body chemistry? Similarly, some forms of psychological illness have been associated with altered body chemistry.

The mind-body relationship seems to work in both directions, and it is not always clear what is cause and what is effect. Psychological stress is an example of psychology affecting biology, with psychosomatic disorders developing out of distressing experiences. It is thought, for example, that psychological stress affects the immune system. There are also common instances of biology affecting psychology, in illnesses and malnutrition.

BRIDGING THE MIND-BODY DIVIDE

Historically there have been three main approaches to the mind-body problem: dualism, materialism and idealism.[2] The first approach accepts a fundamental distinction between experience and the substratum, whilst the other two reject it.

Acceptance of the distinction

We can accept the distinction between experience and an unexperienced physical substratum, and attempt to connect the two in some way. At the risk of simplifying the often complex positions of philosophers, we shall employ a commonly used classification of theories, and describe this first approach as *dualistic,* for two distinct parts of the world have been set up, namely experience and the physical. It is the dualist's burden to show how the two are related to each other.

Rejection of the distinction

Alternatively we can claim that the division of the world into experience and a physical substratum is misconceived, that an error has been made in setting up the two sides of the problem. We could argue that there is only a material or physical world, or that there is only experience. These approaches we can call *monistic* because they argue that the world is of one nature. It is either entirely physical or entirely experience, and the former position we classify as materialism or physicalism, a doctrine of matter or physical entities, and the latter position as idealism, a doctrine of ideas in the broad sense indicated before, denoting the varied contents of experience. These philosophical usages are to be distinguished from other meanings: materialism is often used to denote an excessive interest in goods, possessions, financial success, whereas idealism may refer to an aspiration after the noble, high, perfect.

DUALISM

If we uphold the distinction between experience and the physical, we are faced with the problem of relating the two to each other. A major function of a substratum is to provide a common, comprehensive basis for our private, partial experiences. To perform this function, the physical world must be related to our experiences in some way. We could argue that the connection is *direct,* that there is a causal link between physical events and experiences. If this causal link is taken to act two ways, from the physical substratum to experience, and vice versa, then the dualism is called *interactionism.* If the causal link is thought to act only one way, the dualism is called *epiphenomenalism.* In the latter case, the physical is taken to affect experience: experience or 'consciousness' is considered a passive by-product of physical processes, a 'glow in the brain' having no reciprocal effect on the physical substrate. The physical is taken to be the unifying substratum of the experiential, a substratum that is not itself influenced by the experiential.

These kinds of dualism suppose that there is a direct, causal bridge linking experience and the physical substratum. The interactionist maintains that cause-and-effect processes move both ways across the bridge. The epiphenomenalist restricts the causal sequence to one direction, from the physical world to the world of experience. However, when we attempt to trace the causal sequence, we run into the original difficulty: how can the many facets of our experience, such as colour, taste, and the more complex varieties of psychological experience, be linked with physical processes that by definition lack these facets? It is conceivable that the geometric-kinematic facets of the physical are causally connected with the geometric-kinematic facets of experience, since geometric-kinematic qualities are supposed to be common to both sides of the mind-body divide. But we are still left with the problem: how can geometry and motion, and other physical entities and processes, produce the astructural qualities of experience. How do physical brain-states produce colours, sounds, emotions, meaning? It seems that the experiential-physical divide of the dualists cannot be bridged fully because astructural qualities cannot be derived from something totally lacking astructural qualities.

A major proponent of interactionist dualism was René Descartes. His version of the mind-body divide is rather more polarised than the one elaborated here, for he distinguished between extended, divisible matter in motion (*res extensa,* extended substance) and unextended, indivisible, thinking mind (*res cogitans,* thinking substance). Soul and body are quite distinct. In the *Treatise on Man*

(1664) and *The Passions of the Soul* (1649), Descartes located the bridge between soul and body in the pineal gland of the brain, and argued that it is only here that the soul can exert an influence on the body, by altering the direction of flow of the *animal spirits,* a subtle form of particulate matter derived from the blood. However, Descartes' soul-body link was not properly established—he had not explained how an immaterial soul can change the motion of material fluid. It is not at all clear how distinct substances, one extended matter and the other thinking mind, can be said to interact. It is worth noting that by the term *thinking,* Descartes referred to more than intellectual activity, using it to cover sense-experience as well.[3] Epiphenomenalism, the other version of dualism we have noted so far, was proposed towards the end of the nineteenth century by T. H. Huxley (1825–1895).

Other forms of dualism differ from interactionism and epiphenomenalism in that they deny any *direct* causal connection between the substratum and experience. How, then, are we to relate the two, for the physical world is supposed to provide experience with a complete, unifying basis? The original versions of this alternative form of dualism introduced a third factor into the discussion to bridge the divide, namely God. The *occasionalist* version of dualism was put forward by several of Descartes' followers to overcome the deficient Cartesian interactionist solution. God acts as a go-between, adjusting the physical to comply with mental events such as decisions, and incorporating an awareness of material bodily changes into experience. It is mysterious how God performs the intermediary role, working on both the physical world and experience, and we are not any closer to understanding the relationship. Nicolas Malebranche's (1638–1715) version of occasionalism gave a partial explanation by using the Cartesian idea that any finite substance needs God to recreate it from instant to instant. God recreates the mental and physical substances from moment to moment, making sure that they correlate with each other. Experience and the physical substratum are linked indirectly through their continuous parallel creation by God, and the whole substratum is therefore physical/religious, a combination of the physical world and God.

Another version of dualism that rejects any direct causal connection was Leibniz's *psychophysical parallelism,* which also originated as a response to Descartes' extreme presentation of mind and body as completely distinct substances. Leibniz's theory includes a refinement of Malebranche's version of occasionalism: transformation proceeds naturally within the substances, and does not require the constant creative activity of God. God's activity is confined to the initial creation of substances, when they were endowed with all that they require for their future changes. The mental and physical are synchronised by God at the beginning, rather that at each moment of change. However, this account is not the whole story, for Leibniz's ideas on the mind-matter distinction are rather different from those of Descartes, as we shall see later. It can be argued that Leibniz's system is a form of idealism, rather than a dualism.

MONISM

Monistic theories tackle the mind-body problem by disposing of the 'mind' (*experience* in our presentation) or the physical substratum. This may involve an attempt to show that one is a facet of the other.

1. *Physicalism*

Materialism or physicalism, when formulated as a strictly monistic philosophy, encounters an insurmountable difficulty. For the assertion that all is material or physical, with the accompanying denial of the mental, is obviously false if the mental is taken to include our experiences. Physicalism in the 'strong' sense—the assertion that both experience and the substratum are purely physical—does not get us very far, because some characteristics of experience are clearly not physical. The experience of a colour, the sound of a tune, the emotion of joy, the sensation of pain, are not purely geometric-kinematic or physical events in our experience, although physical body-states can be correlated with them. The denial of mind in a physicalist approach would be more acceptable if mind were presented as something intangible and unknown, such as a 'pure consciousness' divorced from any experiential content. But here we have taken experience as the partner of the physical in the mind-body problem, and its existence cannot be denied.

In practice, then, physicalism is not a denial that experience exists, but a statement that we need concern ourselves only with physical entities in explanations, and that experience is completely dependent on the physical. Without the physical substratum there would be no experience, and experience has no effect on the physical world. This 'weak' physicalism is not really a monism, for it retains the dualistic division into experience and the physical. It is therefore not very different from Huxley's epiphenomenalism. Huxley, however, was keen to point out the world of mind is the only world we know for sure, whereas a physicalist prefers to forget this, and stresses the primacy of the physical.

Physicalism employs a form of *reductionism*, which is the attempt to narrow the many and complex to the few and simple. The reductionist method is not confined to physicalism—we have already encountered it in the theories of psychological atomism, which attempt to reduce complexes of experience into experiential elements. Psychological reductionism is also present in explanations of behaviour or motivation that cast the whole of experience in a small number of fundamental explanatory terms. The power of reductionism lies in its single-minded attention to a narrow range of facets, whilst ignoring a multitude of other facets that would distract from the in-depth consideration. There is some attraction in having just a few basic concepts with which the complex multiplicity of the world can be understood, and there can be little doubt that reductionistic approaches have been immensely productive. However, problems arise when the focus is kept too narrow for too long, and a useful but limited set of explanatory terms usurps its useful limits and is universalised into an all-encompassing explanatory system.

Materialist reductionism was at work in the ancient Greek atomism and in the corpuscular philosophy: it was hoped that a few supposedly basic qualities, the geometric-kinematic qualities of structure and motion, would be sufficient to account for all qualities. It is this attempted reduction that leads to the mind-body problem, for it is found that astructural qualities cannot be derived from structural qualities. We saw that the corpuscular reductionism was stimulated by the unsatisfactoriness of contemporary modes of explanation, which invoked a plethora of *occult* (hidden) qualities. The corpuscular philosophy performed a useful function by stressing the importance of structure and structural transformations, and by eliminating pseudo-explanations, but we have seen that the reductionist expectations are difficult to realise, and lead to the mind-body problem.

Physicalist reductionism is expressed in the view that psychology is nothing more than neurophysiology, which in turn is chemistry, which is itself reducible to physics and mathematics. It is supposed that the complexities of psychology can, in theory, be deduced from a detailed knowledge of quantitative physical science. The materialist idea that everything is ultimately reducible to matter in motion found an enthusiastic exponent in the English philosopher Thomas Hobbes (1588–1679). Hobbes was deeply impressed by the proofs of Euclid's geometry and by Galileo's study of motion, and he believed that mind consists of motions in the body. Intellectual activity is to be understood as motions in the head, and the passions as motions in the heart. In sense-perception, motions of objects outside the body are conveyed through the sense organs to the head and heart, where they interact with the natural motions of the body parts, giving rise to 'ideas'.[4] A nineteenth century illustration of the reductionist attitude is evident in the hope that a study of the anatomical structure of the nervous system would lead to a mechanistic account of physiology and psychology. Important figures included Hermann Helmholtz (1821–94), Emil du Bois-Reymond (1818–96), Carl Ludwig (1816–95), and Ernst Brücke (1819–93). The movement was intent on showing that the only processes at work in organisms are physical and chemical, and utilised the recently discovered connection between electricity and nerve conduction. The movement was a reaction to the vitalistic tendencies of the German nature philosophy—vitalists supposed that there are guiding life-forces at work in organisms that are not reducible to physico-chemical entities.

Physicalism is not infrequently accompanied by deterministic views. This is certainly the case in Hobbes's materialism—mind consists of matter in motion, and motion proceeds in fixed, causally determined ways. Therefore mental activity is causally determined. Our choices are expressions of causally determined physical processes, and free will is illusory. Another idea that has sometimes accompanied physicalism is the concept of the man-machine. The body can be viewed as a physical system, an organisation of matter in motion in the materialist version of physicalism. The human body is a machine, an automaton consisting of complex physical mechanisms. It is imagined that a highly skilled craftsperson would be able to construct a machine that has no experiential flux associated with it, but is behaviourally indistinguishable from a human being. Even if experience would arise in the machine, the experience plays no role in its functioning. Its absence would make no difference. Descartes supposed that animals are purely machines, while human beings are body-machines linked with souls. The idea was developed by French materialists, notably Julian de La Mettrie (1709–51) and Paul Henri d'Holbach (1723–89). In their writings, the materialist position was not simply a philosophical response to the mind-body problem, but was intended to undermine the authority of those religious ideas which promise rewards or threaten punishments in the afterlife. Such ideas could be used for the purposes of social control and to justify theocratic power. The mechanical philosophy provided a way of undermining the religious world-view, even though many of the original exponents had regarded the new mechanical-mathematical system as a strong justification for belief in a supreme God, who governs a rational, orderly universe.

In the eighteenth century the skilled creator of a man-machine would have been a watchmaker conversant with Newtonian mechanics, in the nineteenth century a neurophysiologist, whilst in the second half of the twentieth century the computer scientist assumed the role. The development of computers has provided a fruitful approach to modelling some aspects of psychological functioning, and the brain can be treated as an information processor that performs operations on information inputed via the sensory channels and from memory stores. The mind-body problem appears in cognitive science and artificial intelligence because there is uncertainty whether an adequate account of mental functioning can be given in terms of unconscious information processing, without bringing in the personal psychological constituents of experience, such as the inner speech of thought, conscious decisions, and emotions. Do conscious thoughts, in the form of inner speech or visual imagery, influence the unconscious thought processes, or are conscious thoughts merely

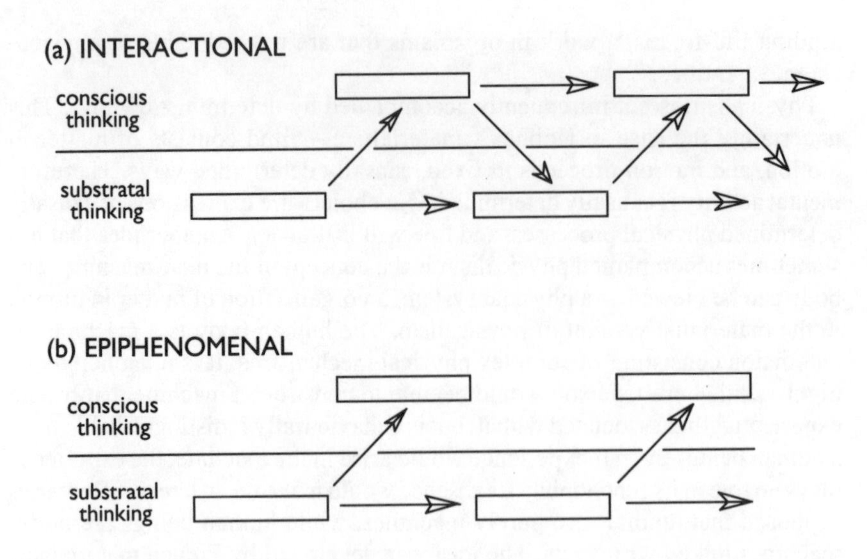

Figure 3.1. The relation between thinking in the substratum and experience: interactional or epiphenomenal? The rectangular blocks represent thought-processes.

epiphenomenal expressions of the latter? Figure 3.1. summarises these two alternatives.

Certainly, it appears to us that our conscious activity—experiences of making decisions, emotional evaluations, understanding meanings, and so forth—has an effect on the unconscious processes that mediate with our bodily behaviour. The physicalist or epiphenomenalist, however, contends that this is mere appearance: experiential contents play no role in information processing.

The 'information processing' form of reductionism does not necessarily reduce experience to the physical substrate of the processing, the biochemical 'hardware' of the brain, but may concentrate on the sequences of logic operations used to process the information, the functions.[5] It does not matter whether the brain-computer hardware is biochemical or solid state. The physicalist, however, may claim that information processing boils down to transformations in physical systems.

2. *Idealism*

Physicalism or materialism is unable to provide a rigorously monistic solution to the mind-body problem. Experience cannot be expressed solely in material or physical terms. Instead, a workable physicalism turns out to be a dualism in which experience is given little or no importance. Experience remains, but is devalued, and denied any causal significance. Hypnotised by the skeletal dance of structure, the materialist ignores the breadth of experience and conceives the whole world, experiential and substratal, in the terms of physical science.

The problem that besets physicalism is not encountered when the monistic solution is applied in the reverse direction. The divide is bridged by postulating that the substratum, as the comprehensive basis of our transient experience, is also *experiential.* This approach can be described as *idealist,* although I prefer to avoid the term because it is applied to a variety of philosophies that are quite different from one another. Idealist theories, in general, maintain that the external world consists of mind, or that mind is the only reality—this leaves plenty of scope for major differences between idealist philosophies, given the lack of consensus over the terms *mind, consciousness* and *ideas.* The discussion here has focused on experience, and the idealist position developed will be the view that the substratum of our everyday experience is itself experiential. To distinguish this approach from other forms of idealism, we could name it *experientialism.*[6]

The philosophies of Berkeley and Kant have been classed as idealist, and idealist notions were influential in early nineteenth-century German philosophy. Notable exponents included Fichte (1762–1814), Schelling (1775–1854) and Hegel (1770–1831). Idealism gained in popularity in Britain and the United States towards the end of the nineteenth century, and a number of contrasting versions appeared. Distinctions are sometimes drawn between absolute idealism and personal idealism. Mind in absolute idealism is regarded as single and objective—there is one Absolute Mind that manifests and underlies individual minds. Personal idealism, on the other hand, stresses the plurality and the independence of minds.

In earlier times, idealist views had some currency in religious philosophies. They have been widespread in Indian philosophy, have had some important expressions in Chinese philosophy through the influence of idealist schools of Buddhism, and in the West have been important in the philosophical tradition of Platonism. Plato never gave a clear expression to his theory of Ideas or Forms, and the theory underwent changes over the course of his philosophical development and in the elaborations of his successors. It seems that the Forms provide a model *(paradeigma)* of which the sensibles are copies, although the exact relationship between the two is never made clear, such as the manner in which the Forms participate in the sensibles. The Forms can be apprehended through *noesis* or *phronesis,* a knowing that is independent of the senses: the curtain can be opened and the substratum revealed. Nature drops her flowing robes to reveal an intelligible realm of even greater beauty.

The tradition that followed Plato, influenced by Aristotle's (384–322 B.C.) concern for the particular, is a little more definite in postulating a world of individual, intelligible objects of which sensory objects are copies. *Nous* (translated as Mind or Intellect) and its intelligible objects constitute the substratum, and *phronesis* of the intelligible substratum, the *kosmos noetos,* is an act of knowing, accessible through moral and intellectual development, and by contemplation.

AN EXPERIENTIAL SUBSTRATUM

In positing physical entities as the constituents of the substratum, the mechanical philosophy selected only certain features of experience, those that are particularly amenable to representation by number and useful for constructing mathematical descriptions. These were the geometric and kinematic features. The resulting physical world proved impossible to picture—we could not imagine it because extension and visual/tactile qualities are not separable in our imagination. Extension and movement in the substratum can be related to extension and movement in our familiar experience, but could not be linked with other facets of experience, such as colour, heat, sound, emotions, conscious thoughts, meaning. In the experientialist response, we reject the purely structural or physical view of the substratum as limited, and admit some astructural qualities into the substratum to make it experiential. In other words, we shall suppose that the substratum is itself an experience. We have adopted a monistic position—our transient experience and the substratum can be linked because both are experiential. The two sides of the mind-body divide consist of experience.

The supposition, then, at this stage of the discussion, is that an experiential substratum supports our plurality of experiences, and that causal influences work both ways between the substratum and our familiar experiences. The dualist idea of a physical brain-state correlated with experiential states is replaced by the idea of experiential brain-states that are closely related to our transient experiences. Indeed, the *transient moments* of our experience could be regarded as special states of the experiential, substratal brain.

There are many matters to consider before the proposed reunion of mind and body through a common experientiality will be at all clear or plausible. If the substratum is experience, why do we not experience it along with our familiar experiences? If the underlying world, including the substratal brain, is experience, it must be experienced in some way—unexperienced experience is contradictory. Yet we are not conscious of the experiential substratum. There are, of course, experiences that are not contained in our familiar experiences, namely the experiences of other experiencing beings, but we need to explain in particular why the experiential substratum is not experienced along with our familiar experiences.

The statement that the underlying world is experiential needs amplification. We would want to determine the experiential characteristics of the substratum, and discover in what ways they are similar to or different from the characteristics of our everyday experience. We would eventually have to work towards re-evaluating the distinctions between qualities according to occurrence, causal role and quantification set out in Chapter Two, for the materialist scheme of attributing only structural qualities to the substratum has been rejected, and needs a replacement.

To begin this task, we can suppose that the contents of the experiential substratum are *structured.* The experiential substratum has taken over the role of the physical world of representative realism, and can absorb the geometric-kinematic structuring and transformation that were the prime features of the physical world. Thus, mathematical descriptions are as applicable to the experiential substratum as they were to the physical substratum, for the latter is simply a denuded version of the former. Thus, the experientialist does not reject the mathematical descriptions of physics, for these describe the structural skeleton of the substratum. However, the experientialist supposes that the structure is only part of the story, and that other characteristics flesh out the substratum.

Another point follows from the original motive for positing a substratum. The incompleteness of our experiential contents suggested hidden objects and hidden causal processes, and was therefore a major stimulus for considering the idea of a substratum. It follows that we should require the experiential substratum to provide a *complete* basis for all our partial experiences. Objects appear and disappear in transient experience, are perceived clearly, obscurely, or not at all, depending on various factors in the perceptual processes. In contrast, we would expect that the current states of all objects are present in full clarity and detail in the experiential substratum. Each state of the substratum must be a complete whole if it is to sustain all the partial experiences of experiencing beings.

We can also say that, unlike our familiar experience, the substratal experience is not limited by the perceptual chains of transmission that lead to the sense-organs. The experiential substratum would be a whole experience, inclusive of substratal perceptual processes outside the body, and also the unconscious resources that underlie each personal flux, the *psychological substratum* introduced in Chapter One. In the experiential substratum, we would presumably find the substratal body of each organism, and all the unconscious processes, structures, memories, and so forth, in the substratal brain that supports the individual flux. The experiential substratum as a whole is a common, universal unconscious for all experiencing beings, with special regions in the bodies of organisms that directly support the individual fluxes. The substratum is, of course, only a universal 'unconscious' with respect to ordinary experience, for it is experiential in nature and is not unconscious with respect to itself. I have assumed that a special, individual unconscious is to be found in each experiencing being, presumably in the substratal brain in the case of higher organisms. We could name these substrates the *personal unconscious* of each individual, the parts of the total substratum that support personal experiences. The form of the contents in a personal unconscious is open to speculation. Personal memories could be encoded beyond recognition, constituting representations that are not resemblances.

I have used the term *personal unconscious* to name the immediate substrate of conscious personality and experience. The term is applied in a more specialised sense in Jungian analytical psychology. I am not sure exactly what contents or processes a modern Jungian psychologist would include in the personal unconscious, but given the psychotherapeutic orientation of the psychology, it is perhaps not surprising to find the term applied by Jung to unconscious personal memories, including painful and unacceptable thoughts and feelings that are repressed from conscious experience. Jung places instinctual and archetypal contents in a deeper level of the unconscious, the collective unconscious, which in some way is common to all.[7] It would not be valid to equate the Jungian collective unconscious with our experiential substratum. Jung's ontology is not too clear, but as far as I am able to gather, the Jungian collective unconscious tapers off into a physical world, and does not include the physical as an essential facet of itself. In contrast, our experiential substratum is a monist response to the mind-body problem, and absorbs the physical aspects into a structured experiential basis.

We have given the experiential substratum structural and experiential completeness. In what other ways can we characterise substratal experience? Fortunately, the epistemological worries over the unknowableness of things-in-themselves are no longer so pressing, for we are supposing that the noumenal world is an experience that is causally related to our familiar experiences, and has some astructural qualities in addition to the geometric-kinematic qualities previously ascribed to the physical substratum. There is now the possibility that the substratum is within our imaginative grasp. It would be tempting to conjecture that some colour qualities belong to the experiential substratum, since we had problems envisaging geometric qualities distinct from colour qualities. What about all the other experiences apart from colour qualities, such as sounds, smells, tastes, warmth and cold, pain and pleasure? Are we to suppose that all colours, tastes, odours, sounds are to be found in the experiential substratum, or just some of these? And what of the 'higher' facets of experience, the complex interplay of emotional feeling, understanding, meaning and volition? Are experiences of anger, love, sadness, hate, expectation, meaning, to be found as such in the experiential substratum?

We would have to consider the organisation of some qualities in the substratum—are the qualities distributed among the extended objects of the substratum? It is fairly easy to imagine a world of extended objects having some kind of *colour* quality, and we are used to ascribing sounds to distant objects.

However, the matter is not as straightforward for taste, touch, pain and other sensations, which we closely associate with our organismic bodies. In familiar experience, many sensations are organised into a body-schema—for instance, a salty taste on the tongue, a headache, a touch sensation of the hand. It is likely that there is much innate cognitive processing and learning involved in the construction of the well-ordered experience, and it is known that the synthesis is open to disruption under certain circumstances. The organisation of taste, touch, pain in the experiential substratum could be very different from the body-organisation of sensations in familiar experience. In summary, then, we have yet to decide which features or qualities are common to both our familiar experiences and substratal experience, and how specific astructural qualities would be related to extended structures in the substratum.

There are causal aspects to be considered as well. We have to reappraise the causal or explanatory distinction outlined in Chapter Two. Would the astructural qualities in the experiential substratum have any causal role, any influence on the course of events in the underlying basis and in familiar experience? We would, for instance, want to be able to trace the perceptual paths leading from a substratal object via the *lumen* to the substratal senses, and finally to the objects of our experience, noting how the various geometric-kinematic and astructural qualities of the substratal object are altered in the process of perceptual representation.

A discussion of causality in substratal experience might have to embrace types of causation that are not normally considered in the scientific accounts of cause and effect in substratal processes. The physical analysis of causation focuses on the relationship between a prior physical cause and the effect that follows, a type of causation that was called *efficient* causation in the philosophy of Aristotle. Now that the substratum is viewed as a comprehensive experience that might include feeling and meaning in addition to the structural qualities, the possibility emerges of non-physical, causal relationships, integrated with physical causation. In our familiar experience, feeling-evaluations and understanding seem to have a role in processes, and the causal influence of a future state on a prior state may even be conceivable, a goal influencing the processes that lead towards it. In the Aristotelian philosophy, this is *final* or *teleological* causation. According to Aristotle, the *telos*, the end or purpose, is achieved through the actualisation *(energeia)* of the potential *(dynamis)*. We would have to consider how efficient causation marries with final causation, and this would require an understanding of the temporal nature of the substratum. In summary, a much broader notion of causality may be applicable to the experiential substratum, and might include some form of final causation, now that the basis has been credited with features other than the structural or physical.

The discussion of an experiential substratum remains highly speculative and would benefit from a grounding in experiential evidence. It is to this possibility that we now turn.

4. EXPERIENTIAL INTIMATIONS

An interesting possibility arises if the substratum is experiential. It may be possible to experience beyond the limits of sense-perception and acquire direct insight into the characteristics of the substratum. In this chapter we shall consider the possibility and look for clues in a type of experience suggestive of an experiential substratum.

EXPERIENCE OF THE SUBSTRATUM

An experiential substratum is an experience. Can this experience become incorporated into our experience in such a way that memories are created, enabling us to remember what has occurred? In a representative theory of perception, it is supposed that under normal circumstances, contact with the substratum is indirect, taking place through perceptual representations and cognitions. In contrast, a *supersensuous* or *trans-sensate* experience would by-pass perceptual representation and draw upon the full experiential extent of the substratum. If such direct experiences are possible, and are capable of leaving memory traces retrievable in ordinary experience, then it is likely that a profound impression would be made, the substratum having a scope far greater than everyday experience. We have supposed that the experiential substratum underlies all streams of experience, and contains the detailed structures and processes of things presented in them. However, it is unlikely that memories of experiences containing substratal content would be very detailed, for the vast scope of the substratum might tax the representational capabilities of an organism. But if some traces are produced, we might find indications of the experiential substratum by examining accounts of extraordinary experiences. The discussion of the experiential substratum would then benefit from the evidence of experience.

MYSTICAL EXPERIENCES

As noted in Chapter One, there is a wide range of experiential states, extending from the familiar group of waking and dreaming states to a host of less common or marginal states, such as hypnotic trances, and borderland states between wakefulness and sleep. Unusual states of experience, so-called *altered states of consciousness,* may occur without obvious reason, or may be linked with illness, the use of psychoactive substances, experiences of intense emotion, or meditative practices. Some marginal experiences are placed in the category of *mystical experience.* Within this category, which itself covers a broad range of experiences, we find a type of experience that is characterised by a greatness of scope and a depth of insight suggestive of content from an experiential substratum. I shall refer to this type of mystical experience as *universal experience,* because the experiences are of very broad scope and may indicate a substratum of universal extent.

It might be hoped that a study of universal experiences would reveal something about the nature of the experiential substratum. Unfortunately, the study of mystical experience is not straightforward, and I can provide only a sketchy treatment of the topic. Some difficulties include:

1. The term *mystical experience* has covered a wide range of experiences, which can differ considerably from one another, and individuals who have had several mystical experiences may describe a number of stages. With this variety of states and stages, there is the danger of mixing characteristics belonging to different types of experience. Thus, there is likely to be some uncertainty in defining the characteristics of the class I have labelled *universal experience.*

2. Although I have assumed that there is a common experiential substratum for all experiencing beings, it does not follow that all universal experiences are identical. Each universal experience may incorporate the substratum from the particular perspective of the experiencing being and therefore involve the cognitions and emotions of the experiencing being. Indeed, accounts of universal experience suggest that some intellectual and emotional responses, reminiscent of everyday experience, occur during the experiences, and this may be a necessary condition for the experiences to be recalled later in ordinary experience. In other words, each approaches the experiential substratum from a vantage-point of place and time, personal cognition, feeling, prior experience and personality, and the resultant blend in the universal experience is unique. According to the Neoplatonic philosopher Plotinus (*c.*205–70), "Of those looking upon that Being and its content, and able to see, all take something but not all the same vision always...."[1] We should not expect complete uniformity in the descriptions of universal experience, although there will be general similarities. Observers on different mountain tops will provide different descriptions of the common landscape, depending on their vantage-point, mood, knowledge of geography, personal interests, the local weather, and so forth.

3. Although mystical experiences are apparently not uncommon, and are by no means the preserve of the few, the experiences are not everyday occurrences and are rarely accessible by choice. Since the experiential substratum is a common basis for all our everyday experiences, it would follow that universal experiences are, in theory, potentially available to everyone, to all experiencing

beings. In practice, however, mystical experience is sufficiently rare and out of the control of the individual to make study of the subject difficult.

4. Individuals may be hesitant to discuss the personally meaningful contents of the experiences with others, for it may be feared that revelations will devalue or betray something precious they have found in themselves, will be dismissed as the product of an over-imaginative or disturbed mind, will be expressions of pride, or may cause harm to those who misunderstand what is related.[2]

5. Studies of mystical experience depend on *descriptions* of experiences, experiences that have been remembered and interpreted to some extent. Accounts of mystical experience may therefore be limited by the capabilities of the memory processes, and by the capacity of the individual to understand the various contents of the experience. The problem of memory may be significant, for it seems unlikely that we would be able to recreate within memory a representation of the all-inclusive underlying world. What is remembered is only a shadow of the experience. William James writes:

> Often, when faded, their quality can but imperfectly be reproduced in memory; but when they recur it is recognized; and from one recurrence to another it is susceptible of continuous development in what is felt an inner richness and importance.[3]

6. To what extent can mystical experience be communicated to others? The ineffableness of mystical experience is often mentioned, but has not prevented many from attempting to describe their experiences. The problems of communication may arise because the experiences are not everyday occurrences, and so there is little common background of experience and descriptive language available. In fact, the problem of ineffableness may not be too much of a hindrance, since the kind of mystical experience we are interested in here is that suggestive of an experiential substratum, which we have supposed may be similar in some respects to the ordinary experience it supports. We may, however, be misled by the poetic, symbolic or mythical language that is used to convey aspects of mystical experience, and caution must be taken to avoid over-literal interpretations.

7. Descriptions of mystical experience come in several forms, often as impersonal descriptions in religious literature, but more recently as personal accounts. In both cases, the experience is likely to be expressed within the framework of ideas that are available and acceptable in the cultural and religious milieu. Some facets of the experience may be left out because they are not part of the traditional view of religious experience—descriptions may be tailored to suit ideas of what mystical experience should be like. We have to be wary

of the doctrinal accounts, which may have become overlaid with theoretical interpretation and misunderstood terminology divorced from experience, and embellished with symbolism and metaphor. All this creates problems when attempts are made to classify and compare the varieties of mystical experience, and decide how similar the experiences may be across cultures, religious traditions and historical periods.

CHARACTERISTICS OF UNIVERSAL EXPERIENCE

I cannot hope to address adequately the problems that beset studies of mystical experience, and my survey of characteristics that may be suggestive of an experiential substratum will inevitably be limited and selective. In describing the characteristic features of universal experiences, I rely on earlier discussions of mysticism and the pool of examples on which these have drawn.[4] It is also worth bearing in mind that our focus here is rather narrow, on the *characteristics* of universal experiences. The characteristics take centre-stage here because we wish to find indications of the nature of an experiential substratum, but in this specialised focus there is the danger of overlooking the broader *context* of the experiences and indulging in a preoccupation with unusual 'states of consciousness'. An understanding of the contents of unusual experiential states is important, but what is ultimately of greater concern is the meaning of the experience in the life-development of the individual. To use an analogy, the wedding ceremony may be a special and memorable event, but it is only a focus between the events that lead up to the union and the married life that follows. In the case of mystical experience, the *special nature* of the event is of interest and worthy of study, but its *place* or *meaning* in the life path is more significant.

In exploring the subject of universal mystical experiences, I have found three mystics and mystical philosophers particularly illuminating, namely the philosopher Plotinus, and two poets, Thomas Traherne (*c.*1638–74) and William Blake. Plotinus is reported by his editor and biographer, Porphyry (*c.*233–304), to have enjoyed four experiences during their acquaintance, and Plotinus himself relates:

> Many times it has happened: lifted out of the body into myself; becoming external to all other things and self-encentred; beholding a marvellous beauty; then, more than ever, assured of community with the loftiest order; enacting the noblest life, acquiring identity with the divine ....[5]

The value of Plotinus in our survey lies not so much in any extended descriptions of his personal experiences, but in the conceptual framework he developed around his mystical insights. With its striking images and its hierarchy of ontological levels, Plotinian philosophy was to exert an immense influence on Western mysticism. At the summit of the Plotinian scheme is the ineffable One, followed by a *Nous* or 'Intellect' that is inseparable from the realm of intelligible objects it contemplates. It is this second, derivative level in the scheme, the intelligible order, the *kosmos noetos,* that seems closest in the Plotinian scheme to the idea of a comprehensive experiential substratum.

Personal descriptions of encounters with the universal are rather more accessible in the writings of Thomas Traherne. Traherne was a clergyman of the Anglican church and a writer of works on church history and ethics, as well as poetry and works of spiritual philosophy and guidance. The most famous is the *Centuries,* which may have been composed for a religious community in Herefordshire gathered around a Mrs Susanna Hopton. The discovery of the *Centuries* in a London bookstall by William T. Brooke at the close of the nineteenth century, and its subsequent identification by Bertram Dobell as the work of Traherne, is a dramatic story, and has provided us with a work that stands out as both a high point of seventeenth-century English literature and a spiritual document of great profundity. Traherne's promise to fill the book with "profitable wonders"[6] and to tell of things "strange yet common, incredible, yet known; most high, yet plain; infinitely profitable, but not esteemed"[7] is achieved in abundance, and we shall have reason to quote from the work on several occasions. One of the most famous passages is the autobiographical description in the third of the five sections of the *Centuries,* in which Traherne relates the mystical apprehension of his infancy:

> The corn was orient and immortal wheat, which never should be reaped, nor was ever sown. I thought it had stood from everlasting to everlasting. The dust and stones of the street were as precious as gold: the gates were at first the end of the world. The green trees when I saw them first through one of the gates transported and ravished me, their sweetness and unusual beauty made my heart to leap, and almost mad with ecstasy, they were such strange and wonderful things.[8]

There are similarities between the ideas of Traherne and William Blake, but also significant differences. Common themes include the visionary state of childhood, Innocence contrasted with Experience, the rejection of materialism and life-inhibiting religious morality, traditional understandings of the obscuring senses, and personal visions of eternity. Struggle and conflict are much more to the fore in Blake's comprehension of the world, although Traherne is also aware of misery and the seamier aspects of life. His writings allude to times of personal despair and to the sufferings of the world, but his vision is so expansive and deep that he cannot limit his optimism. The writings of Traherne and Blake resonate with biblical and Platonic themes, but their styles are very different: Blake, the prophet of Lambeth, is a passionate blaze, whilst Traherne, the rector of Credenhill and Teddington, is a radiant flame. To his contemporaries, Blake was a puzzle: his close friends knew a kindly but eccentric man, gifted with an extraordinary imagination, whilst others thought they discerned the ravings of a madman in Blake's mythopoetic creations and his extraordinary conversational pronouncements. Later generations have acknowledged Blake's literary, artistic and psychological genius, which for the most part went unrecognised during his lifetime. Traherne's works are still undergoing a process of discovery, and have yet to be appreciated fully.[9]

But without further ado, let us begin our survey of the characteristics of universal mystical experience. Several lists of the characteristics of mystical experience have been put together, and one of the most famous is to be found in William James's classic of 1902, *The Varieties of Religious Experience.*[10] The book contains several descriptions of mystical experiences, as well as more general examples of religious experience. James proposed four *marks* that characterise the states of consciousness he called 'mystical':

ineffability: very difficult or impossible to describe,
noetic quality: a state of knowledge,
transiency: cannot be sustained for long,
passivity: no control over what happens in the experience.

Another early writer on mystical experience was the Canadian psychiatrist Richard Maurice Bucke (1837–1902), whom James quotes in the *Varieties.* Bucke is of special interest to us here because he focused on experiences that involve a "consciousness of the cosmos, that is, of the life and order of the universe."[11] At the age of thirty-six, Bucke had a mystical experience that prompted him to study the subject, and his work was published in 1901 under the title *Cosmic Consciousness,* the name he gave to the mystical experiences in question. Bucke distinguished eleven marks of "cosmic consciousness" or "cosmic sense". Some of these are not descriptive of the experience itself, but are concerned with related matters, such as the effect on the person and the age of the person.[12] Of particular relevance to the experience itself is a mark that Bucke calls "intellectual illumination", which is "a clear conception (a vision) in outline of the meaning and drift of the universe."[13]

> ... he sees and knows that the cosmos, which to the self conscious mind seems made up of dead matter, is in fact far otherwise—is in very truth a living presence. He sees that instead of men being, as it were, patches of life scattered through an infinite sea of non-living substance, they are in reality specks of relative death in an infinite ocean of life. He sees that the life which is in man is eternal, as all life is eternal; that the soul of man is as immortal as God is; that the universe is so built and ordered that without any peradventure all things work together for the good of each and all; that the foundation principle of the world is what we call love, and that the happiness of every individual is in the long run absolutely certain.[14]

In particular, the experience brings "a conception of THE WHOLE, or at least of an immense WHOLE" beside which our ordinary attempts to grasp the universe and its meaning are "petty and even ridiculous."[15] One of the most interesting accounts in the book was provided by a woman identified by the initials C. M. C., who had the following experience in 1893 at the age of forty-nine:

> I felt myself going, losing myself. Then I was terrified, but with a sweet terror. I was losing my consciousness, my identity, but was powerless to hold myself. Now came a period of rapture, so intense that the universe stood still, as if amazed at the unutterable majesty of the spectacle! Only one in all the infinite universe! The All-loving, the Perfect One! The Perfect Wisdom, truth, love and purity! And with the rapture came the insight. In that same wonderful moment of what might be called supernal bliss, came illumination. I saw with intense inward vision the atoms or molecules, of which seemingly the universe is composed—I know not whether material or spiritual—rearranging themselves, as the cosmos (in its continuous, everlasting life) passes from *order to order.* What joy when I saw there was no break in the chain—not a link left out—every thing in its place and time. Worlds, systems, all blended in one harmonious whole. Universal life, synonymous with universal Love! How long that period of intense rapture lasted I do not know—it seemed an eternity—it might have been but a few moments.[16]

The writer discovered that she "loved infinitely and was infinitely loved!"[17]

> It was the gladness and rapture of love, so intensified that it became an ocean of living, palpitating light, the brightness of which outshone the brightness of the sun. Its glow, warmth and tenderness filling the universe. That infinite ocean was the eternal love, the soul of nature and all one endless smile![18]

C. M. C. also describes an experience of "being *centred,* or of being *a* centre", of being supported or anchored on all sides by something that provides no obstruction to movement but is "as permanent and solid as the universe."[19]

Another example of mystical experience that shows some common themes is provided by Ancilla, who describes an experience at the age of forty-three in her book, *The Following Feet.* Sitting in a church near Nuremberg in 1934, she felt her 'self' step down from the centre-stage of importance, and was led by a joyful humility into an experience that was both momentary and eternal. In the experience, the world was not drastically changed, having "form, and colour, even good and evil, and animals and people", but was also different from usual, being complete, a whole.[20]

We shall now consider some important features of universal mystical experience that seem to me to be representative of the category. It is worth bearing in mind again that an analysis of experience into its features can be misleading if the integrated quality of the experience is forgotten.

1. *Completeness*

This is the defining characteristic of the universal experience. The scope is very great, sometimes described as infinite. It is a whole and a unity, encompassing all particulars. It extends to the very large and very small, to the near and the far. The all-encompassing nature is experienced spatially, temporally, in understanding and in the feeling of love.

2. *Cognition*

There is a very strong cognitive element in the universal experience. A sense of total comprehension, knowing and meaning seems to be an integral and effortless feature. It is Bucke's 'intellectual illumination', and James called it the 'noetic quality' of mystical states, regarding it as a principal feature along with ineffableness. The following description by the Franciscan mystic Angela of Foligno (c.1248–1309) illustrates both features:

> The eyes of my soul were opened, and I beheld the plenitude of God, wherein I did comprehend the whole world, both here and beyond the sea, and the abyss and ocean and all things. In all these things I beheld naught save the divine power, in a manner assuredly indescribable; so that through excess of marvelling the soul cried with a loud voice, saying 'This whole world is full of God!'[21]

Although particular understandings may be picked out from the experience, it is the total comprehension that strikes the experiencer, a complete and general understanding that is not retained on the return to ordinary experience. It may be thought that something extraordinarily simple and obvious has been realised,[22] that one has always known it at some level,[23] and that many others realise it too throughout the span of time. In some religious philosophies, such as those building on Plato's theory of Forms (as in Middle Platonism and Neoplatonism), the cognitive nature of the substratum may be emphasised by equating it with the *thoughts* of God or a divine mind. For Plotinus, the intelligible order underlying the sensible world, the *kosmos noetos,* is united with the divine mind, the *Nous,* as the object of its thought.

3. *Absence of Flux*

It is a common theme in the mystical literature that the temporal aspect of experience is very different in deep mystical experience. In fact, a cessation or absence of time is sometimes claimed. This characteristic of 'timelessness' or the eternal refers to an absence of flux—there is no sense of shifting from one experience to the next. The word *eternal,* as used here and throughout the remainder of the book, is to be distinguished from *everlasting.* The latter refers to something that endures forever, having an unending life-span, whilst the former refers to a condition in which the sense of flux is said to be absent. The objects in universal mystical experience are permanent or stable in the sense that they do not transform from one state to another across a succession of experiences that seem to replace one another—instead, it would appear that the objects in all their successive states are contained in some way in the one experience. 'Time', as the continuity of temporal states of objects, is contained in its entirety in one experience. The Dominican theologian and mystic, Meister Eckhart (*c.*1260–*c.*1328), describes a form of knowledge, above the sensory and the rational, that apprehends a 'timeless present':

> It knows no yesterday or the day before, or tomorrow and the day after, for in eternity there is neither yesterday nor tomorrow, there is a present *now:* that which was a thousand years ago, and that which will occur in a thousand years, is present there, and so is what is beyond the ocean.[24]

If we take universal mystical experiences to be indicative of the nature of the experiential substratum, we must then question the assumption that kinematic qualities, the qualities of motion, characterise the objects of the underlying basis, at least in the way encountered in our transient experience. We can still ascribe static geometric qualities to the substratal objects, and the successive states of these objects could form a more extensive spatial geometry, as we shall consider in Chapter Six. A greater spatiality is described by Thomas Traherne:

> One would think that besides infinite space there could be no more room for any treasure.... This moment exhibits infinite space, but there is a space also wherein all moments are infinitely exhibited, and the everlasting duration of infinite space is another region and room of joys. Wherein all ages appear together, all occurrences stand up at once, and the innumerable and endless myriads of years that were before the creation, and will be after the world is ended are objected as a clear and stable object, whose several parts extended out at length, give an inward infinity to this moment, and compose an eternity that is seen by all comprehensors and enjoyers.[25]

In the substratum, temporality seems to be incorporated into an enlarged spatial field. The experiential substratum, then, would not undergo instantaneous creation and destruction from moment to moment, but would contain within its permanent whole all transformational states of objects statically displayed in the enlarged spatial field. The substratum contains all the states of objects that appear little-by-little in transient experience. William Blake expresses the difference between the flux-world and the underlying eternity, the world of Imagination—the objects in the mirror of sensory experience are images of "Permanent Realities":

> This world of Imagination is Infinite & Eternal, whereas the world of Generation or Vegetation, is Finite & Temporal. There Exist in that Eternal World the Permanent Realities of Every Thing which we see reflected in this Vegetable Glass of Nature.[26]

The wholeness ascribed to the underlying basis is not merely that of a momentary spatial state of the universe, but is the wholeness of the universe throughout its total spatial and temporal extent. Clearly the possibility of a fluxless substratum is of great significance, and the idea will become a focus of discussion in the remaining chapters.

4. *Luminosity*

References to *light* figure very extensively in the literature of mysticism. The usage may be symbolic or metaphorical, sometimes expressing the achievement of an understanding, as in such non-mystical phrases as "suddenly the meaning dawned upon me" or "the darkness lifted". In other instances, it seems that an actual experience of light, of *lux,* is intended. Light experience occurs in many classes of mystical experience, in addition to the universal type we are considering here.

Plotinus frequently ascribes vision and light to the underlying intellectual principle.

> The life in the Divine Intellect is also an Act: it is the primal light outlamping to itself primarily, its own torch; lightgiver and lit at once; the authentic intellectual object, knowing at once and known, seen to itself and needing no other than itself to see by, self-sufficing to the vision, since what it sees it is....[27]

The Christian mystic Jan van Ruusbroec (1293–1381) describes the Light in which "one becomes seeing":

> Behold, this mysterious brightness, in which one sees everything that one can desire according to the emptiness of the spirit: this brightness is so great that the loving contemplative, in his ground wherein he rests, sees and feels nothing but an incomprehensible Light; and through that simple Nudity which enfolds all things, he finds himself, and feels himself, to be that same light by which he sees, and nothing else.[28]

In our experientialist approach to the mind-body problem, we could interpret the luminous content of universal mystical experience as an indication that colour qualities are actually found in the substratum, and are not confined to sensory and dream experiences. The problem of structural qualities without visual qualities, pointed out by Berkeley, then disappears: the spatio-temporal geometric structures in the substratum do have colour qualities. The structural quality of extension is not distinct from the astructural visual quality (hence the term *astructural quality* is not really adequate).

It is not clear from the evidence of universal experiences what colour qualities might characterise the experiential substratum. The matter is complicated by the variety of mystical states and stages, and by the symbolic uses of colour descriptions, which are not actual descriptions of experiences. Generally, descriptions of white or golden luminosity are very common, and in the Tantric traditions of Buddhism the *Clear Light* is described. Coloured lights are mentioned in the mystical literature, although they are sometimes regarded as derivative, not belonging to the light in its purity, and maybe obscuring the pure light. If the luminosity of the substratum is single-hued, we may ask how the great variety of hues in transient experience is derived. To provide a satisfactory answer, we would probably have to understand in depth how the stable, fluxless luminosity of the substratum links with the shifting luminosity of transient experience.

The luminosity of mystical experiences is sometimes described as solid or crystalline. According to St John of the Cross (1542–91), "In this state the soul is like the crystal that is clear and pure...."[29] Perhaps it is the fluxless character of the luminous state that suggests crystalline solidity. Descriptions of crystallinity may imply transparency as well as solidity, and indeed the luminous world is sometimes described as *transparent.* Transparency seems to follow from the complete scope of the universal experience. The scope of sensory experience is dependent of the transmission of information, and visual experience is incomplete. We usually see the surfaces of objects, and these surfaces hide the interiors of objects and the objects in the background. Substratal experience, on the other hand, would not be dependent on perceptual processes, for it is a complete cognition. There would be no obstruction in a total experience, because objects are present in their entirety, not as images of surfaces constructed through perceptual processes. The theme is found in Blake's writings: he contrasts the opacity of sensory experience ("terrible surfaces" that imprison men in "Selfhood", separating them from the "Divine Humanity") with the transparency or translucency of Eternity: "What is above is Within, for every-thing in Eternity is translucent".[30]

Sense-experience provides some instances of transparency: the 'empty space' between the three-dimensional arrangements of objects, and various transparent materials and objects, such as water, glass, crystals and jewels. Such familiar instances of transparency may provide useful comparisons for pointing to the transparency of universal experiences and the experiential substratum, and are to be found in mystical space symbolism and in descriptions of bejewelled locations and beings.[31]

What other astructural qualities, besides the colour quality, are presented in universal experiences? It is not clear to me whether there is much evidence for tastes, sounds or odours. The occasional mentions in the mystical literature could be intended metaphorically.[32] We may wonder how sound would manifest in a fluxless experience—as a structural variation, as a panoramic cognition-feeling of harmonies? It seems that bodily pain is absent in deep states. As for temperature qualities, some types of mystical experience are characterised by heat, but it is not clear to me whether this is also true for universal experiences. Body experiences are likely to be very different from the familiar body sensations of transient experience since the organisation of astructural qualities would no longer be linked with a distribution of sense-receptors and a cognitive body-schema, as we noted in the previous chapter. The body of experience in the universal mystical state is no longer the organismic body—the compass of skin and interior sensations—but could be construed as the whole extent of the universal experience, encompassing the entire universe and all organismic bodies.

5. *Emotional feeling*

A deep and all-encompassing feeling of love is often encountered in universal experiences, and may constitute an integral characteristic of the substratum. Now, the word *love* can be used to label many states of feeling or types of relationship, some of which have little to do with the love that concerns us here. It is therefore appropriate that we try to gain a clearer understanding of love in the universal context. For instance, it is important to note that love, whether genuine or grossly distorted, is not simply a feeling. In the discussion of familiar experiences in Chapter One, we noted that emotional feelings are not really separable from cognitions and body sensations. In considering love, we should therefore be alert to its cognitive facets, to the understandings or misunderstandings that it involves. Indeed, love—whether love in ordinary experiences or in substratal experience—may be usefully termed a loving attitude, for the love is directed towards something, the person or 'object' of the attitude, and has cognitive, affective and behavioural/active facets.[33] Erich Fromm (1900–80) discussed the loving attitude in *The Art of Loving,* and singled out care, responsibility, respect and knowledge as features that show the active character of love.[34] Love in this sense could also be called *benevolence,* a term that conveys the activity, well-wishing, understanding and concern, but fails to bring across the intensity of the loving cognition.

The loving attitude at the substratal level would presumably have some special features. Firstly, substratal cognition is complete, and therefore love at this level would be based on total understanding and knowledge, in contrast to the partial and often distorted understandings of familiar experience. Secondly, substratal cognition and the object of cognition may not be separable, for it seems that the *knowing* is also the *being* at this level. Thus, the object of the loving attitude is the same as the cognition. Furthermore, the loving feeling and the knowing are sometimes said to be inseparable, to be one and the same. Finally, the active or 'behavioural' aspect of the attitude could be interpreted as the urge towards benevolent or compassionate action felt in the experience, an urge that is perhaps actualised in the long-term development of beings, and displayed in its fullness in the eternal view.

Whereas the loving attitude appears to be an integral feature of the experiential substratum, other feelings in the universal experience seem to be personal reactions to the emergence of the substratal knowing and loving. Feelings of surprise, awe, humour, amusement, relief, joy, or peace may be evoked. There may be relief because a state of being has been reached in which pain is absent, and the sense of peace may derive from the full meeting of needs and strivings. The searching has come to an end, if only in the experience. There may also be unpleasant reactions—fear, confusion, self-evaluative feelings of unworthiness, impurity, horror at the narrowness of one's customary outlook and aims. Indeed, a realisation of the loving attitude is likely to provide a shocking insight into insular self-concepts and attitudes to others developed in the limited scope of transient experience, and could induce a level of self-esteem that is lower than before the experience. The discovery may lead to self-recriminations or feelings of impurity if there is a comprehension that the loving attitude has been contradicted by personal attitudes and actions.

To use a mirror-metaphor—the mirror as a source of self-knowledge—the substratum, with its full cognitions, may be experienced as a clear mirror in which one's self-deceptions, petty glorifications, selfish motivations, poor treatment of others, are fully exposed. The potentially withering experience of encountering the loving attitude has been expressed in a religious framework by a seventh-century Nestorian, Isaac the Syrian (Isaac of Nineveh): he explains that the suffering of sinners in Hell is not a deprivation of the love of God, but the intense sorrow that follows from the realisation that sins have been committed against love.[35] It is sometimes stated that the revelation of mystical contents can be too much to bear, and that a retreat into the shady currents of flux takes place—the loving attitude and the knowledge it brings may be too painful, too threatening to self. Indeed the withdrawal may be a necessary protection against a potentially destructive undermining of the personal self. Protective defence mechanisms may intervene, as they do in the more mundane traumas of life. The 'light' is painfully bright; the 'heat' conflagrates the unprepared soul.[36] To develop an openness to and readiness for the universal experience, the individual may be encouraged to undergo moral purification, and to develop actively the substratal characteristics. The progressive education in the mysteries of love, leading to the vision of absolute beauty, received a famous exposition in Plato's *Symposium.* In theological terms, the process of cultivating universal characteristics aims to bring out the likeness of God, or to lead to an assimilation to God, to *homoiosis.*

Related to love in mystical writings are the experiences of compassion and beauty. It is conceivable that there is an element of anguish in the feeling-cognition of compassion, since compassion involves a knowledge of the suffering of experiencing beings. As for the beauty of the intellectual realm, it is a commonplace in Platonic thought.

6. *Self-and-others*

The sense of self is frequently reported to undergo changes in mystical states. That this occurs in universal experiences should come as no surprise: the self-concept of our ordinary experience, organised around the limited organismic body, personal memories, thoughts and feelings, is likely to be challenged severely by a shift to a vastly expanded scope of cognition and feeling in which the usual, sharp distinction between self and other changes radically. The alteration in sense of self may be experienced as a liberation and union, a loosening of the restrictive boundaries of cognition and feeling that have separated self from the rest of the world. For instance, in the *Select Meditations,* Traherne describes a double self in man, the confined self of man in the world, and the self of man in God, conversant with Eternity.[37] The substratal mirror of understanding seems to reveal two selves, the personal self understood in a new, unsettling light, and the transformed self of universal cognition and feeling.

A terminology that distinguishes between the familiar experiential self and the experiential self of universal experience would be useful. Bucke distinguishes between the *self conscious self* and the *Cosmic Conscious self,* regarding the latter as an evolutionary advance on the former. In fact, Bucke refers to a *duplex self* to indicate the two sides of self. Jung's distinction between *ego* and *Self* could be used, but these terms have their particular meanings and nuances in analytical psychology. We might, instead, distinguish between the *experiential self* and the *experiential Self* (using the capital letter to denote the greater scope of self-experience), or between the *experiential self* and the *universal self, transpersonal self* or *superpersonal self.* Other terms used in the past include the *oversoul, the higher self,* and in Hindu thought, the *atman.* I shall opt for the term *universal self,* the self-experience that may become apparent in universal experiences. Building on the terms used in earlier chapters, we might then make the following tentative distinctions:

(a) The *personal self:* the personal self-system of an organism, consisting of the self in ordinary states of experience, and its immediate roots in the substratum.

(i) The *experiential self:* the self in ordinary experience distinguished from other selves and objects in the environment, the 'myself' described in Chapter One, covering the self-concepts, self-awareness, emotional feelings, volitions, extended body, and body feelings, that appear in the flux of experience. It is the phenomenological self.

(ii) The *personal unconscious:* the hypothesised immediate unconscious substratum that supports the experiential self and includes unconscious self-concepts, emotional attitudes towards self, concepts about others that help to define 'myself', personal memories (pleasant and unpleasant, accessible and inaccessible), perceptual and cognitive processes.

The personal self develops throughout the lifetime, beginning with its formation in infancy.

(b) The *universal self:* expanded self-concept, emotional feeling and 'body', which appear to be revealed in universal mystical experiences.

(c) The *total self-system:* the integration of the experiential self, personal unconscious, and universal self in a total, interactive system.

In making these discriminations, my intention is not to present the self-terms as names for things, substances or persons separate from experience—say, a 'transcendental self' that observes experience—but to provide a vocabulary that may be of use in discussing the self as a *content* of various types of experience. We should also bear in mind that there is considerable uncertainty over the ascription of self-cognitions and feelings to the substratum as a whole. How appropriate is the application of the term *self* in the universal context? Is some kind of self-cognition—a sense of 'I-ness'—an integral part of the experiential substratum? Or is the altered self-concept a transitional phenomenon in which old personal self-identifications have become loosened and reapplied to the substratal experience? In other words, does the universal knowing and loving of the experiential substratum include an intrinsic self-concept? Only considerable familiarity with universal experiences would help us to gauge the matter.

Another term is the *universal mind* of some idealist philosophies, and in theistic systems the idea of a greater self is sometimes joined with the idea of God, at least with the manifest God, contrasted with the unmanifest God or Godhead that has no attributes or cognitions, self or otherwise.[38] Whether a sense of self can rightly be attributed to the experiential substratum then becomes the theological question: is Selfhood to be attributed to the manifest

God? If so, the process of *homoiosis,* assimilation to God, would be an assimilation to a greater self. For instance, in the idealism of *Libellus XI* of the *Corpus Hermeticum,* 'Mind Unto Hermes', there seems to be an exhortation to reconstrue limited self-concepts into what could be called an all-inclusive Self-concept. By encompassing the universe in the mirror of one's thoughts, the mind becomes like God, who contains the world as a thinker contains thoughts.

> If then you do not make yourself equal to God, you cannot apprehend God; for like is known by like. Leap clear of all that is corporeal, and make yourself grow to a like expanse with that greatness which is beyond all measure; rise above all time, and become eternal; then you will apprehend God. Think that for you too nothing is impossible; deem that you too are immortal, and that you are able to grasp all things in your thought, to know every craft and every science; find your home in the haunts of every living creature; make yourself higher than all heights, and lower than all depths; bring together in yourself all opposites of quality, heat and cold, dryness and fluidity; think that you are everywhere at once, on land, at sea, in heaven; think that you are not yet begotten, that you are in the womb, that you are young, that you are old, that you have died, that you are in the world beyond the grave; grasp in your thought all this at once, all times and places, all substances and qualities and magnitudes together; then you can apprehend God. But if you shut up your soul in your body, and abase yourself, and say 'I know nothing, I can do nothing; I am afraid of earth and sea, I cannot mount to heaven; I know not what I was, nor what I shall be'; then, what have you to do with God?[39]

The text may present a meditative exercise in which an attempt is made to embrace the all-inclusiveness of experience in a greater, eternal Self.[40]

Connected with the idea of the universal self of mystical experience may be the notion of the *macrocosmic person,* the cosmos at large, the macrocosm, conceived as a cosmic person. There are numerous religious and mythological instances, including *Purusa* of the Indians, *Gayomart* of the Persians and the Gnostic *Anthropos.* The cosmic person fragmented into pieces is a common theme, a splitting that can be interpreted as a symbol of the division of the eternal universal self into the multiplicity of isolated personal selves in flux.

So far, our discussion of self in the universal experience has been deficient because the *social* dimension of the experience has not been stressed. The cognitions and feelings of an experiential self in ordinary experience, which involve distinct boundaries with other selves, seem to be transformed into a unified cognition-feeling of self-and-other-selves, a 'great togetherness'. In the universal loving attitude, the universal self unites all selves in a unity of multiplicity. The *universal self* is 'selfless' by virtue of this loving unity of selves, and self-experience at this level might be better called *universal self-with-other-selves,* or *universal self-in-love-with-other-selves.*

In a famous passage in the *Centuries,* Traherne begins by affirming that "You never enjoy the world aright, till the Sea itself floweth in your veins, till you are clothed with the heavens, and crowned with the stars: and perceive yourself to be the sole heir of the whole world", but then adds, "and more than so, because men are in it who are every one sole heirs, as well as you."[41] Traherne's stress on the *sole* possession or heirdom of the world[42] may appear inflated or even solipsistic. Indeed, Traherne himself relates that some believed much learning had made him mad.[43] Yet Traherne adds that the soul is but one "sole heir" *among many,* a state of affairs that maintains the distinctness of each soul and adds to the perfection of all..

> THE very sight of other mens Souls, shining in the Acts of their Understanding throughout all Eternity, and extending themselves in the Beams of Love through all Immensity, and thereby transformed (every one of them) into a Sphear of Light comprehending the Heavens, every Angel and every Spirit being a Temple of GODS Omnipresence and Perfection; this alone will be a ravishing Spectacle to that Goodness, which delights to see innumerable Possessors of the Same Kingdome: Much more will the Perfection of the Kingdome it self, which by infinite Wisdome is so constituted, that every one is the Sovereign Object, the First born, and Sole heir, and End of the Kingdome; Every one the Bride of GOD, every one there a King, yet without Confusion, or Diminution, every one distinctly, enjoying all, and adding to each others fruition.[44]

Paradoxically, *all* are *sole* heirs. "Thou hast made me the end of all things, and all the end of me. I in all, and all in me."[45] Perhaps meditating along similar lines, Paracelsus (1490–1541) wrote (quoted by Jung)[46] "... heaven is man and man is heaven, and all men are one heaven and heaven is only one man." Jung calls it the experience of the *coniunctio,* the self discovered to be intimately connected with other selves.[47]

Blake expresses the idea in his conception of *Eden,* the highest of the four states of humanity:

> Then those in Great Eternity met in the Council of God
> As one Man, for contracting their Exalted Senses
> They behold Multitude, or Expanding they behold as one,
> As One Man all the Universal family; & that One Man
> They call Jesus the Christ, & they in him & he in them
> Live in Perfect harmony, in Eden the land of life,
> Consulting as One Man...[48]

The universal self seems to involve a togetherness of selves within the loving attitude, a social or collective self. This would imply that self-esteem and esteem for others, which we noted in the discussion of the personal self in Chapter One, are merged in the experiential substratum, and consist of the universal loving attitude that we have discussed above. We shall return to the idea of self-love in the next chapter.

From what we have noted so far, it should be clear that universal experiences, along with related mystical experiences, are likely to provide a challenge to the personal self-concept, particularly to narrow, rigid self-concepts, and may set in motion conceptual and emotional changes that could take a long time to work through and integrate within the personal self. The process of transformation, of emotional and conceptual readjustment, may be so extensive that it is expressible symbolically as a *death* of the old personal self. A glimpse in the 'mirror of eternity' may precipitate a psychological death, an 'ego-death' that makes way for the reconstruction of a personal self in which the implications of substratal material can be accommodated. Like other transformative life-events, the appearance of substratal content in experience has much potential for enriching and maturing the personality, but the process can bring its difficulties, with ample opportunities for the stirring up of unpleasant material from the personal unconscious, confusions, resistances, devaluation of the personal self, dangerous and compulsive religious striving, inflatory identifications of the personal self with universal content, dogmatic beliefs, and so forth. Psychologists, counsellors and psychotherapists who acknowledge a transpersonal range of experience have begun to explore the role of mystical and related experiences in personal growth, and have paid some attention to the various problems that may arise in the process.[49]

HUMAN NATURE AND THE DIVINE

If we suppose that there is an experiential substratum of the kind intimated in universal experiences, we may wonder how to conceptualise its relation with ourselves, and what contribution this understanding should make to our self-evaluations. The flux of experiential self is highly variegated in its range of cognitions, emotions and actions: as human beings, we are each capable of expressing great love and appalling cruelty, and much else between the extremes. What are we to make of human nature? What light is thrown on the question by mystical intimations of an experiential, universal substratum at the root of the personal self?

A long history of philosophical and religious thinking has sought to place humankind in relation to the 'spiritual' and the 'material', and to reach some understanding of human nature. We touched on this concern in Chapter One, noting the issues of transcendence, immanence, and the indwelling of God. Mystical experiences, which take the experiential substratum from the field of philosophical speculation into direct personal awareness, bring such issues to the fore and can be quite challenging to beliefs that place a wide gulf between experiencing beings and the divine. Individuals have sometimes struggled to express their mystical insights in forms acceptable to orthodox religion. The insights of mystical experience tend to be congenial to notions that admit a divine indwelling and regard basic human nature in a positive light, and may incline thinkers to entertain notions of an immanent God, forms of idealism, or the spirituality of matter.

It is true that the idea of divine indwelling has the potential to encourage an investment of great value in the individual life, and can stand in opposition to distorting mirrors in which the human being is viewed as a purposeless and disposable bag of chemicals or as a creature innately blighted by sin. Yet it is also true that an excessive reliance on the mystical range of experience or the conception of the indwelling divine as a source of value may compromise an appreciation of ordinary life and its essential limitations, of the limited human personality in its variety. This is likely to be the case if the spiritual is thought to be confined to only one part of the individual, a divine core or spark that is valued at the expense of the rest of the person. Such a view is conducive towards material-spiritual dualisms and world-transcending attitudes. In this context, it is interesting to note the appearance in Mahayana Buddhism of the idea of the buddha-nature (Sanskrit: *buddhata*; Japanese: *bussho)* inherent in all creatures. It is this eternal nature that enables every creature to become Buddha. Chan-jan (711–82), the ninth patriarch of the T'ien-t'ai school of Chinese Buddhism, is noted for extending the idea to things that are normally regarded as inanimate. Taking an idealist position, he maintained that nothing exists apart from mind and that the distinction between animate and inanimate is invalid. All things, including people, trees, grass, soil, a particle of dust, have the buddha-nature, and follow paths to the realisation of buddhahood. The idea of the buddha-nature, like that of the indwelling God, may or may not be interpreted in a way that gives value to the personal self: in a negative view, the buddha-nature could be viewed as the eternal core encrusted by the dross of the individual, or in a positive view as immanent in the person as a whole, in perception, thought, emotion, body, and activity.

Notions in Western thought on the divine indwelling owe much to biblical ideas and to Greek religious philosophy. In the Old Testament the affinity of man with the spiritual is brought across in the story of the creation: the first man was created in the image and likeness of God (*Genesis* 1.26), and God breathed His spirit into the nostrils of the man of dust to give it life (*Genesis* 2.7). The New Testament promised a restoration of the image, the *imago Dei,* through the salvatory work of the Son, the true image of God. The fallen image could be reformed. Exactly what was to be understood by the image of God in man, and man's likeness *(similitudo)* to God, and exactly what constituted its reformation, were open to interpretation by Christian writers.[50] The idea could incline towards religious dualism if the divine image was regarded as a soul, or part of a soul, *distinct* from the material body—only the divine image is to be valued, not the human mirror that reflects it. Less inclined to dualism was an old strand of thought that took the person as a whole to be the image of the divine universe, the person as microcosm, or *minor mundus,* a 'little world' reflecting the great macrocosm.

In the overtly mystical sense, the idea of the microcosm points to the experiential presence of the divine in human beings: that each is created in the image of God or in the image of the cosmos is taken to mean that each can find God and the divine cosmos within. The mystical element occurs in the Plotinian understanding of the microcosm:

> For the Soul is many things, is all, is the Above and the Beneath to the totality of life: and each of us is an Intellectual Cosmos, linked to this world by what is lowest in us, but, by what is the highest, to the Divine Intellect....[51]

That each one of us is "an Intellectual Cosmos", or intelligible universe, can be interpreted to mean that in the mystical ascent each finds the intelligible order within.[52] The passage also suggests another strand of microcosmic thought. Each is a microcosm because each partakes in all aspects of the world, from the divine and angelic to the animal and material. Human beings are at the centre of the chain of being extending from the highest to the lowest, and as middle-terms they connect the spiritual and the material. The idea of microcosmic man spanning or uniting the heights and depths was popular in the late Middle Ages, and had some currency in Renaissance concepts of human nature.[53] The microcosm-macrocosm relationship has been applied in other ways too. It may, for instance, indicate the existence of correspondences between human beings, nature and the heavens, as in the widespread systems that related the spiritual, human, animal, vegetable and mineral realms.[54]

In the mystical understanding of the microcosm, the ancient inscription "Know Thyself" on the temple of Apollo at Delphi could be interpreted as an injunction to look 'inwards' to find the intelligible order and the God within. It was supposed that the creature, soul, or divine spark in the soul, could be assimilated to God, and perhaps even become identified *(theosis)* with God.[55] In some cultural and historical periods, care had to be taken in promoting such views. Christian mystical writers were open to accusations of pantheism, or other heretical beliefs, when they described the mystical union with God. Meister Eckhart found himself in difficulties towards the end of his life, and Ruusbroec had to modify his earlier descriptions of union by adding the qualification that no creature is able to become God in the union, describing "How we, though One with God, must eternally remain Other than God."[56]

Where are we left, then, regarding the problem of human nature? Human characteristics are highly variegated across individuals and within each individual, and a simple answer would fail to do justice to the complex nature of human personality. But if we are concerned with an *intrinsic* nature or a *potential* nature, as opposed to a *conditioned* state, then the mystical perspective may tempt us to assert that the substratal foundation of human personality, and indeed the foundation of every experiencing being, is the universal loving attitude. We may then be inclined to go along with the Chinese philosopher Mencius (*c*.371–289 B.C.) in supposing that there is an "original goodness" in each of us, a capacity to respond compassionately to the suffering of others and wish for their well-being, and that the "way of learning is none other than finding the lost mind" in which the loving attitude finds its complete expression.[57] As human beings, we have impressive cognitive endowments and strong social needs, a combination that places us in a good position to bring out the potentialities suggested by universal experiences. Yet the combination also provides us with immense potential to do harm to one another. It is clear that the substratal core may be very well hidden, and that the promise of its flowering in human personality may remain very much a potentiality amid the difficult conditions of life. We shall return to the subject in the next chapter, when we consider attitudes towards time.

SUMMARY

In exploring the characteristics of universal experience, we have encountered several indications of the possible nature of an experiential substratum, but have been left with many uncertainties. Knowing, meaning, loving seem to be clearly indicated, and some kind of light quality could well be an attribute of the experiential substratum, filling in the structural characteristics, although it is not clear how the substratal *lux* is related to the variety of colours in ordinary experience. The occurrence of other astructural features, such as sound, taste and pain, is rather more uncertain. It may be that some astructural characteristics of our ordinary experience require a condition of flux in order to take on their familiar natures, a temporal combination of sub-experiences. Bodily pain, for instance, might require a 'fusing' of experiential parts, which in their latent, substratal form are not painful in the familiar sense, but have experiential contents, including cognitions, that become our familiar pain sensations when expressed in transient experience. This possibility will become clearer when we consider transience and the temporal complexity of the moment, in Chapter Six.

Rather than pursue any further the difficult task of ascertaining substratal astructural/psychological characteristics, we shall focus on substratal structure and motion, for here we can look towards the physical sciences for information. The lack of flux stands out as a substratal characteristic that may be particularly useful in furthering our understanding, for we can explore how the idea of fluxlessness in the experiential substratum links with conceptions of space, time, and motion in the physical sciences. The spatio-temporal structure of the substratum, and its relationship with our familiar experience, will become the focus of attention in Parts II and III.

5. TIME AND ETERNITY

Our approach to the mind-body problem has been to absorb the physical substratum into a comprehensive experiential substratum in which structural qualities are supplemented by other features, including luminosity, cognition and feeling. Universal mystical experiences suggested that the experiential basis might differ from our usual experience in several important respects. In particular, transience, or the characteristic of flux, is often reported to be absent from universal experiences. If the evidence of such experiences is to be taken seriously, then the straightforward ascription of motion qualities to objects in the substratum will need modification. In this chapter, we begin to explore the idea of fluxlessness by considering the philosophical and psychological background.

BEING AND BECOMING

Flux was a subject of great interest to early thinkers. Change is observed throughout nature, in the cycles of the day and the year, in growth and decay, in life and death. Objects require some degree of stability to maintain their forms, but ultimately stability is never more than temporary, and change is always taking place. Old patterns break apart, and new patterns emerge. Materials change into other materials, or change state between solid, liquid and gas. Transformation may occur very suddenly or gradually, perhaps imperceptibly. Nowadays we understand that the earth has had a long history of geological change, mountains rising and crumbling, continents drifting apart. We can speculate on the formation of the earth, sun and planets from a cloud of hot gasses four to six thousand million years ago, and we can make predictions about the eventual fate of the solar system. We observe flux throughout the universe, with galaxies and clusters of galaxies in relative motion, and stars undergoing violent explosions.

There is regularity in all this change, on the Earth and in the heavens, and we may wish to understand the order behind transformations. In recent centuries, there have been promising attempts to formulate mathematical laws of change. The classical laws of conservation, for instance, maintain that certain quantities, such as energy and momentum, remain unchanged from moment to moment. An understanding of change promises greater control of our surroundings, and a knowledge of inorganic and biological processes advances our technological, agricultural and medical skills. We, too, are subject to transformation, and the journey through the life-span ensures that stability and change are always matters of personal concern. Through the span we cannot rest for long, challenged by common life-transitions and unexpected events, by changing biologies and social roles. Individual life never remains the same for long, though the patterns recur from generation to generation.

The theme of change, of life and death, received widespread attention in the creative efforts of the ancient civilisations, and figures in much religious and mythological speculation. How was the world created and how will it end? Why were we born, and why are we subject to disease, ageing and death? What powers govern the transformations of nature? Are these powers personal or impersonal? Can they be placated or controlled?

From a background of religious and mythological thought, a distinctive way of looking at nature emerged in the West in the sixth century B.C. with the Milesian philosophers, who lived in the Greek city-states of Asia Minor. They speculated that everything develops from a primary stuff, and that the structure and transformations of the world are explicable in terms of this *arche.* Thales of Miletus held water to be the basic stuff, perhaps inspired by the mythological accounts in which water is the creative source. Anaximander proposed an abstract basic substance, which he called *apeiron,* the 'indefinite', while Anaximenes chose air as the *arche.* Heraclitus of Ephesus (6th to 5th century B.C.) took a cosmic fire as the basic stuff, which he connected with an intelligent ordering principle, the *logos.* Water and earth derive from the fire, and transformation between the three takes place in a regular fashion, the overall quantity of each being conserved. Heraclitus has come to be associated with the idea that "everything is in flux" *(panta rhei),* and that one can never step into the same river twice.[1] Whatever Heraclitus' position on flux may have been, his theory of opposites ascribed an important role to change or *strife.*[2]

Empedocles of Acragas (*c.*495–435 B.C.) combined some of the earlier *arche* speculations in his theory of the four 'roots' *(stoicea),* in which the cycle of change is regulated by two principles, Love and Strife, and the basic elements are fire, water, earth and air. There were also medical and psychological versions of these theories: in the Hippocratic writings the elements were identified with bodily fluids, the four humours, which disposed individuals to certain personality types and illnesses, depending on the relative amounts of the humours in the bodily constitution. Similar approaches to change are to be found in early Chinese philosophy and science, with the theory of five elements and the comprehensive classification of transformations in the *I Ching,* the Book of Changes, which categorises transformation into sixty-four basic types.

In the Milesian philosophies, change and motion are an integral part of the world, and the later element theories show a continued interest in change. By the time of Empedocles, however, a philosophy had appeared that denied the reality of change, and provided an immense challenge to later Greek philosophers. This was the Eleatic philosophy, the philosophy of Parmenides of Elea (born *c.*515 B.C.) and his followers. Parmenides describes a chariot journey through the portals of Day and Night to a rendezvous with the Goddess, who tells Parmenides the Way of Truth, and the Way of Error which people commonly follow. The argument hinges on the proposition that something either exists *(is)* or does not exist *(is not),* and that which does not exist is unintelligible. If something comes into being and goes out of being, then it *is not* before and after it *is*. Since the state of *is not* is rejected as unintelligible, the idea that things can come into being and perish has to be rejected. Hence, the Way of Truth belongs to the *is* logical alternative, and that which satisfies it is single, continuous, unchanging, uncreated and imperishable.[3] Multiplicity and time are eliminated from the real universe. This is the Parmenidean One, a spherical, timeless Being. The Eleatic cause was furthered by Zeno of Elea (born *c.*490 B.C.), a pupil of Parmenides, who put forward a number of paradoxes to undermine the notions of plurality and motion. Four of Zeno's paradoxes are concerned with motion, and the best known is the race between swift-footed Achilles and the tortoise. The tortoise is the slower of the two but starts further along the race track. The race begins and Achilles reaches the starting-place of the tortoise. In the meantime the tortoise has moved a small distance, and in the time Achilles covers this distance, the tortoise moves a little further. So the race continues, Achilles moving closer and closer to the tortoise, but never quite reaching it.

In practice, the faster runner will overtake the slower, and we are left to puzzle the significance of Zeno's argument. The story raises questions about the divisibility of distances and time-intervals. Achilles must traverse an infinite number of positions and endure an infinite number of instants in order to move at all, for the slightest spatial distance or temporal interval is taken to be infinitely divisible in the story. It can be debated whether the infinite divisibility of space and time is in fact a problem—does it matter whether Achilles has to traverse an infinite number of segments, since together they add up to a finite length that is traversed in a finite time-interval? Alternatively, the infinite divisibility of Achilles' path can be denied. It is then supposed that motion occurs in 'leaps' of finite lengths and finite durations—a moving body occupies only a few of the infinity of positions that make up its path, appearing and disappearing from position to position. Space and time are taken to be atomic, indivisible below certain lengths and durations.

Various theories of atoms were put forward in the ancient world. We have already had cause to look at the atomic theory of Leucippus and Democritus. This theory has been interpreted, following Aristotle, as an attempt to reach a compromise between the Eleatic philosophy and the philosophy of flux. The non-being that Parmenides rejected as unintelligible was introduced in the form of the *void,* to make motion a possibility (an idea first proposed by Melissus, a philosopher of the fifth century B.C.), and the problem of infinite divisibility raised by the paradoxes was rejected by introducing a plurality of indivisible unities. These physically indivisible atoms agreed with the Eleatic doctrine for each constituted an unchanging unity. As well as theories of material atoms, there were speculations about atomic time, a minimal time. A notable instance was the atomism of Diodorus Cronus (fourth century B.C.) who argued that atomic movements—appearance in one position followed by reappearance in the next—are possible. Various forms of atomism were also considered in the Islamic world.[4] It is noteworthy that the idea of 'leaps' has returned in quantum physics, and the modern quantization of space and time could be taken to imply that Achilles has only a finite, but very large, number of positions to cover before he overtakes the tortoise.

The opposition between the timeless Parmenidean One and the 'all is flux' view ascribed to Heraclitus has become a major theme in the history of Western philosophy, and continues in one form or other to this day in the struggles between eternalist and temporalist philosophies. The unchanging *is* and the transient flux have been called Being *(on)* and Becoming *(genesis),* and Eternity *(aion)* and Time *(chronos).*

Western philosophical views about Becoming have rarely been as extreme as the total Eleatic rejection, but there has often been a tendency to ascribe Being a greater degree of reality than Becoming, and this can be seen in the philosophy of Plato. Plato attempted to steer a middle course between the eternalist and temporalist positions. He accepted both Being and Becoming, and brought the two into relationship by associating them with the different levels of knowledge in his epistemological scheme. The highest level, the world of Forms, is timeless and perfect, whereas the lower levels based on sense-perception are subject to change. In Becoming, things cannot be grasped in any permanent way. The objects of perception are glimpsed fleetingly, and no certain or final knowledge is obtainable. In Being, the objects of knowledge were permanently available. However, Being and Becoming are not unrelated: the objects of the sensible world are copies of the eternal Forms, and are said to participate *(methexis)* in the Forms. In the *Timaeus,* Plato expresses a positive view of the sensible universe, and Time acquires a more exalted status than it is usually accorded—it is a moving image *(eikon)* of Eternity. Eternal Being is the model used by the divine craftsman when he fashioned the world of Becoming. In the *Sophist,* Plato even suggests that there is a Form of Motion *(kinesis).*

In the *Timaeus,* Plato accounted for the processes of change by interpreting the four elements in geometrical terms: bodies consist of space bounded by geometrical surfaces. The elements are identified with four regular solids (the tetrahedron, the cube, the octahedron, and the icosahedron) and transformation occurs through the disintegration and reintegration of their component isosceles and scalene triangles. Plato assigned the fifth regular solid, the dodecahedron, to the cosmos, but the solid was later associated with a fifth element, the *quinta essentia* or *aither,* which circulated round the heavens in the Aristotelian cosmology. The explanation of matter in terms of space and boundary was to exert a considerable influence on medieval thought, and as we have seen, matter came to be identified with spatial extension in the philosophy of Descartes.

Ideas of Time and Eternity underwent developments in the Platonic philosophical tradition. Philo Judaeus (*c.*20 B.C.–*c.*50 A.D.), who brought together Middle Platonism and Jewish scripture, regarded Eternity as the life of the intelligible universe and Time as the life of the sensible universe.[5] In the Plotinian development of Platonism, the intelligible realm of *Nous* is eternal, whereas the lower levels of emanation are involved in time. Like Philo, Plotinus maintained that Eternity and Time are two kinds of life. Eternity is not to be identified with the intelligible universe itself, although there is a "certain excuse"[6] for making such an identification. Rather, Eternity is to the intelligible universe as Time is to the sensible universe. Time is "the Life of the Soul in movement as it passes from one stage of act or experience to another"[7] and Eternity is "a life limitless in the full sense of being all the life there is and a life which, knowing nothing of past or future to shatter its completeness, possesses itself intact for ever."[8]

Plotinian philosophy, along with the exotic ideas of Hermeticism, Gnosticism and later Neoplatonism, exerted a considerable influence on Jewish, Christian, and Islamic thought, particularly within the mystical undercurrents of these religions. Concepts of eternity also prospered in the mainstream, St Augustine's (354–430) discussion of eternity being influential, and the work of the Roman philosopher Boethius (480–525) was widely read throughout medieval times. Boethius regarded simultaneity as a characteristic of the Eternity belonging to God. Eternity is the "total, simultaneous and perfect possession" of life.[9] In contrast, the creature set in time is unable to take in at once the total extent of its life.[10]

The idea of an eternal reality, in which all periods of time are present, raises the problem of determinism and free will. Boethius denied that an eternal, divine knowledge compromises free will, but others found it less easy to reconcile free will with eternal knowledge and the pre-destination it seems to imply. If the future is set out in one complete act of knowing, in the omniscience of Eternal Being, then it may be wondered if we have any power to choose a future state and work towards bringing it about? If all is eternally set out, have we any real choice? It may seem that there is only one outcome possible, whatever we decide to do. Can we then be held responsible for our actions? We shall return to the matter in the next chapter.

Interest in the eternal continued beyond the theological and mystical discussions of the medieval period, and was stimulated by the revival of classical ideas in the Renaissance. Later, the notion of an eternal realm appeared in the idealist philosophies inspired by Kant's distinction between the phenomenal and noumenal. Kant had regarded the space and time of phenomenal experience as constructions, and not characteristics of the noumenal world. German idealists, such as Fichte and Schelling, criticised the idea of unknowable things-in-themselves, and stressed the timelessness of the noumenal world. For these idealists, the noumenal has the nature of mind. In Hegel's philosophy, the world behind appearances is the Absolute, a universal mind uniting all the individual minds. Alongside the timelessness of the Absolute, Hegel also proposed a dialectical theory of change, which he traced to the philosophy of Heraclitus.

Although Hegel's ideas soon lost their hold in Germany, they were influential for a time in the English-speaking world, and inspired several idealist philosophers in the late nineteenth and early twentieth century. According to T. H. Green (1836–82), Mind is not in time, but is an eternal consciousness, and acts of knowing within time are a participation with the eternal consciousness. In the idealism of F. H. Bradley (1846–1924), the Absolute is an all-encompassing experience, devoid of relations or qualities, and lacking the appearances of space and time. Bradley's notion of the Absolute experience is clearly different from the experiential substratum we have entertained here, which involves luminous, spatially extended objects. Another absolute idealist of the period was Josiah Royce (1855–1916)—there is an Absolute Experience which is complete, unlike fragmentary individual experience. To the Eternal Consciousness, the whole of time is present.

The reality of both space and time was denied by J. M. E. McTaggart (1866–1925). But McTaggart's version of idealism differed significantly from those of Green, Bradley and Royce. McTaggart's idealism is *personal*—the Absolute is a *community of selves,* a system of substances that have complete knowledge and love of one another. McTaggart deduces the unreality of time from a supposed contradiction in the notion of temporal flow, in which an event changes from future to present to past. An event, or the moment in which the event is contained, has the characteristics of being future, present, and past, a combination which McTaggart views as contradictory.

The tendency to downgrade or even deny the reality of time in the idealist philosophies of the late nineteenth and early twentieth centuries was not left unchallenged. Some were dissatisfied with the deterministic implications they saw in the idea of an eternal world. C. S. Peirce (1839–1914) and William James both rejected strict determinism, and James disliked the absolutist view, with its notion of an eternal reality, the "block universe", which seemed to make free will an illusion. He opposed the absolute monism of the all-encompassing, timeless Absolute, the "all-form", suggesting instead a plurality of temporal existences, the "each-forms", united with one another at the edges, rather than in a single, real Absolute.[11] James made it clear that his opposition was not a purely rational matter: he disliked the block universe of contemporary idealists, because of its intellectual abstraction and its "clean-shaven" perfection.

> The "through-and-through" universe seems to suffocate me with its infallible impeccable all-pervasiveness. Its necessity, with no possibilities; its relations, with no subjects, make me feel as if I had entered into a contract with no reserved rights, or rather as if I had to live in a large seaside boarding-house with no private bed-room in which I might take refuge from the society of the place.[12]

James saw an ally in Henri Bergson (1859–1941), in whose philosophy he found an invitation to discard the idea of a timeless Absolute and embrace instead the temporal:

> Dive back into the flux itself, then, Bergson tells us, if you want to *know* reality, that flux which Platonism, in its strange belief that only the immutable is excellent, has always spurned; turn your face towards sensation, that fleshbound thing which rationalism has always loaded with abuse.—This, you see, is exactly the opposite remedy from that of looking forward into the absolute, which our idealistic contemporaries prescribe.[13]

Whitehead was another influential advocate of flux. His process philosophy stressed the open-endedness of temporal development and the immanence of the past in the present. Whitehead's philosophy of process, like that of Bergson, inspired the Christian Process Theology movement, in which the idea of a distant, timeless God was rejected in favour of a God actively involved in the temporal struggle of evolution.

ATTITUDES TOWARDS TIME

Time, as transience, as change, is basic to our experience, and has often stood as a symbol of life, of the life-journey from cradle to grave, with its joys and splendours, its struggles and horrors. In this symbolic role, time has figured prominently in myths, religions and literature.[14] A persistent theme has been the tendency to relegate time, to demean it, or even deny its reality. The tendency is present to some extent in the legacy of the Eleatic doctrine in Western thought, but disdain of the temporal is to be found much further afield, and has often been part of a general devaluation of the world. The denial of the flux-bound world of everyday experience may be found linked with a repudiation of the senses, thought, the personal self, sexuality, the passions, body, matter, nature, the feminine, life itself. Austerities have often figured in attempts to transcend mundane experience and achieve a supposedly spiritual alternative.

Why has temporal existence frequently been judged unreal, illusory or substandard in some way? Clearly, transient experiences exist—they are the one sure actuality we ordinarily have, an actuality that even contains any conjectures we might formulate on the non-existence of flux or the existence of some greater 'reality'. A philosophical denial must therefore mean something other than non-existence. What, then, lies behind talk of unreality or illusion? Let us consider some possibilities.

1. *Flux is mere representation?* Sometimes 'unreality' seems to be a way of saying that the underlying basis, as the represented, is the genuine original, the reality, whilst transient experience, as representation, is an imitation, an appearance. The argument fails to recognise that a representation has an actuality of its own, whether or not it is a fair copy of the original. A painting is not simply a copy of the subject, but is a thing in its own right, with its own features, and its own causal influences. Furthermore, representations make up only part of our experiences, which contain much more than sensory images.

2. *Flux is partial?* Transient experience may be judged limited, relative, incomplete, imperfect, when it is compared with an all-encompassing substratum, whether physical or spiritual. This may lead to the value-judgement that transient experience is unsatisfactory or unreal. However, incompleteness and imperfection are not be equated with unreality.

3. *Flux implies clouded awareness?* Compared with experiences of the universal, our ordinary, transient experiences may seem clouded and lacking in intensity. Some accounts of mystical experience use metaphors of sleeping, dreaming and awakening to bring across the superior clarity of the experience. The experiencer may be faced with a contrast between the 'mountain-top' experience of limitless light, knowing, love and bliss, and the 'cloud-covered' flux in which these features are greatly diminished, with accompanying uncertainties, stress and emotional ups-and-downs. The shock discovery of a mode of experience statically embracing a sweep of consecutive events may lead to the conviction that 'flowing time' is illusory. It is a reaction to the previously unquestioned familiarity with transient experience. However, once the novelty of the eternal has faded, a resolution may be possible in the acceptance of both Becoming and Being as equally real—although not equally clear and complete—aspects of existence.

4. *Flux obscures the fluxless?* Flux may be blamed for hiding the eternal. According to Eckhart, "There are three things that prevent us from hearing the eternal Word. The first is corporeality, the second is multiplicity, the third is temporality. If a man had transcended these three things, he would dwell in eternity...."[15] It is time that "keeps us from the light. For nothing is so firmly opposed to God than time."[16] However, in a more positive view of time, an

intimate connection between time and eternity may be acknowledged: time provides a path to the eternal, or more positively still, time builds the eternal. As we shall conjecture later, flux and substratal experience are not separable: there is no eternity without time, no time without eternity.

5. *Flux is deceptive?* The perceptions of transient experience may be deceptive if they contain implicit misinterpretations, or lead to understandings that are unwarranted. A representation can be deceptive if it is taken to be an absolute likeness or identity, or if it is interpreted as something that it is not. The mirage is an experiential reality, but it is deceptive when taken to be a pool of water. Likewise, the mirror image is an actuality, but we are deceived if we confuse it with the original. Again, the dream or hallucination is an experiential actuality, but it becomes deceptive when it is not understood for what it is, and is confused with ordinary experience. In representational realism, the dream differs from waking experience, for it is not a direct perceptual representation of the external world. It may, however, be a fair representation of conditions in the individual's personal unconscious. The dream is deceptive when we believe it to be something other than it is.

Some of the epistemological sources of dissatisfaction with flux are illustrated by Plato's philosophy. Plato's simile of the Prisoners in the Cave in *The Republic* is a well-known and striking expression of the idea. The human condition is likened to the state of prisoners held fast in a subterranean cavern. A fire casts shadows onto a wall in front of the prisoners, who take these two-dimensional shadow-representations to be the real objects. But a prisoner who is freed from his bonds can turn to the fire and the objects that cast the shadows, and even make the difficult ascent from the cave to the upper world, the intelligible realm, where the sun shines, the ultimate source of all, corresponding in the simile to the Form of the Good, the highest of the Forms. The limitation of knowledge in transient experience is contrasted with another level of knowing. William Blake frequently expresses the idea. For instance,

> If the doors of perception were cleansed every thing would appear to man as it is, infinite.
> For man has closed himself up, till he sees all things thro' narrow chinks of his cavern.[17]

In Blake's *Jerusalem,* the figure Erin explains:

> The Visions of Eternity, by reason of narrowed perceptions,
> Are become weak Visions of Time & Space, fix'd into furrows of death...[18]
>
> The Eye of Man, a little narrow orb clos'd up & dark,
> Scarcely beholding the Great Light, conversing with the ground:

> The Ear, a little shell, in small volutions shutting out
> True Harmonies & comprehending great, as very small...[19]

Presumably it is the contrast with the more extensive scope of knowing that makes transient experience seem so unsatisfactory. If the 'upper world' has been experienced, there might be a reluctance to return to the cave and a tendency to disdain cave-life. Plato makes an insightful point on the transitions between the lower and higher levels of knowledge, between the cave and the upper world, the dark and the light: a transition either way could be highly disorientating. We might add that the disorientation might include a devaluation of the human affairs in the cave, the intensity of the experience causing a blindness to the value of mutable human experience. A dualism is set up between the eternal, regarded as the 'spiritual world', and the temporal, regarded as the 'material world'. Indeed, the Platonic simile of the prisoners in the cave tends in this direction, with its unflattering picture of human ignorance and confinement. The tendency is not complete in Plato, for his account of the sensible world in the *Timaeus* is fairly positive—Plato's demiurge fashioned the temporal world as a beautiful copy of a beautiful, eternal original. Nor does Plato suggest that the released prisoner should stay in the upper world: the prisoner is to be encouraged to return to the cave for the good of the many, for the knowledge of the upper world can be usefully applied for the good of those still in bondage. Plato has in mind the teaching and execution of Socrates—the new perspective gained in the upper world may be met with ridicule and even violence by the troglodytes firmly entrenched in their cave-perspectives.

SUFFERING AND THE MYTH OF THE FALL

Besides the largely epistemological concerns, there have been other motives behind the devaluation of transient experience. These have often stemmed from the potential of transient experience to be unpleasant, varying from mild and fleeting discomfort to intense and prolonged suffering. Time is made a symbol of suffering, or the agent or arena of suffering: time is a devourer, a destroyer, a crushing wheel, a raging fire, a sea of drowning souls, a battleground. Indeed, life in the temporal world can be very difficult, with its conflicts, dangers, diseases, cruelties. The body is fragile. Feelings are vulnerable. The self is threatened by events in the outer world and by conflicts within. Loved ones are similarly vulnerable, adding greatly to our anxieties. There is the knowledge that death is inevitable, promising non-existence or a continued existence of uncertain nature. There would be little point in delineating the varieties of dissatisfaction and suffering that 'flesh is heir to'—suffice is to say that there are frequent periods in the collective life and in each individual life when unpleasant and distressing experiences come to the fore.

The suffering encountered in temporal flux and the search for deliverance have been persistent themes in mythology and religion. The mythographers devised various tales to account for the origin of the world and man, of sickness and death, of evil. Why is there death, disease, famine, war, cruelty? Is there a life in which the sorrows of temporal existence are absent? How can such a life be attained? Not uncommonly, the mythic account involves three stages: a blissful original state following a creation, a state of suffering and searching, and a state of resolution, which may be the initial state regained or a new development. When the concluding stage is viewed as a return to the initial stage, the intermediate stage of flux is likely to be viewed as an unfortunate disturbance.

In the original state, which sometimes follows a divine creation, there is a paradise or a golden age in which an unsullied mankind lives in harmony with nature, blissful, happy, free from sickness and conflict. This state comes to an end through a sudden fall or a gradual deterioration. Not infrequently the change is said to come about through an act of self-assertion (disobedience, ambition, self-will) or harm to others (lack of benevolence, murder, the eating of meat)—the society of nature is disrupted and a fall from innocence occurs, followed by a nostalgic yearning for the lost home or paradise. Human beings are no longer unconscious participants in nature, but outsiders painfully sensitive to their separate existence and their vulnerability. For instance, in the ancient Mesopotamian tale, the hero Gilgamesh is shaken by the death of his friend Enkidu, a man of nature. He realises his own mortality and searches for an elixir, the plant of immortality. The fall may be a loss of innocence through knowledge, sometimes a realisation that there is something wrong with the world. Siddhartha, the prince who becomes Buddha, wakes from the slumber of palace life when confronted by signs of the human condition: sickness, age and death. A fourth sign, a holy man, inspires him to search for a solution to the problem of suffering.

In some myths of the fall, it may be mankind in general that has descended into a world of suffering and death. In others it is the individual soul that falls, exiled from its divine origin into the world of matter and darkness. This latter theme is common in Orphic, Pythagorean, Gnostic and Manichaean thought, and versions are to be found in Neoplatonism. Plato's image of the cave may have drawn on Orphic or Pythagorean thought, in which life in the cave is viewed as a death for the fallen soul. Empedocles, for instance, seems to have bemoaned his fall into the Sphere of Strife, to wander for many lives in "this roofed cave", although he conceded that the intelligent use of sensory experience would lead to clear understanding. In *Pagan and Christian in an Age of Anxiety,* E. R. Dodds describes the views in late antiquity: it is often the Pythagorean *tolma,* self-assertion or wilfulness, that is held to be responsible for the fall.[20] In other versions it is the soul that chooses to descend, through a love for Nature, or through the soul's narcissistic attraction to its image in the mirror world of matter. Initially, Plotinus subscribes to some of these views, but in his mature writing, sharpened by his criticisms of Gnostic attitudes, the descent is regarded as instinctive, a natural process without sin, a consequence of the manifestation of the One.

The second stage of the mythic process is life in the world of transformation, a world sometimes symbolised as a churning sea of space and time, a field of suffering, a sickness, a gaping wound, a barren wasteland once fruitful. The picture may be painted very grim indeed, and from some experiential perspectives, individual and collective, such pictures are no doubt justifiable. According to Dodds, the turbulent period of the later Roman empire was a time when pessimism in religious thought came to the fore: man is insignificant, and there is something unreal about mortal life—it is an insubstantial dream, a delusion, a vicious drama, a comedy, an absurdity. The sensitive individual feels out-of-place in the world, an alien in a foreign country, exiled from the homeland above the planetary spheres. In world-views yet farther removed from the sparkle of classical Greek rationalism, there appears a still darker picture of the world: in some Gnostic views, the demiurge assumes a sinister nature, is regarded as an evil creator presiding over a world of suffering. The universe is no longer divine and beautiful: it is a place of darkness and matter in which the divine sparks of light are ensnared. Escape is sought from the hostile world to the good Father beyond.

In the cosmic drama, the second stage comes to a close with the end of our familiar time, an end that is viewed as either individual liberation from the cycle of rebirth, or a collective salvation when there will be "time no longer".[21] In Zoroastrianism, an ancient religion of Persia that exerted a considerable influence on the eschatologies of later religions, the restoration *(frashokereti)* of the world followed a universal judgement at the end of a historical process of twelve-thousand years' duration.

The image of the Fall lends itself to usage outside purely mythic and religious contexts, to symbolise any change of conditions that is experienced as a decline or loss. Physical sickness, for instance, may be experienced as a fall from health, and the image of the fall could be applied to transitions in the life-span if they are experienced as difficult, including transitions from childhood to adolescence, or from adulthood to old-age. A variety of other changes may also be experienced as falls, such as the break-up of a relationship, the loss of a job, or a bereavement. These may involve a fall from a state of comparative emotional stability to one of upset and unsettled readjustment, and a call for changes to the self-concept. Other falls can be seen in the transpersonal areas of experience: in Chapter Four, we noted the potentially disturbing effects of emerging substratal material in mystical experiences as one type of experience that may precipitate a turbulent process of change in the self-concept. The fall could also refer more specifically to the end of a mystical experience, the shift from a luminous, blissful state to the comparatively limited scope of ordinary experience. Traherne provides a graphic description of the possibility:

> After that sight it is better perish and be annihilated, than live and be bereaved of it. The fall from so great a height would fill the Soul with a cruel remembrance, and the want of its former glory and bliss be an infinite torment.[22]

There has been considerable progress over the last hundred or so years in understanding 'falls' and the experience of loss. The social and psychological causes of personal suffering have received much attention and we are in a position to understand how negative attitudes, conscious and unconscious, towards self, others, and life in general, may be influenced by life-experiences. The subject is too broad and complex to examine here in any detail and we shall restrict ourselves to a brief look at an especially important psychological form of the three-stage process of fall and restoration. This interpretation acknowledges the importance of social relationships in the development and maintenance of the self-system. The three-stage process begins with an inhibition of an intrinsic human capacity for joyful, loving, social relatedness, is followed by an experience of self in isolation, and may find its resolution in the reparation of the feeling of social relatedness.

The formulation of this psychological story of human development owes much to the stimulus provided by certain weaknesses in Freud's pioneering psychoanalytic theory. The theory had the strength of emphasising the role of childhood experiences in the acquisition of inner psychological conflict, but was deficient in several respects. One area that attracted criticism was Freud's depiction of the personality at birth as a cauldron of chaotic, primitive instincts, driven to seek pleasure and reduce tensions. In Freud's scheme, the personality is innately dark and chaotic from the start, with no inborn drive towards social relatedness. As Ian Suttie (1889–1935) pointed out, the psychoanalytic mirror of human nature was comparable, in its attitude towards the new-born child, with the doctrine of Original Sin. Suttie, a British psychoanalytic 'heretic' in the mould of the fifth-century British monk Pelagius, argued that the infant is born with a social impulse to give and to respond, and that "the greed and hate, 'the ape and the tiger within us', 'original sin', proclaimed by Freudians and theologians alike as characteristically human"[23] is the result of early love-privations. The 'beast within' is not naturally self-centred and rapacious, but becomes so when it is abused, manipulated, unappreciated, neglected, starved of unconditional love, overstimulated, excessively controlled.

The notion of an inborn striving to relate to others, a social need that is liable to frustration and distortion, has found other advocates, within psychoanalytic thought and in other psychological systems. A number of Freud's followers, including Alfred Adler (1870–1937), Karen Horney (1885–1952), Erich Fromm and Harry Stack Sullivan (1892–1949) moved away from classical psychoanalytic theory by rejecting the notion of an innate destructiveness and by emphasising the role of social-environmental influences in the development of innate potentialities. Mainstream psychoanalytic theory has also moved towards a more social understanding, with such developments as the Object Relations school. John Bowlby's ideas on bonding, separation and loss have also been influential. The humanistic movement in psychology, in which Abraham Maslow (1908–70) and Carl Rogers (1902–87) were leading figures, opposed the pessimistic conception of human nature in psychoanalytic thought. According to Maslow, our needs and abilities are essentially good or neutral, and we have a tendency to develop or actualise intrinsic potentialities. The tendency to actualise may be frustrated by environmental influences. Rogers felt that "the basic nature of the human being, when functioning freely, is constructive and trustworthy".[24] The core of personality is positive: "the innermost core of man's nature, the deepest layers of his personality, the base of his 'animal nature,' is positive in nature—is basically socialized, forward-moving, rational and realistic."[25]

Explanations of what is thwarted, when and how the thwarting occurs, and what reparative experiences can be usefully undertaken in later life, vary across the wide range of modern psychotherapeutic theories, but to state the matter very generally, it may be supposed that during some periods of an individual's development, especially in the formative early years, a person's sense of worth and social feelings of love, tenderness and trust, are liable to be undermined by poor relationships, the belittling attitudes of others, losses, privations, separations, social and cultural conditioning, to such a degree that fear, anxiety, insecurity, guilt, anger, feelings of threat to self, a sense of being unworthy of love, isolation, come to permeate experience. Defensive reactions may be provoked, defences that are liable to distort the self-image further, hinder relationships and restrict the enjoyment of life.

If such developments constitute a 'fall' in psychological development, an estrangement that we all inevitably undergo to some degree, it may be wondered what resolution may be aimed towards. Clearly, one way forward would be to move towards an open, joyful, loving attitude to self and others. The idealised state of childhood may become a symbol for the attitude if we, as jaded adults, witness moments of its natural expression in children. Actual childhoods, of course, are often very different from the idealised image, a fact that has received increasing acknowledgement in recent years, but the image of the child remains a powerful symbol for qualities that we may wish to find in ourselves. Maybe what we see is a loving attitude, a trust in life and in others, an innocence and openness, a creativity and spontaneity, a natural spirituality, a sense of wonderment. In the account of the 'psychological fall and restoration' provided in Eric Berne's Transactional Analysis, the *natural child* facet of the personality is given much importance, and Berne associated the natural, uncorrupted child with the capacity to relate to others in a loving, aware, spontaneous fashion that is not exploitative and manipulative.[26]

The importance of self-love or self-esteem has received considerable recognition in twentieth-century psychological thought, in the work of Rogers, Fromm and many others, and has been regarded as a basis for the capacity to love.[27] The modern psychological view contrasts with many traditional religious and moral attitudes, which have commonly taken self-love and the love of others as mutually exclusive, a view that results from a failure to make a distinction between healthy self-love and the self-preoccupation that derives from a lack of self-love. To understand the relationship, we need to remind ourselves of an idea mentioned in Chapter One: the self is established in a social context, and responses from others contribute to the attitudes we form towards ourselves—this was the 'looking-glass self' idea of Cooley. Now others may provide clear or distorting mirrors, and the self-image we see reflected by others may be correspondingly clear or distorted. Children who are shown love come to understand that they are intrinsically worthy of love, whilst children who accurately or mistakenly believe they are not loved develop a distorted self-image, a sense of being intrinsically unlovable. According to this line of thought, esteem from others in the early years provides a basis of self-esteem by showing us that we are worthy and valued individuals, deserving of love. A firm basis of self-esteem in turn enables us to love others. If self-esteem is not well-established, the loving attitude may be obscured by self-preoccupation, anxiety and anger. Thus, in the psychological view, the reformation of the fallen or sullied Image consists of an undistorting of the self-image, a re-imaging in which one comes to esteem oneself. The transforming mirrors provided by others in later relationships may encourage the process, but some relationships may also prove a hindrance, for it is not unusual for 'mirrors' to be sought that confirm and reinforce the familiar, distorted self-perceptions.

Self-repression and the suppression of others, in the supposedly laudable devaluation of self to avoid selfishness, were criticised by William Blake, who in some ways anticipated the insights of modern depth psychologies.

> And Priests in black gowns were walking their rounds,
> And binding with briars my joys & desires.[28]

Yet the relation between self-love and love of others was not appreciated in early psychoanalytic thought: it was supposed that a limited quantity of libido or mental energy was available to the organism, which implied that the investment of libido in self, or *narcissism,* would result in a lower investment of libido in others, *object cathexis.* The implication is that the more one values oneself, the less one values others. If valuing is taken to be a measure of loving, then the more one loves oneself, the less one is able to love others. As Fromm pointed out, love is an attitude, and as such it is not exhaustible. For an undistorted loving attitude, both self and others are objects. 'Myself' is just one self among many other selves, and will not be devalued if a truly loving attitude holds. To use a venerable analogy, the loving attitude is like the sun that shines impartially on all things.[29] If it shines on one, it shines on all. If one is unillumined, it shines on none. If we are unable to love ourselves, it is unlikely that we shall be able to love others in an unmanipulative, unconditional manner.

Also of relevance to our discussion is another of Freud's ideas that met with justifiable criticism, from Carl Jung, Erich Fromm and others. This was the reductive supposition that the religious experience of unity, the "oceanic feeling", is a regression to an "early phase of ego-feeling" antedating the full differentiation of the ego, and "a first attempt at a religious consolation" in the face of threats to the ego.[30] Although regressive tendencies may accompany experiences that reveal universal content, it is clearly inadequate to identify the universal unity with infantile ego-feeling, for we have seen that universal experiences involve all-encompassing cognitions and a universal loving attitude, a scope of experience that is not to be equated with the infantile feelings and cognitions considered in Freudian theory. It would be more realistic to suppose that the infant striving towards love and relationship in the early days of development is made possible by the substratal qualities underlying the infant's personality. Unconscious resources make possible the infant's social impulses and provide a basis for the more cognitively developed experiences of love in later relationships, in which self-other differentiation is greater. We can take universal mystical experiences as indications of a condition of love and unity in the deep substratal regions of our psychologies, a condition from which we have become partially separated, but which makes its existence felt in infant love and in adult love.

On the question of regression, Ken Wilber makes a useful distinction between *pre* and *trans* states: the view that transpersonal experiences are nothing more than regressions to purely infantile or pre-personal experiences is as fallacious as the view that pre-personal content emerging in disturbed adolescent and adult experience is purely mystical.[31] Wilber quotes Erich Fromm, who expresses the point cogently, explaining that the unity sought in mystical religion is not the regressive unity of a pre-individual harmony, but a unity that has been achieved after a period of separation and alienation.[32]

Thomas Traherne's experience of fall and restoration illustrates the theme of lost childhood, and seems to contain overtly mystical content in the *pre* as well as in the *trans* stage. In the autobiographical accounts in the *Centuries,* it is a loss of mystical apprehensions in infancy that Traherne describes, although there may have been other contributions to his 'fall', and it appears that in an earlier work by Traherne, the *Select Meditations,* there is much less reference to the mystical intimations of childhood.[33] Whatever the case may be, in the

Centuries Traherne relates that as an infant in the "Estate of Innocence", he had the joys and knowledge of the spotless and pure eternity, and was blissfully ignorant of the sufferings of the world. Traherne supposes that we are born without sin, and that

> our misery proceedeth ten thousand times more from the outward bondage of opinion and custom, than from any inward corruption or depravation of Nature: And that it is not our parents' loins, so much as our parents' lives, that enthrals and blinds us.[34]

In the *Centuries,* Traherne's understanding of original sin and the Fall differs from the Augustinian notion that men have been born in a sinful state ever since the Fall of Adam corrupted human nature. Traherne's thought on this matter is sometimes linked with Pelagius, but there is support for a stronger link with the early Christian Father, Irenaeus (*c.*130–*c.*202). It is a view advocated by Patrick Grant,[35] who describes Traherne's familiarity with the theology of Irenaeus and the similarities between their understandings of man and the Fall. Both emphasise the childlike quality of the unfallen condition, the innate dignity of man, a fall through the conditioning by society's distorting ways, man's personal responsibility for sin, and restoration as a return to a state of divine infancy.

Traherne's understanding of sin and the Fall clearly relates to his own experience: childhood innocence was not to last, eclipsed by an "apostasy" that Traherne ascribed to the "rude, vulgar, and worthless things" of the world, the "customs and manners of men", the taint of "wrong desires" of others, and the "evil influence of a bad education".[36] He recounts that he found his way back to the mystical apprehensions by unlearning the ways of the world and becoming "as it were, a little child again that I may enter into the Kingdom of God", a reference to *Matthew* 18.2–7. Traherne also connects the "amendment" of his fallen state with a growth of self-love. His orientation here is primarily mystical—the self-love that brings true Felicity is the love of God. The theological background to the idea is to be found in various Christian writers, including Augustine, St Bernard of Clairvaux (1090–1153), Thomas Aquinas (*c.*1225–74), Meister Eckhart and Marsilio Ficino.[37] In Traherne's mystical understanding of self-love, assimilation to God brings the realisation that one shares in God's nature, and that God's Self-love, which is a love for all, has become one's self-love, replacing the selfishness of the personal self.[38] Describing the development of his self-love, Traherne tells us:

> That pool must first be filled that shall be made to overflow. He was ten years studying before he could satisfy his self-love. And now finds nothing more easy than to love others better than oneself: and that to love mankind so is the comprehensive method to all Felicity.[39]

Traherne's understanding is not entirely mystical. He supposes that we are always subject to wants, and that if a want is satisfied a previously unnoticed want takes its place. Wants are not to be rejected, for they constitute a bridge between man and God, and between man and man.[40]

> Till we are satisfied we are so clamorous and greedy, as if there were no pleasure but in receiving all: When we have it we are so full, that we know not what to do with it, we are in danger of bursting, till we can communicate all to some fit and amiable Recipient...[41]

According to Traherne, the satisfaction of receiving is a preliminary: when our needs are "infinitely satisfied", we are able to overflow towards others. To 'climb the ladder' to reach this stage we must begin with self-love, which is "the first round, and they that remove it, had as good take away all."[42]

Traherne was one of several seventeenth-century writers, including the Cambridge Platonists, who were provoked into defending human nature by the controversial philosophy of Thomas Hobbes, in which self-love was viewed as mere selfishness, an urge towards self-preservation and the principle motivating force in human beings.[43] The opposition to Hobbes's ideas was intense, Traherne and the Platonists forming a mystical strand among the reactions of moralists and churchmen. From a rather different perspective in the following century, Rousseau (1712–78) also challenged Hobbes's concept of human nature, arguing that Hobbes had overlooked the principle of compassion, which derives from an ability to identify with the sufferer. Rousseau distinguished between *amour-propre* and *amour de soi-meme:* the former refers to socially learned pride and self-seeking competitiveness that create discord among people, whilst the latter denotes a natural tendency towards self-preservation.[44] Much earlier, Aristotle had distinguished between self-love and selfishness, showing considerable insight into social psychology in his suggestion that "friendly relations with one's neighbours ... seem to have proceeded from a man's relations to himself."[45] Aristotle argues for a positive interpretation of self-love *(philautia),* distinguishing it from the mere selfishness it is commonly understood to mean.[46]

THE VESSEL OF TRANSFORMATION

We have observed that the outcome of the three-stage process may be conceived in two ways. The resolution may be viewed as a return to a former state of order and health, which in the mythic drama is a restoration of harmony following a painful and futile slip into time. In the psychological context, this kind of interpretation of the fall is paralleled by the view that psychological unrest and disturbing symptoms are no more than unfortunate lapses from health. In the alternative view, the process may be viewed as leading to growth, progress, evolution, or some kind of change for the better: the outcome is an advance rather than a return. The innocence regained is not simply the innocence of the child, but an innocence established in a mature, developed personality. It is supposed that the fall into suffering plays an indispensable role in the scheme of things. The urge to dismiss or transcend the world of flux is then likely to be replaced by an interest in working with the world. There is a Heraclitean realisation that progress may sometimes involve conflict, that growth takes place through transformations that sometimes proceed fairly smoothly and easily, and sometimes with extraordinary hardship. In the psychological context, a simple distinction between health and sickness is seen to be insufficient, and it is appreciated that life necessarily involves dislocations, difficult periods of transition, if psychological growth is to proceed. It seems that the forging of a mature personality involves a period of separation from the intrinsic resources of relatedness and loving, the necessary alienation described by Fromm in the passage noted before. John Keats (1795–1821) was well aware from his own difficult but creative life that the "vale of Soul-making", in which divine sparks of intelligence are tutored into personal souls, is "A Place where the heart must feel and suffer in a thousand diverse ways!"[47]

An ancient understanding of suffering is to be found in the *tragic* view of life. Suffering brings a possibility of insight: "man must suffer to be wise." It is a view that needs qualification, lest it become an excuse for a masochistic acceptance of meaningless suffering, or the rationalisation of the sadistic taskmaster who seeks to 'improve' others. We must also "know joy to be wise", and know it well. On occasions suffering has been elevated into a virtue and actively sought, but such instances are likely to strike the psychologically-minded as expressions of self-dislike, and as misdirected strivings after recognition or love.

The tragic drama, according to Aristotle, is not simply a parade of disasters, but has a development with a beginning, a middle and an end: the initial happiness or prosperity of the tragic figure changes to misery through an error of judgement, and the ensuing suffering and struggle lead to insight. We see here the threefold structure that we noted before in religious and mythological contexts. The Greek tragedians drew their stories from ancient myths, and it has been suggested that tragedy originated in the rites of the god Dionysius, the festivals that celebrated his sufferings or passion.[48] There is a link with the widespread theme of the suffering god, whose death agony is followed by resurrection.

Although the challenge of suffering may promote personal growth, and lead to a mature self in which substratal qualities have become fluently integrated into an individual personality, it is very often hard to discern much that is productive in the sufferings of human beings and animals. Pronouncements on the positive consequences are likely to sound hollow or platitudinous in the face of the deep pain and the sheer destructiveness we so often hear about and sometimes experience. Religions and mythologies have, in their various ways, attempted to address the issue, and continue to do so, for in our age, as in every age before, there has been much private and public suffering. Many have found difficulty in reconciling the depth of suffering in the world with the idea of a benevolent and all-powerful creator.

Perhaps the question of suffering can never be satisfactorily answered in the intellectual terms of discursive reasoning. In the whole feeling-cognition of mystical experience, some appear to have reached an experiential understanding. The account of the experience quoted in the previous chapter, from Bucke's *Cosmic Consciousness,* provides a significant example of the insight into suffering that can occur in universal experiences. It is the experience described by C. M. C., whose earlier life had been marked by a restlessness and unhappy searching. She recounts that an illness, physical and psychological, exacerbated her condition, leaving her with a painful sensitivity to the sufferings in the world.

> What I had hitherto known or realized of life was as the prick of a pin to the thrust of a dagger. I had been living on the surface; now I was going down into the depths, and as I went deeper and deeper the barriers which had separated me from my fellow men were broken down, the sense of kinship with every living creature had deepened, so that I was oppressed with a double burden.[49]

Over the following years her "infinite need" was unanswered: "the great tide swept on uncaring, pitiless, and strength gone, every resource exhausted..."[50] until she reached a point in her crisis at which she could only submit. Through the mystical experience that followed, C. M. C. came to understand that her suffering was a phase in "spiritual evolution", and she was able to exclaim: "Welcome centuries, eons, of suffering if it brings us to this!"[51]

> How foolish, how childish, now seemed petulance and discontent in presence of that serene majesty! I had learned the grand lesson, that suffering is the price which must be paid for all that is worth having; that in some mysterious way we are refined and sensitized, doubtless largely by it, so that we are made susceptible to nature's higher and finer influences—this, if true of one, is true of all. And feeling and knowing this, I do not now rave as once I did, but am "silent" "as I sit and look out upon all the sorrow of the world"—"upon all the meanness and agony without end." That sweet, eternal smile on nature's face! There is nothing in the universe to compare with it—such joyous repose and sweet unconcern—saying to us, with tenderest love: All is well, always has been and always will be.[52]

C. M. C. came to the mystical realisation that in some way "all is well." For most of us, however, our personal suffering is never so comprehensively understood, but we may sometimes intuit that there is a meaning, although difficult to grasp. Very often it is only after much time has elapsed that the meaning of a difficult period or experience may become apparent. In the thick of the struggle, the meaning may be impossible to see, and the idea that there is indeed a meaning may be found absurd or repellent.

Generalised questions about the meaning of life and suffering are too abstract to be addressed satisfactorily, as the existential psychotherapist Viktor Frankl has pointed out. Rather than lose ourselves in abstract questionings that admit no adequate or absolute solutions, he argues that we would do better to look at the specifics of our personal experiences, to find meaning and to make meaning in our lives. Frankl supposes that there is indeed a *super-meaning,* an ultimate understanding of suffering, and he suggests that we bear our inability to grasp this super-meaning, rather than endure the meaninglessness of life argued by some existentialists.[53] One may strive to retain a kind of optimism, "to say yes to life in spite of everything." This *tragic optimism* is a recognition that there is some meaning in suffering, and involves an active attempt to address the pain, guilt and transitoriness of life. It is not a capitulation into despondency, inertia, and self-pity over the apparent futility of life; nor is it a facile pretence that all is well, in spite of much clear evidence to the contrary.[54] The "all *is* well" of the mystics seems to apply to the Eternal Present, the world in its completed aspect, in which all the dramas of flux are understood and have their resolutions. For the Transient Present, the use of the future tense seems more appropriate: "all *shall* be well". This is the form of the well-known expression of Julian of Norwich (1342–*c.*1423), which Jesus communicates to her in the 'Thirteenth Revelation', explaining the necessity of sin and the purging role of suffering.[55]

Before we leave the topic of suffering, it will be instructive to consider an ancient stream of thought and practice that recognised the possibility of creative transformation in suffering. The *alchemical* opus is of particular interest to us here because it has a bearing on the dualisms of spirit-matter and mind-body, and because it has been linked with mystical and psychological thought. To some extent, alchemy constitutes an early stage of chemical and metallurgical science, but it is also clear that many alchemists carried out their art with intense religious devotion, and that a few may have combined the practical work of the laboratory with a process of mystical transformation.

In the nineteenth century the spiritually transformative aspects of alchemy received some attention, notably in *A Suggestive Inquiry into the Hermetic Mystery* (1850) by Mary Anne South (later Mrs Atwood), who linked practical alchemy with mesmerism. In the twentieth century, psychological interpretations appeared, first in Herbert Silberer's *Problems of Mysticism and its Symbolism* (1914), then in Jung's exhaustive studies. Jung found much of psychological interest in the images and processes of the alchemists. He believed alchemy to be more than rudimentary chemistry, elaborate religious symbolism, or a mystical art, seeing in the alchemist's work a largely unconscious attempt to transform the psyche through a projection of psychological contents onto material processes.

Alchemy, like its modern scientific descendant, was rooted in and worked with the natural world, but unlike modern science, its underlying assumptions derived from ideas that predate the differentiation of qualities in the mechanical philosophy. Alchemy was a philosophy of nature, a *Naturphilosophie,* whereas chemistry is a discipline of natural philosophy, of modern science. Both nature philosophy and natural philosophy concern themselves with the multiplicity of change in the world, but the former had a broader scope, taking as its field of study the interrelationships between nature, humankind and the divine, whilst the latter has limited itself to a detailed study of physical structures, processes and causes.[56] Nature philosophy has tended to be poetic, holistic, wide-ranging, amorphous and undisciplined, whilst natural science is very often analytical, reductionistic, well-structured, and highly successful within its very narrow focus. A classic illustration of nature philosophy in conflict with natural philosophy was Goethe's (1749–1832) *Farbenlehre,* or *Theory of Colours,* which emphasised the experiential or phenomenological study of colour, the interplay of coloured *lux.* It was a stand against the physical theories of *lumen,* theories that ignored the experiential nature of colour by interpreting light and colour solely as *lumen,* as particle beams or wave radiations in the material world.

To the alchemist, nature was a vessel of creative transformation in which minerals, plants, animals and human beings underwent development. It was supposed that in the course of time ores ripened into metals of increasing perfection. Human beings, immersed in nature, could take part in the labours of nature as co-workers, and the alchemist attempted to accelerate the regeneration of matter into nobler forms. To the spiritually minded alchemist, the work of ripening matter was not separate from the work of spiritual growth—creation was to be perfected through the simultaneous redemption of humankind and the natural world. The chemical and metallurgical transformations provided a rich source of images, including images of painful transformation. The violence of the material processes, the tortures of fiery and chemical dissolutions, the generation of evil-smelling poisons, were experimental actualities in the alchemist's laboratory and were also parallels for the general processes of transformation in the microcosmic crucible of the person and the macrocosmic vessel of the universe. A new stage of development had to begin with a fall into death, an alchemical reduction to the original state, the *prima materia,* or primal chaotic matter. The old form had to be rendered into its primary material constituents, from which a new form could be assembled by the alchemist. A new synthesis followed the analysis into basic constituents. It is the old myth of death prefiguring rebirth, expressed in the chemical sphere. Thus, the process of transformation in the alchemical vessel, the *vas hermeticum,* involved a purposeful descent into darkness and suffering, a crushing between the wheels of time, to enable a re-integration into a more advanced form. The dangerous and painful phases were ascribed an important role in development—there would be no spring without winter, no growth without decay, no resurrection without disintegration and death.

Only after long and arduous work could the goal be attained, which for the technological alchemist was the generation of common gold, or a transformative stone *(lapis philosophorum)* of immense value in chemical operations, or a life-prolonging elixir. For the mystically-minded practitioner of alchemy, the goal was the achievement of the spiritual gold, the heavenly or spiritual stone, or the 'immortality' of eternal life. Rock and stone are very old symbols for the immutable basis and source of life, the *petra genitrix,* and were to provide a bridge between alchemical and Christian symbolism. There are several references in the Bible to the corner-stone or foundation-stone that is cast aside or stumbled upon—in the Old Testament, the stone refers to God or Israel,[57] in the New Testament it is Christ, the living stone described by Peter the Rock.[58] Connections were readily made by Christian writers between the alchemical and the Christian stone, the stone that is rejected by the ignorant, but is a treasure buried in the dark earth of the *prima materia,* awaiting resurrection from the tomb or from its imprisonment in the sealed heart. For example, referring to a verse in the *Revelation of John* (2.17), the Christian mystic Jan van Ruusbroec described a Sparkling Stone, a calculus barely noticed when trodden underfoot. It is a pebble "small and round, and smooth all over, and very light", "shining white and red like a flame of fire", accompanied by light, truth and life. This sparkling stone is Christ, "for He is, according to His Godhead, a shining forth of the Eternal Light, and an irradiation of the glory of God, and a flawless mirror in which all things live"[59]—just as the stone is trodden upon, so Christ was despised and crucified by those who failed to recognise him. Jung elaborates on the *lapis*-Christos parallel, and the stone "trodden underfoot in the dunghill", in his work *Psychology and Alchemy,*[60] and relates Gerhard Dorn's exhortation: "Transform yourselves from dead stones into living philosophical stones".[61] Material bodies are transfigured into spiritual bodies, which are the living stones built into the temple of God.[62]

The transmutation of base lead or flowing mercury[63] into the incorruptible gold of the heavenly Jerusalem symbolised the realisation of a state of being immune from the ravages of time, the eternity in which the warring elements in the vessel of flux are conjoined in the incorruptible body of the stone. Paradoxically, the central goal of alchemy, the *lapis,* is said to be everywhere about us and within us, even in the vilest of things, and goes unvalued by all: the eternal is immanent in nature, but few recognise that it indwells in matter and in humankind. In fact, the round alchemical vessel, which in its cosmic aspect was the world of Becoming, the spherical universe of transformation, was sometimes identified with its product, the *lapis*.[64] The round of transformation is equated with the circle of eternity, the flux of matter with the immutable bedrock. In this way, the path, the second stage of the mythic process, is also the goal, the outcome of the process, and the dualisms of matter and spirit, of time and eternity, could be relinquished in favour of a more positive conception of the temporal, at least by a few alchemists. The rock as *matrix,* as source of flux, completed the picture, uniting all three stages in the symbolism of the stone, for the stone is at once the starting-place, the journey and the goal. Jung supposed that the symbol of the *lapis* was not a conscious invention of individual alchemists, but had its roots "in the border regions of the psyche that open out into the mystery of cosmic matter",[65] the *psychoid unconscious,* an inaccessible level of the psyche that reaches to the material world. On the mind-body relation, Jung's preference seems to have been towards some form of double-aspect theory: he supposes that "irrepresentable, transcendental factors" support the "one world" of psyche and matter, which are "two different aspects of one and the same thing."[66] The "one world" is Jung's *unus mundus.* His interest in the connection between psyche and matter was stimulated by observations of links between psychological phenomena and seemingly unconnected events in the outer world. As these meaningful coincidences eluded the usual causal explanations, Jung termed them *acausal.*[67]

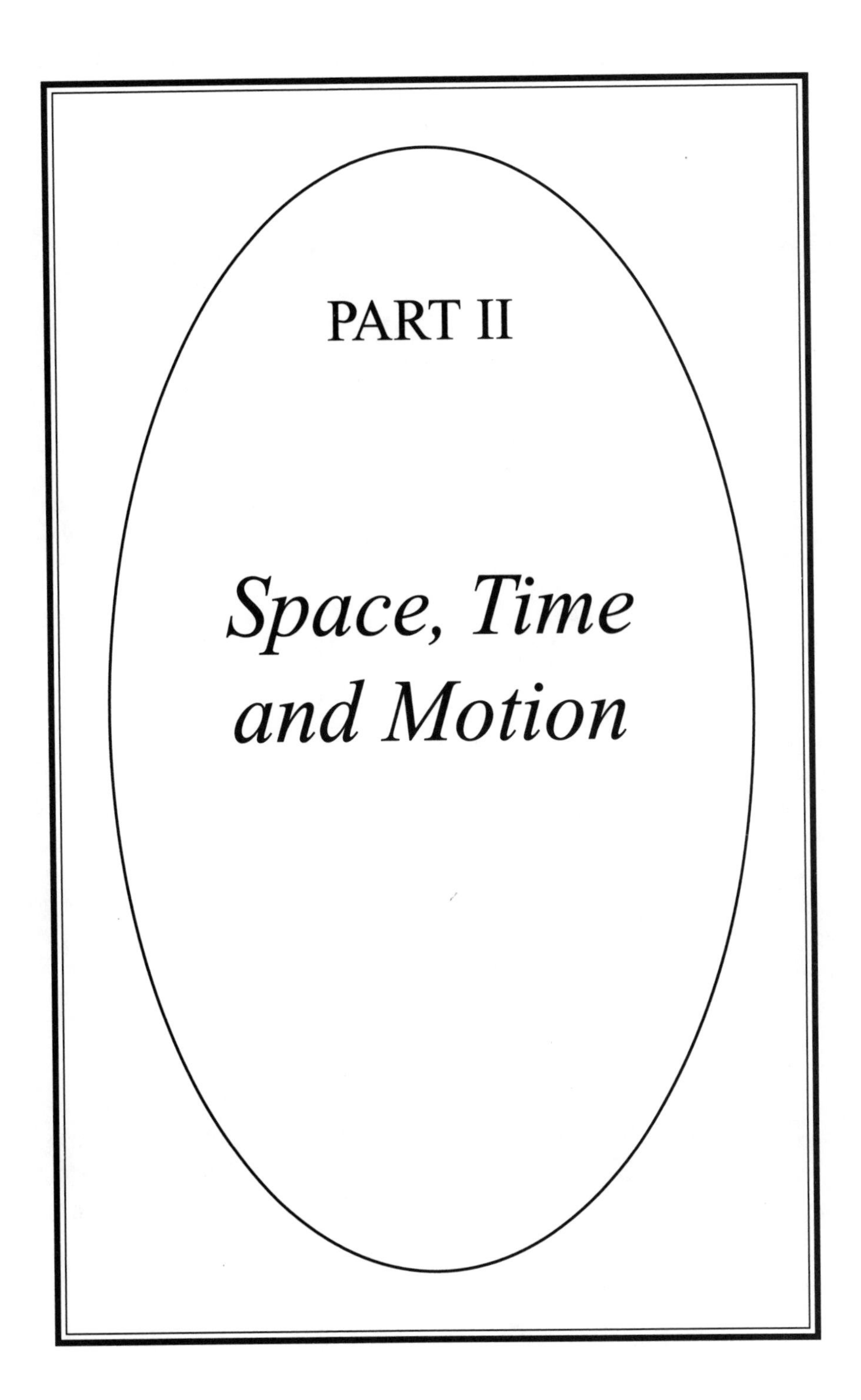

PART II

Space, Time and Motion

6. THE SPATIALIZATION OF TIME

Until the first decade of the twentieth century, there had been no concept of a fluxless substratum in the physical sciences. The timelessness of the mystics, the stone of the alchemists, the Being of the philosophers, had no equivalent in the world-view of scientists, who envisaged only a physical world in flux, a world of Becoming. In 1907, there emerged the idea of a physical substratum in which space and time are fused into a whole. The idea, due to the mathematician Hermann Minkowski, was a development of Einstein's Special Theory of Relativity (1905). The absolute world of Minkowski, *Minkowski spacetime,* has frequently been interpreted as a static, four-dimensional space in which all physical events are laid out, a substratum in which the flux of time is absent. Some have expressed dissatisfaction with this understanding, arguing that the static interpretation of spacetime is invalid, or that spacetime is merely a conceptual tool and not an ontological actuality. In this chapter, spacetime and its relationship with flux will be discussed in general terms. The special spacetime of relativistic physics will be considered in Chapter Nine.

THE LINEAR ORDERING OF EVENTS

To make sense of our experiences, we need to order them, to place events in temporal relationships of *before, simultaneous* and *after.* We order recollected experiences into a linear sequence leading from our earliest experiences up to the present, and we speculate how the sequence might continue into the future. These are 'maps of time', temporal schemas in which the memories of past experiences are ordered, contexts for current experiences provided, and future experiences anticipated or planned. We carry a number of such temporal maps, ranging from the private maps of personal experience, to family histories, national and cultural time-scales, geological and cosmic time-scales.

Events are ordered into a linear, temporal sequence, and this abstracted sequenceforms the basis of everyday clock time and the physical time of the sciences. There has been some tension in philosophical thought between the time of transient experience *(psychological time)* and the ordering of moments in an abstracted time sequence *(physical time, mathematical time).* Not infrequently, the abstracted time has been regarded as a real temporal ordering of the world, with the psychological time of transient experience viewed as incidental. Such a view is likely to be adopted when the physical substratum is taken to be primary, an 'objective reality'—this has usually been the case in scientific work. In recent times, a number of thinkers, such as Henri Bergson, opposed this tendency, and placed the emphasis on the complex temporality of experience. In bridging the mind-body divide, we may have to reconcile the two views of time, bringing together the sequential temporality ascribed to the substratum with the complex, superimposed temporality of transient experience.

THE TEMPORAL COMPLEXITY OF THE MOMENT

Let us consider the temporal complexity of the experiential moments, of 'psychological time', which distinguishes them from the point-like moments of physical/mathematical time. Several philosophers of flux, including James, Whitehead and Bergson, have argued that each individual moment of experience, each transient moment, contains a *span* of temporal states. James expressed it thus:

> ... the practically cognized present is no knife-edge, but a saddle-back, with a certain breadth of its own on which we sit perched, and from which we look in two directions into time. The unit of composition of our perception of time is a *duration,* with a bow and a stern, as it were—a rearward- and a forward-looking end.[1]

Some of the past is in the present, giving to the moment a 'duration'. James called this temporally-complex moment the *sensible present* and quoted a passage by E. R. Clay, in which the moment is called the *specious present.*[2] This experiential moment, containing a temporal span, has also been called the *psychological present,* the *perceived present,* the *mental present,* and the *psychic present,*[3] to distinguish it from the abstracted, discrete, isolated moment of *physical, mathematical* or *clock time.*

An example frequently cited to illustrate the temporal span of the moment is the experience of music. A succession of musical notes is not a mere string of isolated sounds, but a tune. The experience of each part contains something of the earlier parts, and looks forward to later parts, giving to each experience a breadth of past carried over into the present, and a future anticipated. The moment is more than a temporal state: as a span of temporal states, it is a temporal process. Speech is another instance of the content of the moment reaching beyond the temporally instantaneous. The experience of listening to speech is not simply a one-by-one apprehension of words or their constituent sounds, the phonemes. A complex sentence, with its parts temporally distributed across a sequence of successive experiences, can be understood in its entirety, which suggests that the meanings of earlier parts of the sentence are carried along into experiences containing the later parts of the sentence. Furthermore, the later parts of a sentence can sometimes be anticipated before they are read or spoken. Experience is cumulative and anticipatory. It is Janus-faced in its rearward and forward-looking directions.

In what way does the experiential present have a temporal span or duration? There are various possibilities, but we shall focus on one interpretation: the temporal span of the moment consists of an *organisation* of temporally-sequential experiential parts in *one* experience. Exactly how these sequential states might be organised in the experiential simultaneity of the moment is not at all clear, but it is well recognised that memory plays a role, since memory is the means by which the past is recorded and brought into the psychological present. Various kinds of memory have been postulated for different types of experiential content, and memories have been distinguished with different storage, coding and recall characteristics. There is the *sensory memory,* which is said to retain experience very briefly, and is illustrated by the co-presence of after-images in a moment. In these after-images, we have the clearest sense of the experiential simultaneity of sequential temporal states. Motion brings out the co-existence of sequential images by distributing them spatially: as I watch my arm sweep before me, I see a faint arc of after-images, together in the experiential present. The blade of a fan or the propeller of an aeroplane imprints in each moment a trail of images that are superimposed into a continuous circular blur, and stroboscopic lighting can be used to reduce the number of after-images to a countable number. The sensory memory seems to consist of *experiential* content that recurs from experience to experience, and the content fades rapidly across the experiences, perhaps in a couple of seconds or so.

The other types of memory are not directly experiential, but are inferred from the recurrence of experiential content after a period of absence from experience. It seems that these memories, if they are ascribed any existence beyond the experiential effects credited to them, involve a storage of content outside experience. The content may be retrieved and returned to experience, often in a modified condition.

It is noteworthy that memory processes organise stored experiences in a way that contains information on the temporal relations of the experiences. For instance, a short sequence of numbers, such as a telephone number, can be repeated in the order in which the numbers were heard. Two kinds of storage memory have been distinguished, short-term storage and long-term storage. Short-term storage is a temporary store—the experiences are not recallable after a fairly short period, say ten, twenty or thirty seconds. A telephone number can be recalled immediately after it is heard, and for a short while afterwards, but it will not be recalled after longer periods unless efforts are made to prolong its life in the short-term store, by bringing it back into experience every few seconds. Alternatively, the telephone number can be stored in the long-term storage memory, which can hold accessible information for much longer periods. We may speculate that all these kinds of memory contribute in some way to the temporal complexity of the moment, the shorter-term memories

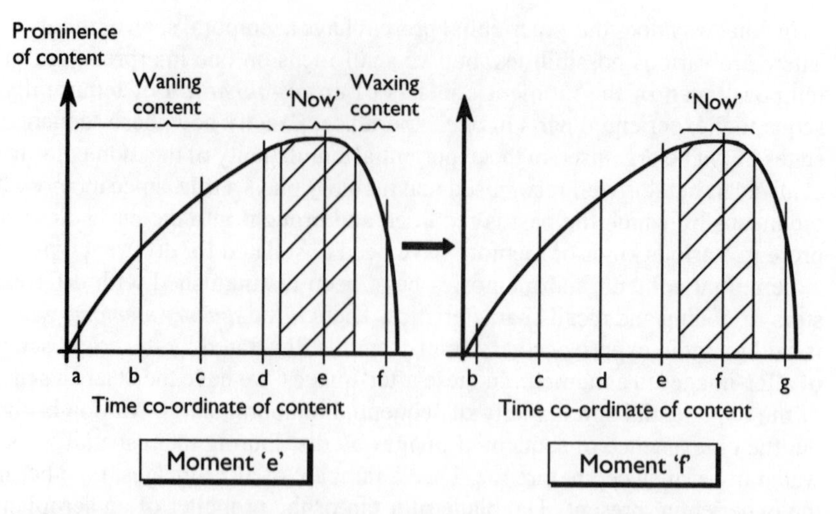

Figure 6.1. *Drops* of experience: diagrams of two consecutive moments, 'e' and 'f', showing how the experiential prominence may vary across each span of content. The most prominent contents may be interpreted as the 'now', even though more advanced temporal content is present. Contents no longer at maximum prominence are labelled *waning,* whilst contents building up to maximum prominence are labelled *waxing.*[4]

giving the moment the more immediate quality of temporal succession, and the long-term store making possible the full temporal richness of human experience. The temporal span of the moment at the 'forward-looking end' presumably derives from expectations and the ability to anticipate or predict events, through memories and interpretations of similar sequences of experience. There is also a possibility that the most prominent temporal content in a moment may be interpreted as the present experience although it is not the most advanced in the temporal span of content (see Figure 6.1.).

TIME-DISTANCE GRAPHS

Returning to the abstracted physical or mathematical notion of temporal moments, we observe that the ordering of events into a simple sequence lends itself to spatial representation by a line. This spatial ordering of sequential events is the key to transforming flux into the eternal—it constitutes the *spatialization of time,* loved by some, loathed by others. A temporal state is represented by a point on the line, and the interval between two temporal states is represented by the line-segment separating the points. The length of the segment is proportional to the time interval between the two events, as measured by some standard clock. This is uniform mathematical time, a linear sequence of point-moments. The line can be used to represent a short time interval, such as a minute or an hour, or it can be used to order longer sequences of events, such as the course of an individual life, or an epoch of history. In this way, time is spatialized, represented as a line, a spatial extension. A notable feature of the line, and of spatial arrangements in general, is that all parts are presented together. So when the one-by-one events of flux are ordered in a spatial sequence, they exist together, all-in-one. Flux-time is little-by-little, spatialized time is all-together.

The linear representation of time can be combined with a linear representation of a space dimension to produce a graph that shows changes of spatial position with time. Time is taken to be an independent axis, and is drawn at right angles to the space axis. In our three-dimensional space of ordinary experience we can produce graphs of a one- or two-dimensional space with a time axis, but not of a three-dimensional space, since one of our three space dimensions is used to represent the time axis.

Consider a bead M moving with a constant velocity along a straight wire W, two metres long, from one end A to the other end B. The motion can be represented by depicting the bead at several stages on its journey along the wire. These 'snapshots' (say, at one-second intervals) can then be stacked above one another in temporal sequence (Figure 6.2.). The dots and lines represent the successive states of the bead and the wire respectively. These can be replaced by a single graph, with a time axis and a single space axis for the wire (Figure 6.3.). The position of the bead at any time is given by the slanting line. This type of graph is commonly used to represent the change of position of an object with time. The axes are calibrated in the units of time and length, allowing the position of the bead to be stated numerically for any time. The system of Cartesian co-ordinates provides a diagrammatic 'union' of space and time, each

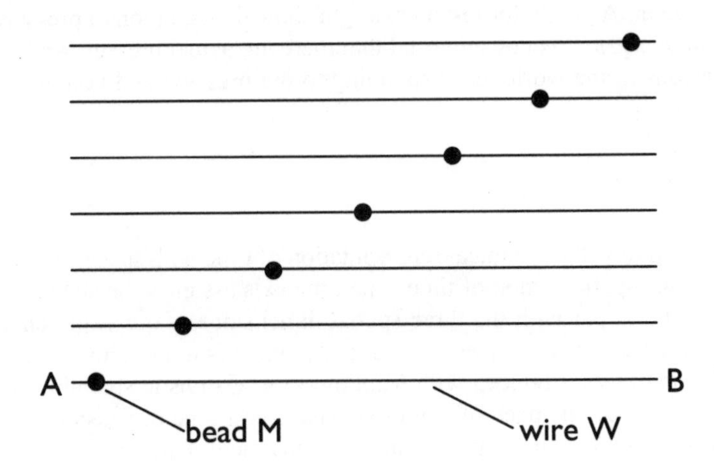

Figure 6.2. Position of the bead M along a wire at equal time-intervals.

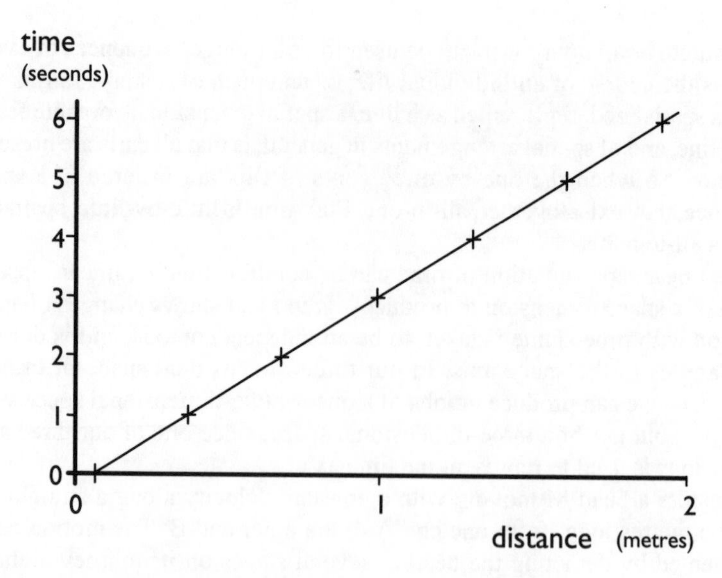

Figure 6.3. Graphical representation of the motion of the bead M.

point in the graph having one temporal and (in the general case) three spatial co-ordinates. The time axis of the co-ordinate system is similar to the space axes, but is divided into units of time instead of units of length.

The graph can be regarded as a convenient way of showing changes in the spatial relations of an object to other objects, without supposing that it represents a substratum in which space and time orderings are combined into one extended space. Graphs are often used to display information, with no suggestion that they are more than convenient ways of showing the variation of one magnitude with another. A graph, for instance, might show the variation of pressure with volume of a gas. It is not supposed that there are actual pressure and volume dimensions in the world, corresponding to the pressure and volume axes of the graph.

SPACETIME

Alternatively, the graphical representation of time with space can be a step towards the spatialization of time. The time axis assumes the status of a real dimension, on par with the three spatial dimensions of our experience. The successive states of an object are arranged along this fourth dimension. Using the terminology introduced with Minkowski's relativistic spatialization, the higher dimensional space of combined space and time dimensions is called *spacetime,* and the line representing the sequence of successive states of a particle or object is called its *worldline.* Each point on the line is called a *worldpoint,* a *point-instant,* or more commonly, an *event* (Figure 6.4.).

The worldline is the course of development of a thing in spacetime, the sequence of its successive states. An object made up of particles would consist of a bundle of worldlines, a worldline for each particle. The bundle is sometimes called a *worldtube.* If we associate life with the continuing object, then the bundle of worldlines might be called the *lifeline.* For a complex organism, the lifeline would comprise a worldtube of worldlines, a worldline for each particle of the organism's body. The lifeline can be regarded as the life journey of the organism, and the rest of spacetime constitutes the fellow-travellers and the landscape. However, when using such analogies, care must be taken not to suppose that a particle wanders up a worldline, or an organism up a lifeline. The worldline is not a path or track that a particle follows, but a sequence of the particle's temporal states arranged to form a line in spacetime. The traveller is at every stage of the journey.

Spacetime can have a variety of forms. Spacetime was introduced by Hermann Minkowski in response to Einstein's Special Theory of Relativity, and the spacetime of his theory, *Minkowski spacetime,* has special features which we shall examine in Chapter Nine. Although the idea of spacetime arose in the context of relativistic physics, it could have appeared in earlier centuries if there had been the stimulus. A number of pre-relativistic spacetimes can be constructed, which embody different views on space, time and motion. Here we shall consider the simple case of Newtonian spacetime, the spacetime that embodies the assumptions of Newtonian physics,[5] namely the assumptions of absolute time and absolute space.

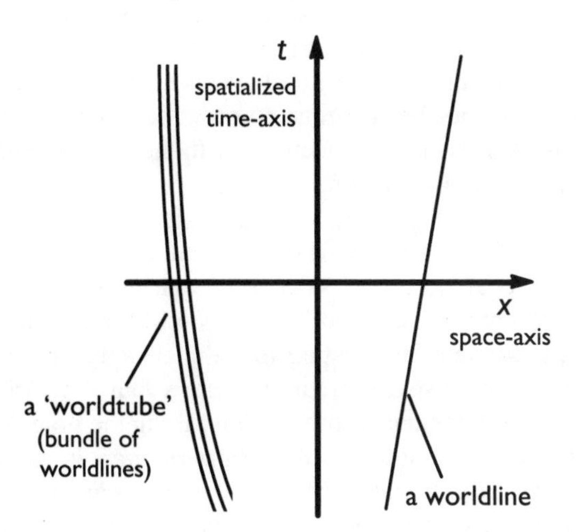

Figure 6.4. Sequences of worldpoints in spacetime: worldlines and bundles of worldlines.

Absolute Time: time exists independently of objects and their states, and enables motions to take place. It proceeds uniformly, irrespective of the existence of bodies. "Absolute, true, and mathematical time, of itself, and from its own nature, flows equably without relation to anything external...."[6] The flow of time applies to the whole universe—each moment the whole universe changes from one state to the next. The events in each state are said to be *simultaneous* and are ascribed the same time co-ordinate. Each moment of absolute time across the universe could be called a *universal Now*. A *single* temporal sequence of all events can in theory be constructed.

Absolute Space: an infinite, immobile container or receptacle exists that is everywhere the same. "Absolute space, in its own nature, without relation to anything external, remains always similar and immovable."[7] It is the arena in which bodies move and interact with one another. The postulates of geometry, summarised by Euclid (*c.*365–300 B.C.) in the *Elements (Stoicheia),* are assumed to apply in Newtonian absolute space. These include the parallel axiom: one version, due to the Neoplatonic philosopher Proclus (410–85), states that a line intersecting one of two parallel lines will intersect the other.

Translating these assumptions into a spacetime representation, absolute time becomes the *absolute time dimension,* a single, spatialized time dimension that is applicable to all objects in the universe, whatever their states of motion. Absolute space is each three-dimensional cross-section of the spacetime. Each successive spatial state of the universe, each moment of physical time, each 'universal Now', is represented as a cross-section of the spacetime diagram at right angles to the absolute time axis. All events in this perpendicular slice of spacetime have the same absolute time co-ordinate and are therefore classed as simultaneous. A Newtonian spacetime, with the absolute time dimension and one space dimension, is shown in Figure 6.5.

The representation of time as a dimension similar to space can be interpreted as truly reflective of the structure of the substratum. In Newton's approach, space and time are regarded as things that truly exist, as 'substances'. It follows that the spacetime corresponding to Newton's scheme should be interpreted as an actuality, as an actually-existing four-dimensional space in which the spatial three-dimensional spaces are joined into a four-dimensional whole, a 'stacking' of three-dimensional cross-sections along the time dimension.

The spacetime world is said to be *static* or *permanent* in the sense that it is fluxless—it is not subject to transformation. The terms are not meant to imply that spacetime remains unchanged *in the course of time,* a meaning that is ordinarily intended with the terms: for instance, "the glue is permanent" or "the

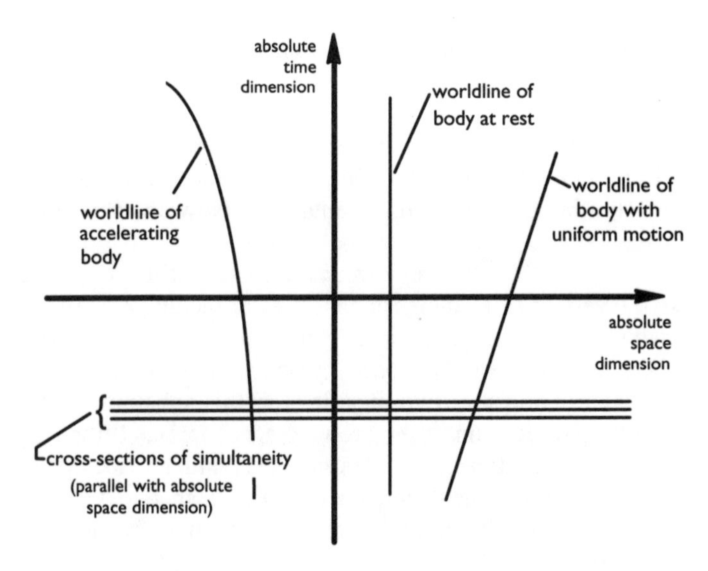

Figure 6.5. Newtonian spacetime with one space-dimension. Straight lines parallel to the time axis correspond to objects *at rest* in the absolute space of Newtonian physics. Other lines correspond to objects *in motion:* straight lines correspond to motions with uniform velocity, curved lines to accelerated motions. The gradient at any point on a curved line corresponds to the instantaneous velocity of the particle.

situation is static". Spacetime, as usually conceived, is *tenselessly* static or permanent. There is no extrinsic flux-time in which spacetime can transform. Time is contained within spacetime, as spatialized time. Spacetime displays statically all changes, motion and activity within itself. It is a static presentation of change.

The spatialization of absolute time in Newtonian physics yields a four-dimensional spacetime that contains all the successive states of things arranged along the absolute time dimension. We could also imagine a substratum that involves both spacetime *and* an additional time, an extrinsic time in which changes to the spacetime can occur. This has not been a popular idea among philosophers. The introduction of a time additional to the spatialized time of spacetime is usually rejected: in the words of Moritz Schlick,[8] "time is already represented within the model and cannot be introduced again from outside." Although I do not favour the introduction of an extrinsic time in which spacetime can transform, I do not think that it can be ruled out so easily, for the introduction is no different from the assumption of a flux-time in the classical idea of a world in flux. We could imagine, for instance, that an incomplete spacetime 'grows' along its time dimension, as successive 'Nows' are created at the advancing front. Or we could imagine a spacetime that has states erased as the Now advances. Let us summarise these mixed models, along with the pure flux and pure spacetime models:

1. *Pure flux:* The entire three-dimensional universe is created and destroyed from moment to moment. Only the current state of the universe exists, constituting the universal, instantaneous Now of a flux-time.

2. *Growing spacetime:* A four-dimensional spacetime is created by successive layers of three-dimensional states of the universe forming at the 'growing face'. At any moment, only the spacetime body of past states and the current state exists. The spacetime is 'open', with future states yet to accumulate. 'Time' has two meanings in this substratum: it is the spatialized time dimension of the growing spacetime and it is the flux-time in which the spacetime grows. This model is similar to the first model, the substratum in flux. The difference is that each successive state constituting a moment of flux-time carries the past with it in the form of a spacetime past.

3. *Diminishing spacetime:* This is a four-dimensional spacetime from which successive layers of three-dimensional states are erased as the Now advances into an already existing future. Again, time has two meanings, the spatialized time of the diminishing spacetime, and the flux-time in which layers are successively erased.[9]

4. *Pure spacetime:* A spatially and temporally complete four-dimensional spacetime exists tenselessly, containing all temporal states of the universe. There is no flux in which the substratum transforms, no flux-time in addition to the spatialized time dimension of the spacetime.

The fourth option, the complete spacetime, would seem to be an appropriate candidate for the structure of the experiential substratum suggested by universal experiences, for it is fluxless and complete, embracing all states past *and* future. It is suggestive of the greater spatiality in which Traherne finds all moments to be "infinitely exhibited", all times and places in an eternal whole.

We now know that Newtonian physics is not entirely in agreement with experimental evidence, and the Newtonian spacetime has to be replaced with a relativistic spacetime. In Chapter Nine, we shall discover that the relativistic spacetime has no one, single time dimension, no *absolute* time applicable to all bodies in motion. This surprising result has led some to conclude that the physical world cannot be in flux, for there is no unique time direction in which the substratal universe could evolve through flux, whether by the instantaneous creation-destruction of states (model one) or by the accumulation or erasure

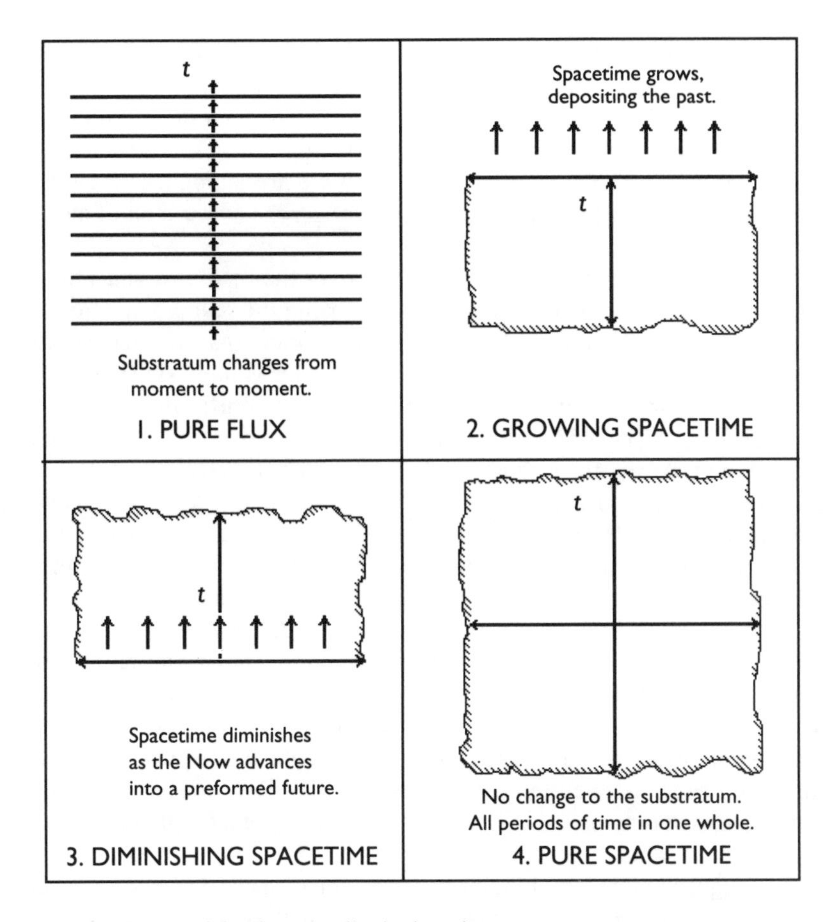

Figure 6.6. Four models of temporality in the substratum.

of states (models two and three). The lack of a unique time dimension means that we cannot single out unique spatial states of the universe, the 'universal Nows' of the universe, and we therefore cannot envisage the substratum as transforming from state to state, from 'now' to 'now'. It is concluded that flux, as a succession of world-wide instants, is not possible and that the underlying physical world must be a static, four-dimensional spacetime (model 4). The details of the argument need not concern us here, and the absence of the universal Now in relativistic physics, *the relativity of simultaneity,* will be explained in Chapter Nine. The argument has been criticised by Milic Capek, who has contended that the lack of universal Nows in relativistic physics is no reason for rejecting Becoming: he supposes that we are tempted to reject flux because our ideas are unconsciously entrenched in the Newtonian world-view, in which it is assumed that Becoming consists of a succession of world-wide instants, the universal Nows.[10] If we give up this assumption, and separate the idea of Becoming from the idea of universal Nows, then the elimination of universal Nows in relativistic theory is not such a threat to the idea of a substratum in flux. Yet it is not clear how we are supposed to envisage Becoming in the physical world, if it is no longer the succession of states of the universe, the universe in flux.

Of particular interest to us is the debate over the reality of spacetime. Is spacetime merely a convenient way of organising the relative positions and motions of things observed in flux, or is there an actual spacetime substratum? Some philosophers and physicists responded to the Minkowski spacetime of relativistic theory by denying that time is really a fourth dimension. Hans Reichenbach (1891–1953),[11] for instance, concluded that time is not a fourth dimension of space—the idea is a useful geometrical representation, but is not reflective of a real spacetime structure. As we shall see, a major reason for rejecting the actuality of the spatialized time dimension has been the form that spacetime takes in relativistic theory—it is not a straightforward combination of space and time dimensions. Opposing the view that spacetime is an actuality, a 'substance', is the relationalist view that things or events can be in spatio-temporal relationship with one another without having an actual spatio-temporal substratum in which to locate them. Space, time and spacetime are not substances, but the relations between things. In the case of time, the relationalist argues that there is no time in addition to the sequence of states of things, no time independent of bodies. In this view, spacetime, with its spatialized time dimension, is a four-dimensional system of relations between physical bodies and their states.

The suggestion that time is a fourth dimension of space does not necessarily imply that the time dimension is exactly equivalent to the other three dimensions. The spatialized time dimension is the dimension along which the successive states of objects are arranged, whereas the three spatial dimensions constitute the space in which objects are extended.

One further point that deserves mention is the *dimensionality* of spacetime. The spatialized time dimension provides one dimension (1-D) and the space dimensions are three in number (3-D). The overall dimensionality can be expressed as (3+1)D, three space and one time dimensions. Is there any significance in these numbers? A unidimensional time is normally assumed because it is imagined that the history of a body consists of a single sequence of temporal states. In special relativity, the single, absolute time dimension is replaced by relative time dimensions defined by the worldlines of each body. Time is still essentially unidimensional because the temporal development of each body occurs in one dimension. Two-dimensional times have been put forward, but these need not detain us here.[12] More interesting is the tridimensionality of space, a question that has been discussed by several philosophers and scientists.[13] The number of space dimensions has important implications for physical laws. Of special interest is the importance of three-dimensional space for the wave propagation of distortion-free, sharp signals. Assuming a representative theory of perception, we can say that the clear sensory representations of our transient experience would not be possible in a universe with a different number of space dimensions.[14]

CAUSALITY AND SPACETIME

In a spacetime substratum of the type suggested by universal experience, all places and times exist together in a complete whole. The entire temporal span of the universe, including the full life-journey of each individual, would be laid out in total. One reaction to this picture of complete temporality might be to claim: "Whatever I do now is of no consequence in the unfolding of future events, for future events are already set out. Therefore, my actions are of no consequence." This modern fatalistic reaction to the idea of spacetime is comparable to earlier fatalisms. Given that the omniscient God or Mind knows everything that will happen, it may be concluded that divine knowledge compromises our freedom and implies pre-destination. Similarly, it might be thought that the idea of spacetime, whether physical or experiential, implies fatalism and the absence of free will.

We shall not go very far into the complicated subject of free will and determinism: it is one of the most discussed problems in philosophy, and requires careful treatment of the central terms, such as causality, reasons, explanation, free will, responsibility. However, a few points are worth making, if only to highlight some of the uncertainties.

1. *Fatalism is to be distinguished from determinism.*

The fatalist supposes that our actions play no part in the unfolding of future events. Whatever action we may take, the future unfolds in only one way and "the future cannot be changed". Consider an example in a world that has an experiential, spacetime substratum: a person has an unusual experience that provides access to substratal content. Let us suppose that this content incorporates an authentic, precognitive insight into an event in the following week. The person attempts to avoid the event, but it occurs all the same. The fatalist concludes that the future cannot be changed. In contrast, the determinist supposes: "Whatever happens now is in complete, causal relationship to previous and future events. The action we take now is part of the causal chain leading from past to future events." The determinist rejects the fatalist's view that actions are of no consequence: actions have causal consequences and are themselves causal consequences of previous states. In the case of the person who attempted to avoid the precognised event, the avoidance actions are actually part of the causal chain leading to the event, as indeed is the precognition of the event. For if the precognition had not occurred, the avoidance action would not have taken place, and the future would have been different in some way. The cognition of the spacetime substratum, with its complete scope of past and future states, is directly involved in the causal chain leading to the event revealed in the complete cognition.The determinist supposes that we take part in the causal chain of events. Our psychological processes (or some physical substrate underlying them, in the materialist/epiphenomenalist view) are part of the causal chain, and the sophistication of these personal processes gives us some independence from the immediate environment. The inner world of cognitive maps, representations, imaginative thinking and feeling, enables the person to be a causal centre of activity in the world at large. We contain causal processes in ourselves that provide a basis for action. This is the notion of *self-determinism.*

Sometimes it is thought that self-determinism does not give the person any real freedom or moral responsibility because the state of the person is determined by antecedent states of the psychological flux, or by unconscious influences. One response may be to suppose that there is something else in the constitution of the person that acts as a cause, but is not an effect of previous conditions. It may be viewed as a 'self' or 'soul' that is unconditioned by previous events in the personal flux of desires and motives, but which has the power to intervene in the flow. We may wonder, however, whether the intervention is truly without cause, for we may ask what inspires the intervention and the form it takes. Furthermore, is an intervention without a cause really conducive towards freedom? Maybe the important point to grasp is that causes do not lie entirely in previous conditions, but can derive more generally, with the future having a role to play—a final causation or teleology. If we suppose that our personal psychologies are supported by a universal substratum containing past, present and future (or that personal selves are part of a self-system involving an eternal, universal self), then the possibility of teleological influences cannot be dismissed lightly.

2. *Spacetime does not necessarily embody determinism.*

The general idea of spatialized time or spacetime favours neither determinism nor indeterminism. We could imagine a spacetime in which there are strict causal relations between successive events, or we could imagine a spacetime in which the events are not strictly connected. In a fully deterministic case, conceived along conventional lines, the present is the effect of the past and the cause of the future. Any one temporal state is completely implied by the immediately prior state and completely implies the immediately following state. In a Newtonian spacetime universe, the temporal states consist of three-dimensional, spatial cross-sections of spacetime, and the determinist supposes that each cross-section has complete causal links with the cross-sections immediately before and after. In the relativistic spacetime, the causal relations are not quite the same, owing to the lack of a universally-definable present or Now. In a fully indeterministic spacetime (a universe in which there are no physical regularities or laws), the spatial cross-sections have no causal relation to one another. If we had complete information about one spatial state, we would not be able to reconstruct the prior state or predict the following state. Between the extremes of complete determinism and complete indeterminism lie partial determinisms: complete information about one state of the universe would allow us to reconstruct past events and predict future events to some extent.

The relations between events in spacetime have usually been regarded as fully or largely deterministic, reflecting the causality that we deduce to be at work in nature and which is described in physical laws. In the Newtonian spacetime, one spatial cross-section would be the complete cause of the next, whilst in the relativistic spacetime, the relations between regions of spacetime would be more complicated, but still deterministic. Yet it is possible that complete physical determinism may not hold, and that some element of randomness is at work. Current scientific understanding does not settle the issue, but quantum theory has led some to believe that there is an element of indeterminism in the universe, as we shall see in Chapter Fifteen, and it has even been argued that this quantum indeterminism is the basis of free will. Much earlier in the history of ideas, in the Hellenic world, the Epicurean philosophers maintained that atoms sometimes swerve spontaneously, without cause, and that the element of chance counters the physical determinism that would otherwise be implied by the atomic theory.[15] Similarly, the American philosopher C. S. Peirce hoped to support free will by claiming a form of indeterminism—in his theory of *tychism,* chance is an integral factor in our universe at its current stage of development. However, is it really necessary to weaken determinism in order to support free will?

3. *Does determinism imply an absence of free will?*

The apparent threat of determinism to free will and moral responsibility was one reason why William James rejected the idea of a block universe. Yet we have just noted that spacetime or the block universe does not necessarily imply determinism. We can, in any case, go on to question whether determinism is really a threat to free will. Many philosophers have argued that determinism and free will are compatible, but the question remains a subject of dispute. To the compatibilist, chance or random elements detract from free will rather than support it, for they introduce a chaotic element that is beyond the control of the individual. We cannot be held responsible for our actions if they are disrupted by random elements. The compatibilist is likely to favour the deterministic version of spacetime, for determinism is taken to be a requisite for free will and moral responsibility.

4. *We may have to broaden the concept of the causal relation.*

To the physicalist or epiphenomenalist, determinism holds in the physical world: causal linking is purely physical, between the physical contents of successive temporal states. The structural or physical content of a temporal state completely determines the content of the following state and is completely determined by the physical content of the previous state. The dualist or the experientialist, on the other hand, can ascribe a causal role to the 'psychological' and astructural contents of transient experience in the causal linking of temporal states. A complete determinism may hold, but it may be a determinism that involves astructural and psychological facets as well as physical. In other words, the laws describing a purely structural/physical spacetime may be insufficient to account for the development of events, not because of random disturbances, but because physical causation is only part of a more general, experiential determinism, a determinism that includes both physical and psychological causal linkings.

However, standard notions of physical and psychological determinism that merely consider the causal connections between *successive* temporal states may be insufficient. The form of determinism considered in classical science—the efficient causation linking or associating the prior state (cause) to the following state (effect)—may be only part of the story, and contents normally ascribed to much earlier and later times may directly influence transformations in the present. The possibility of more elaborate causal connections was hinted at above, in the notion of a precognitive experience acting as a psychological cause, and in the idea of a factor at work in personal flux that can draw on the full temporal scope of the substratum. If the substratum is experiential and if its contents can become part of our transient experience or have some activity in our personal psychologies at an unconscious level, then the spacetime as a whole or some significant part of it may act as a causal influence. Thus a more elaborate determinism might regard future states as causes, as well as effects, of earlier states. All events would be causally knit together in the spacetime whole, a causal interrelationship that may extend to the physical structuring of events. As we shall see, there are suggestions of this in quantum physics, and the spacetime model developed in later chapters has a structural unit that is linked with every other unit throughout the entire spatio-temporal substratum.

Certainly, the idea of an eternal whole, which is a universal feeling-cognition, has the potential to broaden the understanding of causality beyond the narrow concept of efficient causation, which seems to make everything a slave of the past. Instead, we may find that in the well-knit whole, everything is to some extent both a cause and an effect of everything else. The full meaning or purpose of an event is to be found in its total role as cause and effect throughout the substratum, an entire web of causal relations that could only be appreciated in a universal cognition. Yet we might also wish to distinguish various degrees of causal significance or meaning. There might be events in an individual life or the collective life that are particularly significant in their casual roles, as seeds for future trains of events or as goals towards which past trains of events lead and in which they find their meaning. We may agree with Blake that "To create a little flower is the labour of ages",[16] and add that the labour is not a blind process of efficient causation, but is purposefully directed towards an end.

We are entitled to attribute meaning or purpose to the temporal development of substratal contents because we have taken the step of interpreting the substratum as an experiential basis. The notion of a substratum characterised by feeling-cognition, or 'intellect', allows us to entertain causal connections between events that would be difficult to envisage in a universe determined along purely physical and efficient causal lines. In a universe that is organised in an orderly and meaningful fashion, with an intellectual-feeling principle at work, we might suppose that broader connections between events are possible, interrelations or 'sympathies' between the meaningful parts of a well-ordered whole. For example, in the Stoic view of the cosmos, the organising principle, the *logos,* provided a basis for natural law and cosmic sympathy *(sympatheia).* As we have noted in Chapter Five, Jung's encounters with meaningful co-incidences in his work on the unconscious suggested to him that there were indeed connections between events that could not be explained in terms of efficient causation.

TRANSIENCE AND SPACETIME

Milic Capek has argued that spatialization is a "perennial philosophical illusion"[17] deriving from the Eleatic strain of thought: spacetime is the eternal Parmenidean One in modern guise, demoting Becoming to the status of appearance. Capek cites Kurt Gödel as one who had acknowledged an affinity with the legacy of Parmenides,[18] for Gödel saw in the theory of relativity "unequivocal proof for the view of those philosophers who, like Parmenides, Kant and the modern idealists, deny the objectivity of change and consider change as an illusion or an appearance due to our special mode of perception."[19]

In his eagerness to defend Becoming, Capek dismisses spatialized time as fallacious, a distortion of relativistic theory. Certainly, Becoming is in need of defence against attempts to deny it, for it is an experiential actuality. However, we may wonder whether the defence necessarily entails the rejection of a spacetime substratum for our transient experiences. If we wish to retain the two, we are faced by a challenge that Capek imagines every system of 'timelessness' fails to meet: how is transient Becoming, an undeniable experience for us, to be derived from static Being? How is transient experience to be related to the tenselessly stable substratum? In the next section we shall consider some of the difficulties that arise when attempts are made to answer this question. But in order to put the objection into perspective, it is worth noting that flux is mysterious whether or not an underlying static spacetime has been posited. The concept of spacetime merely highlights the puzzle of flowing experience by bringing out a contrast with a static organisation of events. There was no clear conception of flux in classical physics, and no notion of a static spacetime to highlight the deficiency. The instantaneous creation-destruction model of a universe in flux, for example, does not help us to understand flux. Extrinsic flux-time, whether the flow of an actually-existing substance called 'time' or a relational succession of states of matter, is included in the system without further explanation.

Such terms as *flowing time, passing time* or *the passage of time* are not very happy ways of expressing the transience of our experience, for they objectify time into a *thing* that flows or passes by. They imply that time is like a river that flows by an observer sitting on the bank, or like a landscape that flashes by an observer seated in a train. We then think of flowing time parading its changing contents before a timeless perceiver or 'consciousness', the observer on the river bank or in the train. This in not an appealing idea if we have doubted the separation of consciousness from the objects of consciousness, the experiencer from the experienced. Instead of one experiencer who views many temporal experiences, there are many temporal experiences, each containing a state of the experiencer. The problematic ways of conceptualising time, which imply a relative motion between time and observer, have been named "the myth of passage" by Donald Williams,[20] and have been the subject of some philosophical discussion. But however confusing or inappropriate the use of time language may be, the transience of our ordinary experience is indisputable, and its relation with static spacetime requires an explanation, if spacetime is to be taken seriously as an actuality.

One suggestion maintains that the sense of Becoming originates from the passage of consciousness along worldlines. Consciousness encounters the eternally-existing events one-by-one, like car headlamps progressively illuminating little portions of a dark road. There would have to be a large number of such crawling consciousnesses to account for the large number of trains of

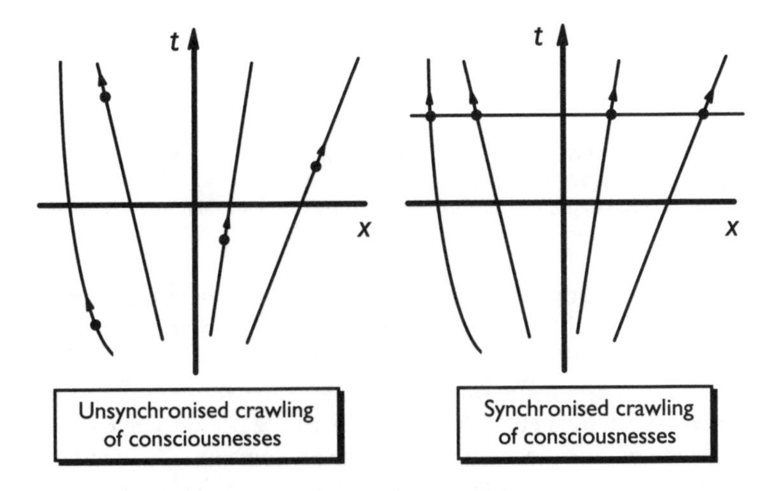

Figure 6.7. Unsynchronised and synchronised crawling of consciousnesses through spacetime. The diagrams show the positions of the consciousnesses in spacetime at a moment of extrinsic time.

transient experience associated with experiencing beings (unless, of course, a solipsist position is adopted). For a Newtonian spacetime, it might be supposed that all the consciousnesses sweep in synchrony along the worldlines, illuminating for a fleeting moment one entire cross-section of simultaneity. In the case of the growing or diminishing spacetime, the passage of consciousness would presumably be located in the active face of the spacetime. It might be wondered whether consciousness is to be found crawling along all worldlines, or is confined to the worldlines of fairly complex organisms that have brain-state representations. It might also be wondered whether it is necessary to have a grand synchronised sweep of consciousness through spacetime: consciousness might creep up each worldline independently (Figure 6.7.).

The idea of unsynchronised crawling consciousnesses suggests some bizarre possibilities. Two or more consciousnesses might crawl up different stretches of the same worldline, or a consciousness might crawl backwards along the worldline path, reversing the direction of time flow, perhaps encountering another consciousness crawling in the other direction.[21] There is another unattractive feature of the unsynchronised version: two people could be communicating with each other, but only one has 'consciousness' at that time—the consciousness of the other might have a very different time-coordinate in the spacetime. This possibility may be acceptable to those who suppose that 'consciousness' or experience has no role in directing events.

The idea of crawling consciousness arose in the context of relativistic spacetime. For example, there is the oft-quoted statement by the mathematician Hermann Weyl (1885–1955):

> The objective world simply *is,* it does not *happen.* Only to the gaze of my consciousness, crawling upward along the lifeline of my body, does a section of the world come to life as a fleeting image in space which continuously changes in time.[22]

In this view, spacetime is unknown, unexperienced, except at those regions along worldlines at which consciousness is currently moving. It is presumably the sense-representations in spacetime that consciousness is supposed to illuminate as it passes, for we do not experience whole cross-sections of simultaneity. Each moment of transient experience contains images of events from a variety of cross-sections, since there are transmission time-lags in the perceptual processes. For instance, the stars we see in the sky are not those in our current cross-sections of simultaneity—the starlight has taken many years to reach us. In any case, relativistic physics makes the definition of a cross-section of simultaneity arbitrary, for the universal Nows of the Newtonian spacetime are no longer applicable.

The idea of crawling consciousness is sometimes rejected because it introduces another time in addition to the spatialized time of the spacetime. The account makes reference to temporal processes, such as the 'crawling' or 'movement' of consciousness, and is similar in this respect to the growing and diminishing spacetimes mentioned above. The passage of consciousness along a worldline is a temporal process, and so the idea makes use of a flux-time additional to the spatialized time of the spacetime. Spacetime has to be placed in another time sequence for consciousness to be able to crawl through it, and there may even be a temptation to spatialize this extra flux-time sequence. J. W. Dunne[23] sought to derive a theory of time that would account for precognitive experiences in dreams and he took the idea of an extra time dimension seriously, suggesting that the transfer of consciousness occurs in a fifth dimension. This fifth dimension, a second spatialized time dimension, is supposed to make precognition possible, and provide an explanation for the experience of Becoming. To account for the temporal transfer of consciousness in the fifth dimension, Dunne went on to postulate another dimension with a moving consciousness, which in turn derives its Becoming from a further dimension and moving consciousness. This continues *ad infinitum.* Dunne's theory of *serial time* therefore derives Becoming from an infinite regress of spatialized time dimensions and moving consciousnesses.

The 'crawling consciousness' idea has implications for the mind-body problem. It could be argued that crawling consciousnesses play no role in the physical spacetime substratum. Consciousness is a passive observer moving along pre-existing worldlines and illuminating pre-existing structures without affecting them. Consciousness and worldlines are connected in some way, since the consciousnesses are supposed to follow them, but there is no causal action with spacetime events. Interactionist dualism and epiphenomenalism cannot be applied. The traditional interactionist and epiphenomenalist interpretations of the mind-body problem would require consciousness to be localised at each physical region along the worldline, permanently connected rather than crawling from one to the next. The epiphenomenalist might argue that there is a 'glow of consciousness' spread along each worldline, a product of the physical spacetime structure, whilst the interactionist dualist might argue that the causal relationship is both ways. Neither is able to say what the relationship is, because the indistinctness of the idea of consciousness means that it is impossible to decide how consciousness is related to spacetime structure. The association of transient experience with parts of the unchanging worldline implies that transient experience is tenselessly permanent.

The other dualist solution—psychophysical parallelism—could be applied to the relation between a physical spacetime and transient experience, but the parallelist would not envisage a consciousness crawling up the physical spacetime because there is no direct connection between the physical and mental in the parallelist solution. Instead, God or some such agency would correlate the experiential flux with the static physical spacetime.

From our experientialist standpoint, the 'crawling consciousness' idea is not attractive. The whole of spacetime is taken to be experiential, with the experiencer and experienced contained together in the experience. A crawling consciousness is incompatible with this experiential picture: experience does not need an external experiencer, for it is experience already. If, then, the idea of crawling consciousness is not attractive, how is the characteristic of transience and its direction to be explained?

THE ARROW OF TIME

One way of thinking about time directionality, or *the arrow of time,* is to say that there is a thing called *time* that moves in a certain direction. The directionality of time is the direction in which time flows. The language is open to criticism because it objectifies time into something that moves, and is therefore similar to such unsatisfactory phrases as *the passage of time* or *the flow of time.* To avoid the unwanted objectification of time into a thing distinct from experiences and processes, and to state more carefully what may be meant by the 'directionality of time', it will be useful to distinguish between three aspects of time directionality, firstly in our transient experience and then at the level of the substratum. The various kinds of time directionality are summarised in Figure 6.8.

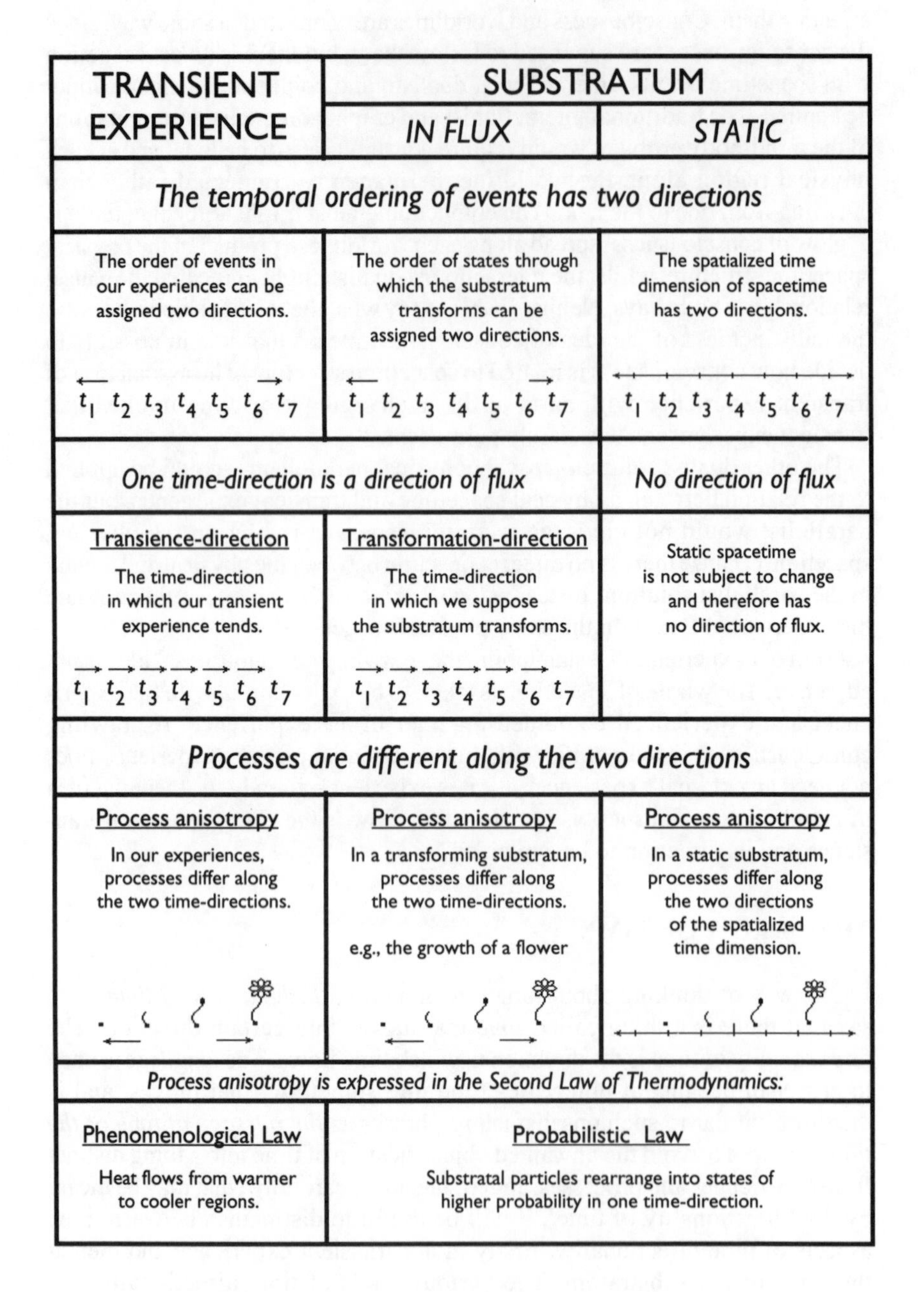

Figure 6.8. Summary of time-directionality terminology.

1. *Direction in transient experience*

1.1. Time as a sequential ordering of events in our memories, and in the inner duration of the experiential moment, has *two* directions, and I shall refer to these two directions as *time directions*. The time directions can be distinguished from each other in the following two ways.

1.2. Experience has the quality of transience, an apparent shifting along experiential states, and this transience is inclined in one of the two time directions, a shifting or trend from one state towards the next state. I shall refer to this directionality of transient experience as the *direction of transience* or *transience-direction.*

1.3. If we examine the ordering of experiences in the transient moment and our memories, we discover that sequences of events, or processes, are different along the two time directions. Consider, for instance, the process of river-flow: in one time direction, a river flows downhill, whilst in the other direction the river would flow uphill. Or consider the life-cycle of a daffodil: in one time direction, the daffodil grows from a seed and then flowers, whilst in the reverse direction the flower ungrows into a seed. Processes are different in the two time directions, and I shall refer to this asymmetry as the anisotropy of processes, or *process anisotropy.*

Processes may appear symmetrical (isotropic) when they are very simple and are not examined closely, such as the swinging of a pendulum or the collision of two billiard balls. Only an ideal pendulum, free from friction losses at its pivot and totally independent of the environment, would demonstrate a swinging process that is isotropic in both time directions.

An important example of process anisotropy is the formation of traces or representations. In one time direction, the trace follows the event, whilst in the reverse direction the event follows the trace. Now, in our familiar experience, we find that the trace follows the event, that the direction of transience is aligned in the event-to-trace direction of the process. For instance, in our transient experience we observe a vehicle traversing muddy ground to leave a track, which is a trace of the vehicle's path. In the reverse process, which we do not experience, the trace precedes the event: the vehicle follows a pre-existing track that disappears as the vehicle passes along it. Similarly, in our experience we find that a river erodes land, creates a valley and transports eroded material to the sea. The valley is a trace of many years of downhill flow. In the reverse process, the river would flow up a pre-existing valley, gradually filling it with material transported from the sea. Our memories are special instances of traces. A man on a boat, carried along by the river, has memories of the journey down the river to his current position, and the part of the journey that is contained in memory he calls the 'past'.

Now transience-direction and process anisotropy come together because we find that the direction of transience is always aligned in just one of the two anisotropic process directions. We find that, in our experience, a river flows downhill, a seed grows into a flower, wood burns to ash. We would be surprised to experience the reverse processes, water flowing uphill, a flower ungrowing into a seed, ash unburning to wood. Such reverse processes are sometimes illustrated to humorous effect by reversing the direction of play of ciné film, and in our imaginations we can perform the reversals too.

Why is the transience-direction of experience always aligned in just one of the two process directions? I have assumed that this alignment is always the case, but it would be hasty to exclude the possibility of unusual experiences in which the experiential transience-direction is aligned in the unfamiliar direction of process anisotropy.

2. *Direction in the substratum*

So far our discussion has focused on transient experience. We have considered the directionalities of what is sometimes called *psychological, personal* or *subjective time*. We must now consider how to interpret the meaning of 'the direction of time' when applied to the substratum, and in particular, to the physical world of realist science.

2.1. Again, we can distinguish two *time directions* in the sequential ordering of events. In the case of a spacetime substratum, these two time directions are the two directions of the linear, spatialized time axis.

2.2. If the substratum is taken to be in flux, as in the classical, pre-spacetime conception of the physical world, then we can ascribe to it a *transformation-direction*. The substratum is undergoing transformation from moment to moment, and this transformation implies a direction of change from one state to the next. It would be natural to suppose that the experiential direction of transience mirrors this substratal transformation-direction, for the substratum has the role of supporting our experience. If the substratum is static, like spacetime, there is no transformation-direction, for there is no flux, no transformation from moment to moment.

2.3. Substratal processes, like the processes in transient experience they support, would be anisotropic. In a representational theory, the daffodil of transient experience, which grows through an anisotropic sequence of states, is a representation of a substratal daffodil that similarly grows through an anisotropic sequence of states. *Process anisotropy* applies to a substratum in flux and to a static substratum:

2.3.1. For a substratum in flux, we have to explain why the substratum transforms in one direction of process anisotropy, and not in the reverse direction. Why is the transformation-direction aligned in a particular direction of process anisotropy? The substratal river flows downhill, rather than uphill.

2.3.2. For a static spacetime substratum, process anisotropy still holds, even though there is no transformation-direction. Processes are displayed statically as sequences of states along a spatialized time dimension that has the two time directions. The spacetime structuring of processes is not the same in the two directions, and is therefore anisotropic. For instance, in one direction of the spatialized time dimension, the daffodil seed precedes the flower, whilst in the other direction the flower precedes the seed.

It is necessary to make these distinctions because a discussion of the 'arrow of time' is otherwise likely to be confused. The importance of distinguishing between the directionalities of time in our transient experience and in the substratum has not always been appreciated. Adolf Grünbaum recognised the importance, and distinguished between what we have called here the process anisotropy of the substratum (2.3.) and the transience-direction of our transient experience (1.2.):

> we must clearly distinguish the anisotropy of physical time from the feature of common sense (psychological) time which is rendered by such terms as "the transiency of the Now" or "becoming"....[24]

In this work we are particularly interested in the static spacetime conception of the substratum, and we are therefore faced with a difficult question: how is experiential transience (and its direction) to be related to a spacetime substratum that has process anisotropy but is not itself in flux?

Before addressing this question, it will be instructive to look in greater detail at the nature of process anisotropy, for much discussion of time's arrow by physicists has focused on process anisotropy. In the following section, *Thermodynamics and Group Processes,* we consider the problem of linking physics with process anisotropy. The reader may wish to omit this section on a first reading, and proceed directly to the section entitled *The Transience of the Moment.*

THERMODYNAMICS AND GROUP PROCESSES

There has been much debate over whether the laws of physics—which a realist takes to be descriptive of substratal processes—provide an explanation for 'the arrow of time'. As I understand the matter, physics has something to say about process anisotropy but leaves unanswered the problem of linking process anisotropy to experiential transience and its direction.

It is by no means obvious how process anisotropy comes about, for the laws of physics are, in general, time-reversible—processes described by the laws of physics could proceed in either time-direction without contradiction. Process anisotropy is not deducible, in general, from the laws of physics. If a system is transformed into one state by a process, time-reversibility means that there is an inverse process that can restore the system to its original state. Time-reversibility is clear in the physics of motion, which, we have noted, has long provided the basic explanatory model for other areas of physical study. The film of a collision between two billiard balls can be played in either direction. Both showings of the collision would seem equally plausible to us and in accord with the laws of mechanics (however, if we inspected the details closely, such as traces of the motions on the billiard table, we would discover asymmetry). Directions of motion and signs of velocity are reversed, but the accelerations and forces are unchanged. A film of a more complex process, such as the life-cycle of a daffodil, would not look equally plausible in the two directions of play. Nevertheless, the growing and the ungrowing processes would both be in accord with the laws of physics. The physical laws in themselves give us no cause for regarding the life-cycle process of the daffodil as irreversible, as anisotropic, although the process clearly is irreversible.

However, there is one exception to the time-reversibility of physical laws, and this is one of the fundamental laws of thermodynamics, the study of heat. The Second Law of Thermodynamics, originally formulated in the nineteenth century, assigns a transformation-direction to processes. Initially the law was simply a statement about processes in transient experience, not a law describing substratal processes. It described experiential transience-direction, not the transformation-direction of a substratum in flux. In its simplest form it is a statement about heat flow in our experience: "heat, of its own accord, does not pass from a colder to a hotter body." Expressed in a more technical form, a quantity called the *entropy,* coined by Clausius (1822–88) and meaning 'transformation-content', is said to *increase* during processes. Entropy, in the study of heat, is a measure of the unavailableness of heat energy for performing mechanical work. The increase of entropy (the increasing unavailableness of mechanically useful heat energy) was taken to indicate the 'direction of time'. Now, the second law in its original form tells us about processes in *transient experience,* about the alignment of the transience-direction (1.2.) with one direction of process anisotropy (1.3.), the anisotropy of heat flow. It is phenomenological, describing the phenomena, and says nothing directly about the noumena, the substratal physical processes. Initially, thermodynamics was concerned with readily measurable properties ascribed to a system, such as temperature, pressure, and volume, and the second law of this 'phenomenological thermodynamics' was not concerned with substratal anisotropic physical processes (2.3.) underlying the heat flow processes in experience. It is simply a description of the evolution of heat processes in transient experience.

The urge to incorporate the various branches of physics into one explanatory picture soon deprived thermodynamics of its ideally phenomenological status by introducing a mechanical model of the substratum. Heat, in the kinetic theory, is the energy of substratal molecules in motion. The introduction of a molecular substratum, described by the time-reversible physical laws of classical mechanics, posed a problem, for the process anisotropy of heat flow at the experiential level (1.3.) is not mirrored in the time-reversible laws of mechanical interaction in the substratum. It was not obvious that any process anisotropy occurred at the molecular level of the substratum. A collision between two molecules in the kinetic theory is not anisotropic. Mechanically, it is quite proper for the heat motions of particles to become concentrated in one region, implying a heat flow from a colder to a hotter part, which contradicts the phenomenological Second Law of Thermodynamics.

Following the successful treatment of thermodynamics in terms of a statistical distribution of particle-motions by James Clerk Maxwell in the mid-nineteenth century, the physicist Ludwig Boltzmann (1844–1906) argued that the Second Law *does* have a basis in the motions of the molecular substratum, and that the basis is *probabilistic* in nature. He contended that the Second Law is explicable as a *statistical* consequence of kinetic theory: an isolated *(closed)* system of components moves to adopt a state from the more numerous (and therefore more probable) varieties of states available. The idea can be illustrated with the example of milk poured into a cup of coffee. For an instant, the milk particles and coffee particles are separate, each of the two kinds of particle being confined to distinct spatial regions in the cup. But intermixing of the milk and coffee particles, in accordance with the time-reversible laws of mechanics, takes place very rapidly and the initial state of separation is not encountered again in the lifetime of the cup of coffee. In the statistical argument, it is pointed out that there are comparatively few unmixed states of the coffee and milk particles, compared with the very many well-mixed states. It is therefore much more probable, the argument goes, that the cup of coffee will be in one of the numerous well-mixed states than in an unmixed or largely unmixed state. Molecular processes are anisotropic, moving towards the high probability states of a system, and entropy is interpreted in probabilistic terms. Thus, process anisotropy is established in the shifting substratum of particles (2.3.1.), and

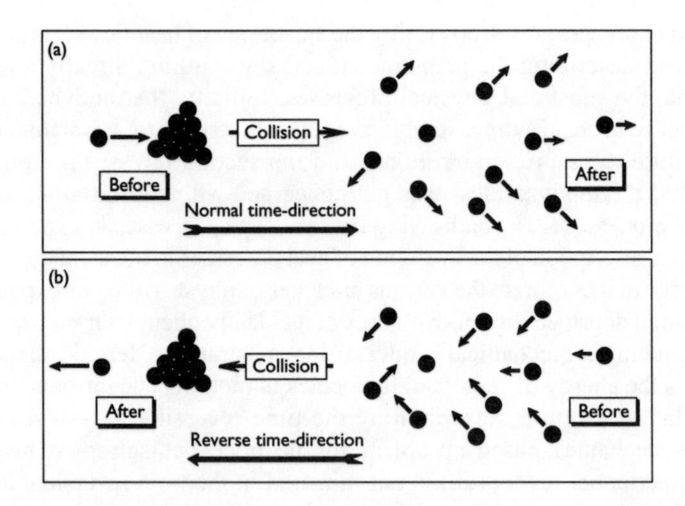

Figure 6.9. Collision of particles: an anisotropic process shown in its two time-directions. The small arrows indicate the directions of motion of the particles. Note that the directions of these arrows are reversed between the two time-directions.

the transformation-direction (2.2.) is aligned in the direction of more probable states. The process anisotropy (1.3.) and transience-direction (1.2.) of our transient experience are then linked directly to the substratum of particles in flux and its trend towards high probability states. Boltzmann's statistical derivation, called the *H*-theorem, was questioned by some, notably J. Loschmidt, E. Zermelo, H. Poincaré, and P. and T. Ehrenfest. It can be objected that the time-reversibility of particle motions in a closed system implies that the low-probability unmixed state will reappear eventually, although the recurrence will take a very long time if there are many particles. The milk and coffee mix would eventually pass through the unmixed and largely unmixed states.

The probabilistic/entropic explanation of time directionality has been disputed ever since its formulation. We shall not go into the complexities of the entropic arguments, which were elaborated by Hans Reichenbach and developed further by Adolf Grünbaum. One important question concerns the status of probabilistic explanations. Statistics and probability provide the scientist with a valuable means of coping with a lack of detailed knowledge of a system. But is it valid to accord probability a role in determining the course of processes towards particular states? Statistics and probability then become facets of the processes themselves, and are not just mathematical tools that we use when our personal knowledge is limited. The question of the status of probabilistic descriptions arises again in the quantum theory, as we shall see in Chapter Fifteen.

Whatever the status of probabilistic explanations may be, the application of statistics points to a feature of the physical world that has a significant bearing on the question of process anisotropy—physical interactions occur among a *multiplicity* of parts. Many components are usually involved in physical interactions, and this plurality enables a process anisotropy to manifest that can be explained in terms other than probabilistic and entropic. The sequence of events describing an interaction between two independent, isolated particles can be envisaged in either time direction without appearing odd, but this is not usually so for interactions in groups of particles, as in the flow of heat, the mixing of milk and coffee, the flow of a river, or the life-cycle of a daffodil. The laws of mechanics describe the individual interactions of the particles, and are completely time-reversible, but the participation of many particles introduces the possibility of anisotropic process.

Consider the collision between particles shown in Figure 6.9. In one time direction, a single particle approaches and collides with a stationary group of particles, scattering the particles in all directions at various speeds. In the reverse time direction, a large number of particles converge from different directions with an amazing degree of co-ordination to form a stationary group with a single particle moving away from the group. In the first case, a single motion gives rise to a diverging multiplicity of co-ordinated motions, whilst in the second a multiplicity of co-ordinated converging motions gives rise to a single motion.

To consider process anisotropy in a group of particles in greater detail, we can look at the case of a stone cast into a pond.[25] In the familiar time-direction, the stone drops towards the pond, hits the surface and sinks to the bottom. Water waves diverge outwards from the point of impact to the sides of the pond. The single motion of the pebble towards the pond is dissipated into a multiplicity of motions, including the wave motions of water particles, heat motions of earth-particles round the pond, and sound motions of air-particles.

In the reverse sequence, a vast number of particle-motions in the earth, water and air are co-ordinated in such a manner that circular waves are generated on the water surface and the pebble is thrust upwards from the bottom of the pond into the air, leaving the water surface undisturbed. The same is true for the uphill flow of the river or the ungrowing of the daffodil into a seed. All these processes are in accordance with the laws of mechanics and physics describing the interactions of individual particles, but they require a remarkable co-ordination of apparently unconnected motions. The co-ordination is not an occasional instance, of the sort we might encounter in our ordinary experience (say, five trolleys converging and colliding simultaneously in a supermarket). In the reverse direction of anisotropic group processes, the remarkable co-ordination or orchestration is the rule, not the exception.

The pebble-and-pond sequence of events is similar to fundamental processes in nature: the propagation of changes. In one direction, an event sends out many signals, whilst in the reverse direction many signals converge on the event. Note, for instance, the emission of a spherical shell of light radiation from a body, which is an example cited by Popper and was first considered by Einstein in 1909.[26] Some regions of the expanding shell are soon absorbed by other bodies in the vicinity whilst other regions are absorbed much later by distant bodies. In the reverse sequence, a large number of widely distributed bodies have to conspire over a long period to emit light radiation in such a way that a spherical shell of light is created, which contracts upon a single, absorbing body.[27]

The anisotropy between the two time-directions of group processes can be expressed as follows:

1. In the familiar process direction, an interaction is followed by a co-ordinated multiplicity of changes. This could be termed *subsequent co-ordination,* co-ordination that follows the interaction. Figure 6.9.(a) shows an example of subsequent co-ordination.

2. In the reverse process direction, a co-ordinated multiplicity of changes precedes the interaction. This could be termed *prior co-ordination,* a co-ordination that precedes the interaction. Figure 6.9.(b) depicts an example of prior co-ordination.

Can these two kinds of group process occur in the same time direction? For instance, can rivers in one part of the universe flow downhill, whilst rivers in another part of the universe flow uphill, both in the same time direction? In our region of the universe we do not experience such mixing, and I suspect it unlikely that a universe conceived as a physically *interconnected* whole could support the mixture of co-ordination types in a common time direction.

The idea of the two anisotropic process directions is linked with the notion of causality. It is tempting to attribute the co-ordination between a multiplicity of changes to a single, unifying cause, for the co-ordination is simply an expression of this common source. In the normal time sequence, the initial, simple event provides a unifying explanation for the co-ordination of the subsequent plural effects, in keeping with the commonly-held scientific view of causation. The efficient cause precedes the effect. But in the reverse sequence (prior co-ordination), the co-ordination of plural events *precedes* the interaction and cannot be explained as the consequence of a unifying efficient cause.

In summary, we do not have to look to a probabilistic interpretation of the Second Law of Thermodynamics to find anisotropy in the substratum. Time directions are distinguishable in group interactions that have an *orchestrated* complexity of events at one side of the interactions. However, we have merely shown that process anisotropy occurs in particle interactions in the substratum, and have yet to fathom how the process anisotropy of the substratum and transient experience may be related to experiential transience and its direction.

Our experience tells us that the transience-direction of experience is aligned with subsequent co-ordination, the process-direction in which an interaction is followed by the complex orchestration. Why is the direction of transience so aligned? One approach to this question might be to examine the role of anisotropic physical processes in sense-representation and trace formation, hoping that a link will be found here—our experience is closely linked with representation, with perceptual images and memory traces in the case of higher organisms. According to a representational theory, we rely on signals from the external environment to build up sensory images of the world.

In the normal process-direction (subsequent co-ordination), a representation or trace follows the original. Light travels from an object to the eye, and a brain-state representation is eventually constructed. In the reverse process-direction (prior co-ordination), the original follows the representation. A brain-state representation would develop out of the brain, without external stimuli, and then undergo deconstruction, with nerve signals outputted to the sense-organs. In the case of vision, light would be transmitted from the eye to the object. Similarly, in the reverse direction, memories of events would precede the actual events, but would fade before the events occur.

In both time directions, then, there are representations and memories, but the temporal relationships with the represented differ, coming either before or after the representation. Image formation in one process-direction is image dissolution in the other process-direction. The important point to note is that the existence of sensory representations and memories is not dependent on the process-direction. This is very clear in the case of a static spacetime substratum. Spacetime structure is anisotropic along its time dimension, but traces and perceptual representations nonetheless exist within it. In one direction, traces precede the event; in the other, traces follow the event. Thus, in the 'crawling consciousness' theory, a consciousness could crawl in either direction along the worldline of an organism and encounter sense-representations or brain-states.

THE TRANSIENCE OF THE MOMENT

Process anisotropy, we have seen, can be traced to physical events in the substratum, through arguments that invoke probability and entropy, or through a consideration of the asymmetry of *group* processes. The process anisotropy of spacetime, however, remains unconnected with the transience of our familiar experience and the direction in which it tends, the transience-direction. How, then, are we to account for transience and its direction, if the process anisotropy of substratal spacetime fails to provide an obvious solution?

Perhaps the process anisotropy of events in a *physical* spacetime substratum is insufficient to account for transience and its arrow. Adolf Grünbaum goes some way towards this recogniton, with his support of Hugo Bergmann's "exclusively psychologistic conception"[28] of flux, the idea that transience depends on consciousness:

> the transient now ... has no relevance at all to the time of physical events, because it has no significance at all apart from the egocentric perspectives of a *conscious* (human) organism and from the immediate experiences of that organism.[29]

Unlike Grünbaum, however, we would not consider substratal events as purely physical, and the "psychologistic" nature of transient experience would be rooted in the astructural qualities and psychological features of the substratum—the experientialist approach to the mind-body problem admits astructural and psychological features into the substratum, in addition to structure. The survey of universal mystical experiences in Chapter Four suggested that universal cognition, a loving attitude, and light, are inseparable from the structural facets of the substratum. Substratal process anisotropy would not merely consist of asymmetrical structural organisation, but would involve an *understanding* of processes, a feeling-cognition of the differences between the two process-directions. Even though the experience as a whole is tenselessly static (fluxless), its structure would be given a dynamic quality by the intrinsic understanding-feeling of its developmental trends. Perhaps we can use the analogy of a book to help illustrate the point: the book as a whole is an all-at-once existence, but its intelligible content draws us along from cover to cover.

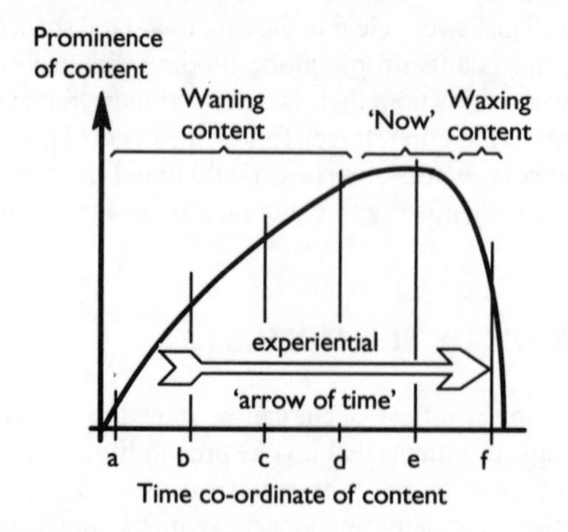

Figure 6.10. The transience of the moment: each moment has the quality of transience through its varied experiential content, including understandings and feelings. The diagram shows the transient moment illustrated in Figure 6.1., with an arrow inscribed to symbolise its *intrinsic* transience.

As a mere structure of pages covered with lines of characters, the book has no dynamic trend, no special 'direction', but the unfolding of *meaning* draws us along through the text.

Now, we might conjecture that our ordinary experience gains its transient qualities through astructural, cognitive and feeling contents. Transience is not something additional to these contents. Each transient moment, each 'specious present', may take its characteristics of transience and transience-direction from its temporal span of sensation, cognition and feeling. Each moment, each 'drop' of transient experience, may derive its quality of transience through a span of temporal content of different levels of experiential clarity or intensity, a span of partial perceptions, understandings and feelings (Figure 6.10.).

Let us summarise the argument. The substratum consists of a total experience, a Being-experience, that contains temporal sequences of events arranged through spacetime. The temporal structuring of experiential spacetime provides the linear *physical time* or *clock time* that physical scientists employ in their descriptions of the world. Transient experience, Becoming-experience, consists of individual moments, each of which derives its quality of transience from complex perceptual, cognitive and feeling content. It is this complex temporality of the transient moment that constitutes the *subjective* or *psychological time* studied by psychologists. The moments of transient experience are little parcels of thinking, feeling and perceiving, set in the greater experience of the substratum. As a whole, the substratum is fluxless, but the little islands are transient by virtue of their complex content. Finely-crafted regions with a shifting quality are knit into the great tapestry.

If we picture the substratum as a spacetime experience in which many transient moments are set, we have yet to explain why the moments are experienced separately from the total experience. Their span of temporal content seems to enable them to stand on their own as experiences, echoing the temporal span of eternity, but, unlike the total experience, they are partial understandings and feelings, and look towards later moments for completion. If the accounts of the mystics are to be believed, the search for completion ("the pursuit of the whole") is satisfied only when the forward striving relaxes and the transient moment opens to the substratum, admitting the fullness of the eternal Now.

The idea that each moment of transient experience has its own quality of transience would agree with the observation noted in Chapter One: transient experience appears to be seamless. We do not distinguish individual moments or gaps between moments. If each moment is a complete transient experience in itself, there is no need to imagine a shift from moment to moment, a linking of sequential moments. Becoming is intrinsic to each moment. All moments distributed throughout spacetime stand on their own as intrinsically transient experiences (a qualification to this statement will be suggested in Chapter Twelve). Each drop of the stream contains the flow in itself, and it is the individual 'flow' of each moment that constitutes the flow of the experiential stream.

As the moments of our ordinary experience are parts of a tenselessly permanent whole (the experiential spacetime substratum), it would follow that our experiences also have a tenseless permanence. All transient moments, as special regions of spacetime, share the tenseless permanence of spacetime-Being. It would be incorrect to think of a transient moment as fading and the next moment arising to replace it. Transient life-experiences cannot arise or fade, for we have not introduced an extrinsic time-sequence or flux-time in which this could occur. There is, however, a quality of fading and arising *within* the complex composition of the transient moment. Socrates accepts the bowl of hemlock. A bird sings in the garden. A cat sleeps by the fire. I write this sentence and you read it. Paradoxically, the transience of the moment is permanent. The fleeting experience, although eternal, has the quality of transience, and cannot be grasped. We say goodbye and move on, but the saying-goodbye and the moving-on are permanent.[30]

There is a further point to consider: the normal alignment of the transience-direction with the substratal process anisotropy might sometimes change, if the transient moment can have an unusual composition in which the earlier parts of the temporal span are emphasised, or the temporal ordering is inverted in some way, giving the impression of reversed transience-direction. Obviously, the details of a reversed composition are obscure, for details of the ordinary composition are obscure, and I make the suggestion merely to point out that an experiential time-reversal could be contained within each moment, along with the slowing or speeding effects that are sometimes reported in exceptional states of consciousness.[31] The reversals and shifts in the quality of transience would be due to a disturbance in the composition of the transient moment. In this theory, there is no need to go outside the individual moment and regard experiential time-reversal as a reversed shifting *across* moments (for instance, a crawling consciousness retreating down a worldline).

The account of transience given here, which calls on the intrinsic astructural and psychological features of experience, on partial cognitions and feelings, including memories, and overlapping temporal content, requires further development before it can be said to account satisfactorily for the relationship between Being and Becoming, but it may be a step in the right direction. The idea that structure alone is sufficient to account for the transience of experience has been abandoned, and it has been conjectured that 'psychological' features united with structural process anisotropy may lie behind transience and its direction. A greater understanding of the composition of the transient moment, and its roots in the complexities of the personal unconscious (including unconscious cognitions and feelings), is required before the explanation can be made more convincing.

7. THE ENIGMA OF MOTION

Of the many kinds of change that occur within the stream of experience, the transformation called *motion* has been the key to the development of modern science. In Chapter Two, we saw that the application of mathematics to the study of motion lay behind the success of the mechanical philosophy in the seventeenth and eighteenth centuries, and led to the modern physical pictures of the world. The triumph of classical mechanics was the culmination of a long history of observation and theory, stretching from the Babylonian charting of celestial motions, through the achievements of Greek mathematical astronomy and Aristotelian physics, to the work of Copernicus, Kepler and Galileo—to mention only a few of the outstanding contributions. In spite of its remarkable success, the classical edifice was flawed, for it stood on unsound foundations. Newtonian mechanics rested on concepts of space and time that came under scrutiny in the late nineteenth century, and underwent major changes in the early twentieth century. However, the spectacular advances brought about by relativistic physics and quantum mechanics have not fully clarified the mysteries of motion, both in the physical theory and the philosophical background.

Motion raises a number of problems. We have already come across one area of uncertainty. The paradoxes of Zeno, intended to demonstrate the unreality of motion, raise questions about the number of temporal states assumed by a moving body as it traverses a distance. Is the number finite or infinite? Does motion proceed continuously or in leaps? However, the problem that is of great interest to us here is the old debate over relative and absolute motion, a debate that has considerable relevance to speculations about the existence of a substratum behind our relative perceptions. If we adopt a realist attitude to the substratum, we may try to obtain a true and unique account of the motions of objects, for we may believe that behind the relativity of sense-experience there exists a substratum with definite attributes, containing objects with definite states of motion. However, it turns out that the search for the true motions of bodies in the substratum does not proceed very far, because our observations always yield *relative* descriptions of motion, never the *absolute* motions of the hypothesised substratal bodies. The idea of the substratum had promised to unify our relative experiences by tying them to a common, comprehensive world with well-defined attributes, an absolute world. On closer inspection we find that the motion of bodies, the centre-piece of physical science, cannot be pinned down absolutely, and the relativity of motion leads us to question the idea of an absolute substratum.

In this chapter we consider the problem of relative motion and in the next we look at pre-relativistic attempts to find an absolute, including Newton's concept of absolute motion in an *absolute space.* In Chapter Nine, we explore the insights of relativistic physics, which pushed aside Newton's absolute world, and consider the relativistic substratum introduced by Minkowski, the absolute world of *Minkowski spacetime.*

THE STUDY OF MOTION

Nowadays, the term *motion* is reserved for changes in the arrangement of objects or their parts. In earlier times, the word had a more general philosophical application, referring to all types of change. The wider usage derived from Aristotle's physics, which included all transformations of nature within its scope. Thus, the Greek word corresponding to our term 'motion', *kinesis,* was applied to changes in the Aristotelian categories of quality, quantity and place. For example, the fading of a colour is an instance of 'motion' in the category of quality. The kind of change in which position is altered is a change in the category of place, and was termed *phora*. In English it was translated as *local motion,* or *locomotion,* because it consists of a change in the location of a body.

The study of locomotion is now part of a branch of physics called *mechanics,* "the science of motion", which has come to be sub-divided into *kinematics, dynamics* and *statics.* It is the treatment of forces in dynamics that is usually held to distinguish dynamics from kinematics. Exactly what is meant by this distinction depends on one's understanding of force. The positivist prefers to discuss the observed accelerations of bodies, rather than unobserved forces and masses, and dynamics becomes a science of the comparative accelerations of bodies. In contrast, a typical non-positivist explanation of the three branches, as we might find in a conventional textbook of mechanics, makes the following distinctions:

Kinematics: the study of motions of bodies *without* any consideration of the agents or causes that are responsible for altering motions. Kinematics describes the following changes:

displacement:	change of position in a direction;
velocity:	rate of change of displacement;
acceleration:	rate of change of velocity.

We could continue the *'rate of change of'* definitions indefinitely, the next being the rate of change of acceleration. But these further rates of change are not sufficiently important quantities in mechanics to receive special attention. The role of direction is to be noted in the above definitions. Displacement, velocity and acceleration are quantities that have both magnitude and direction, and are called *vector* quantities. They are usually represented by bold letters (**r**, **v**, **a**), and, geometrically, by directed lines or arrows. They are contrasted with *scalar* quantities, which have magnitudes but no associated direction. Scalar quantities include mass and time, and are usually represented by italic letters *(m, t)*. Speed, the magnitude of a velocity, is a scalar quantity.

Dynamics: the study of the motions of bodies, *with* consideration of the causes of motion. The kinematical description of displacements, velocities and accelerations is supplemented with descriptions of *forces* causing the changes in motion, and *masses* of bodies resisting the changes in motion. The mechanics of Newton's *Principia* (1687) was the first comprehensive system of dynamics. The acceleration of a body is important in dynamics, because it is taken to be a measure of the force acting on the body.

Statics: the study of bodies at rest with one another, owing to a balance of forces.

In using the terms *kinematical* and *dynamic* in the present discussion, I shall follow the common usage: forces characterise dynamic descriptions or laws, but not kinematical descriptions. In this sense, the mathematical astronomy of the Greeks can be called kinematical, because there was no treatment of physical force in their mathematical modelling of planetary motions. In contrast, Newton's universal law of gravitation is dynamic because it describes forces that act between bodies.

Motions can be distinguished into motions along *straight* paths and motions along *curved* paths. In a translation, all the parts of a body are displaced through equal distances in just one direction. The motion is one-dimensional. This kind of motion is called *rectilinear.* In a *curvilinear* motion, such as a rotation, some parts of a body move through greater distances than others, and there is a change of direction from instant to instant. In the two-dimensional, circular, rotational motion of a wheel, a point on the periphery covers a greater distance than a point near the axle, and all parts constantly change their direction of motion. As we shall now consider, circular motion was held in great esteem until the seventeenth century.

MOTIONS CELESTIAL AND TERRESTRIAL

In the early study of motion, it was natural to distinguish the motions of bodies on the earth, which appear complex, disorderly and short-lived, from the motions of celestial bodies, which appear simple, regular and everlasting. On earth, bodies drop to the ground, come to rest, are disturbed by collisions. In contrast, it appears that the heavenly bodies follow unwavering circular motions around the heavens, circulating round the earth once a day, rising in the East and setting in the West. In the daytime we see the east-to-west journey of the sun across the sky. On a clear night, we can follow the east-to-west journeys of the stars, moon and planets. From our centres of observation on the earth's surface, we can imagine that the sky we see above the horizon is hemispherical, and that the sky as a whole is a sphere enclosing the earth, a celestial sphere studded with stars. The sphere rotates once a day about the earth, defining a north-south polar axis, and stars trace circular paths around this axis.

The heaven of stars is awe-inspiring, wresting the attention from the mundane world of the terrestrial plane. In the heavens, Plato saw "an eternal moving image of the eternity which remains for ever at one",[1] an everlasting semblance of the eternal Being, fashioned by the creator, the demiurge. Following earlier notions of a spherical god or cosmos, Plato explained the appropriateness of the rotating sphere for the shape of the divine cosmos: the sphere contains all other figures within itself, excels in completeness and uniformity, and is endowed with uniform circular motion "which most properly belongs to intelligence and reason".[2] Suggested by celestial motions, justified by geometrical and religious arguments, uniform circular motion became the ideal motion of the ancient world, and geometric accounts of celestial motions were to utilise uniform circular motions or combinations of such motions. Indeed, the efforts of Copernicus, which played such an important role in changing cosmological understanding, were motivated by the ancient ideal of uniform, circular motion.

The ancient astronomers who sought to model celestial motions using geometry were faced with a considerable challenge. The simple daily *(diurnal)* motion of the stars about the polar axis is not emulated by the motions of all celestial bodies, the most noticeable exceptions being the sun and moon. In

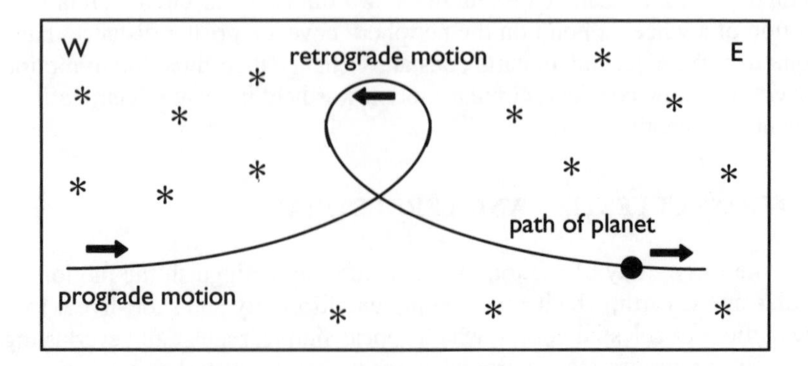

Figure 7.1. A retrograde motion of a planet against the background of stars.

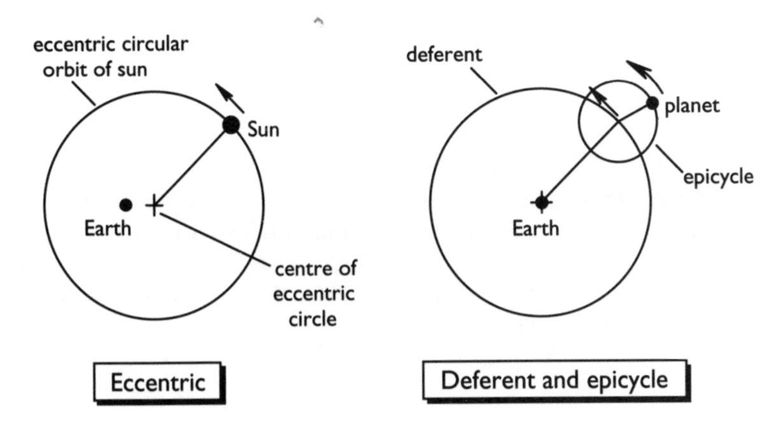

Figure 7.2. Off-centre circular orbits: eccentrics and epicycle-deferents.

ancient times, five other bodies were discovered that deviate from the uniform circular motion exhibited by the stars (the *fixed stars)*. These were the five planets, Mercury, Venus, Mars, Jupiter, Saturn. In the old usage, the term *planet* (Greek *planetes,* 'wanderer') included all the wanderers, the sun and moon, as well as the five planets. These seven wanderers depart from the diurnal motion of the fixed stars, showing an independence that suggested the activity of souls or intelligences. The motions of the planets lag behind the east-to-west motion of the stars, and follow paths round the celestial sphere through the band of stars called the *zodiac.* This band is centred on the yearly path of the sun through the fixed stars, called the *ecliptic.* The sun and moon show significant departures from uniform circular motion, and the five planets show overtly discrepant behaviour in their *retrograde* motions—the laggardly planets are sometimes observed to speed up, temporarily advancing faster than the stars. With additional north-south motions above and below the ecliptic, the five planets trace looped paths against the backcloth of stars (Figure 7.1.).

Attempts to model the irregular motions of the sun, moon and planets, using systems of ideal circular motions, provided a major stimulus to the development of mechanics, and, for a long period, advances in mechanics were confined to the study of celestial motions. Eudoxus (*c.*400–347 B.C.) devised a mathematical system of concentric (homocentric) spheres, centred on the earth, with the five planets assigned four spheres each, and the sun and moon assigned three spheres each, to account for their irregular motions.This system, extended by Callippus (born *c.*370 B.C.), lived on in the extraordinarily influential cosmology of Aristotle, who seems to have ascribed the mathematical spheres a physical reality. The concentric sphere system was soon replaced in the accounts of astronomers by more promising mathematical theories, which used off-centre circular orbits *(eccentrics),* and a combination of circles *(deferents* with *epicycles)*—see Figure 7.2. The development of these alternatives to the theory of concentric spheres is associated in particular with Apollonius of Perga (third to second century B.C.), Hipparchus of Rhodes (second century B.C.) and Ptolemy (*c.*100–*c.*170 A.D.).

It was not until the seventeenth century that terrestrial motions began to receive adequate, quantitative attention, first in the work of Galileo, who ascertained the correct mathematical description of bodies falling to the ground, the *law of free-fall.* Galileo found that the distance s fallen by a body is proportional to the square of the time t elapsed from the beginning of the fall. For a body with no initial velocity,

$$s = \frac{1}{2}at^2$$

It follows that the velocity of the body increases uniformly with the time elapsed, and not with the distance travelled, as had sometimes been thought.

$$v = at$$

Furthermore, the free-fall acceleration a is the same for all bodies, if air-resistance effects are excluded. This is counter-intuitive: we tend to think that heavier bodies fall more rapidly, unless our pre-conceptions have been corrected by the insights of classical mechanics.

The mathematical treatment of terrestrial motion, and its integration with celestial motions in Newton's dynamics, finally displaced the circular ideal that had dominated thought since the Greeks. Rectilinear motion—uniform motion in a straight line—became the *natural* motion in classical mechanics, both on the earth and in the heavens, and circular motion was reinterpreted as a *forced* or *constrained* motion.

MOTIONS NATURAL AND CONSTRAINED

The theory that dominated the physics of motion until the seventeenth century had distinguished between natural and forced motions. According to Aristotle, natural motion arises when a body is free from constraint and can actualise its potential. The different kinds of body found in nature (*stoicheion,* 'element') have natural places to which they move when freed from constraint. There are two kinds of natural motion, one terrestrial and one celestial. Below the sphere of the moon, in our terrestrial world of generation and corruption, the four elements engage in natural motions towards their natural places, earth towards the centre of Aristotle's spherical cosmos, and water, air and fire to places successively further out. These elements follow their natural rectilinear motions, falling to or rising from the centre, in accordance with their tendencies of heaviness *(gravity)* and lightness *(levity)* towards their natural places. However, in the terrestrial region, natural motions are often constrained, and the elements are unable to reach their natural places.

The other natural motion in the cosmos takes place in the celestial region above the sublunary realm, in the superlunary realm. Here, the natural motion is *not* rectilinear, but circular. The four elements, with their rectilinear motions, are not found here—instead, a fifth element, or quintessence, the *aither* or *quinta essentia,* is located in the celestial region, and this element follows a natural circular motion, which is everlasting and unconstrained. Moving outwards from the stationary earth at the centre of the cosmos, we encounter the planetary bodies carried by their crystal spheres, both planet and sphere made of *aither.* The moon is the first, the slowest of the planets in its motion around the earth, and Saturn the last, which is closest in speed to the rapidly-rotating, outer shell of the universe, the sphere of fixed stars. All change and motion in the cosmos ultimately derive from a single cause, a First Mover, or *proton kinoun,* which is itself unmoved. Aristotle's closed, spherical universe inevitably raised questions about the existence of things beyond the outermost boundary.[3]

Besides the natural locomotions of the elements, there was another kind of motion posited in Aristotelian physics: violent or forced motions. These were said to occur when a body was projected, given an impulse or force. The motion is continued by the surrounding medium that rushes in behind the body and pushes it forward. The process relies on a *plenum* to maintain the motion, a fullness of matter—motion could not take place in an emptiness, in a vacuum. The plenum is a distinctive feature of Aristotelian physics, and seems to be a response to the empty space or void *(kenon)* postulated by the atomists. Instead of occupying space, a body has a place *(topos),* which it has by virtue of another body enclosing it. 'Place' is defined as the fixed boundary surface of the containing body, the interface between the body and its container. Nature is a plenum, not matter interspersed with void.

When the Aristotelian cosmology lost its hold, the idea of natural and forced motions lived on in other forms. For Copernicus, whose ideas led the way to the sun-centred model and the final collapse of the Aristotelian cosmology, the natural motion was still the uniform circular motion idealised by the philosophers and early Greek astronomers, but was now applied to the daily rotation of the earth. Later, Kepler held the natural state to be rest, and he ascribed to matter an inherent resistance to disturbance from the state of rest—a body had a tendency towards rest, a laziness or *inertia.* To explain the continued motion of the planets around the sun, Kepler supposed that the sun exerts forces that drive the planets along their orbits. Galileo seems to have had a mixed view, for in his discussions of terrestrial motion he utilised natural circular motions as well the tendency of bodies to resist change from rectilinear motion, a rectilinear inertia. In Descartes, the natural motion is fully rectilinear:

bodies would continue in straight-line motion forever if it were not for the deflections caused by impacts with other bodies. In Newton's mechanics, uniform, rectilinear motion was accorded prime importance as the First Law of his three axioms or laws of motion:

> Every body continues in its state of rest, or of uniform motion in a right line, unless it is compelled to change that state by forces impressed upon it.[4]

It is clearly an ideal law, for Newton also tells us that gravitational force is universal. Bodies always have forces impressed on them, and so their motions can only approximate to a uniform rectilinear motion. The ideal motion described in the First Law, uniform and rectilinear motion, can be called *inertial motion:* it is a motion that is resistant to change when a force is applied. The First Law is also known as *the Law of Inertia.*

It seems that inertial motion was not exactly a natural motion for Newton, at least not in much of his thought, for he ascribed to matter an 'innate force' *(vis insita),* a power of resisting changes to its state of rest or uniform rectilinear motion. By invoking a power that maintains a body in its state of motion, he differs from later exponents of classical mechanics: inertial motion came to be interpreted as a natural motion, a *persistence* that requires no cause or explanation. Forces need only be invoked when changes to uniform, rectilinear motion occur. It was this second kind of force, the externally impressed force constraining a body from its inertial rectilinear motion, that Newton described in his Second Law of Motion:

> The change of motion is proportional to the motive force impressed; and is made in the direction of the right line in which that force is impressed.[5]

The First Law implies that a body which deviates from its state of rest or uniform rectilinear motion is subject to an external force. This deviation, an acceleration, may show as a change in the magnitude of the velocity, or in the direction of the motion, or in both the magnitude and direction. In the case of a uniform circular motion, a force causes the direction of motion to change continuously, but the speed (magnitude) of the motion remains unchanged. The Second Law tells us that the extent of the deviation from inertial motion is proportional to the strength of the external force. Without going into the complexities of what exactly Newton may have intended with his Second Law,[6] we can look instead at the familiar modern statement of the law, in which the vague term *motion* is replaced by *momentum* (mass multiplied by velocity, $m\mathbf{v}$), and *change* is replaced by *rate of change:*

> The rate of change of momentum of a body is proportional to the applied force, and takes place in the direction of application of the force.

Expressed in modern vector and calculus notation:

$$\mathbf{F} = \frac{\mathrm{d}}{\mathrm{d}t}(m\mathbf{v}) = (m\mathbf{a})$$

Force = rate of change of momentum = mass × acceleration

The *inertial mass m* of the body is the measure of the body's resistance to the impressed force. The greater the mass of a body, the smaller is the acceleration produced by the force.

Newton's idea of an external force constraining rectilinear motion proved to be of immense value in understanding the planetary motions. The motions of the planets, following the elliptical orbits ascertained by Kepler, were explained by Newton as continual deflections from rectilinear motion to give a closed orbit, the deflections caused by the gravitational force acting between the sun and planets. The moon is constantly falling to the earth, but its linear inertia carries it into an orbit round the earth. Newton proved that an inverse square law of gravitational force followed from the elliptical figures of the motions, an idea that had been entertained by Robert Hooke (1635–1703) and others, but which had not received a mathematical demonstration.

Yet difficulties lurked behind the impressive re-evaluation of natural and forced motions. Newton was aware of one problem that had been neglected by Descartes. Descartes proposed the law of uniform, rectilinear motion, but also held a thoroughgoing notion of relativity. However, the relativity of motion suggests that the ascription of a particular motion to a body, whether curved or rectilinear, uniform or accelerated, is arbitrary. If this is the case, how can we be justified in framing laws of mechanics that make a distinction between uniform, rectilinear motions and accelerated motions? The ascription of uniform, rectilinear motion to a body seems to be arbitrary, dependent on the state of motion of the reference from which the motion is gauged. Newton addressed the problem with the concept of *absolute space,* an absolute reference for motions and a real feature of the world.

If we are interested in ontological questions, including questions about the *causes* of things, the formulations of classical mechanics provide another source of dissatisfaction: we may wonder *why* uniform, rectilinear motion constitutes the natural motion. The inertial motion described by the First Law is a given in Newtonian dynamics, an ideal deduced from the non-ideal, constrained motions we observe on the earth and in the heavens. There is no attempt to address why uniform, rectilinear motion is the natural motion. Following the hints of the philosophers Berkeley and Mach, to be noted shortly, the realist may be tempted to conjecture that the rectilinear motion of a body is physically connected in some way with the whole universe of bodies, for the motion is relative to this universe of bodies. 'Natural' rectilinear motion, then, would not be the *innate* tendency of a body, perfectly manifested in space if forces or other bodies were absent. Instead, it would indicate a connection between all bodies in the universe, a connection that underlies both the inertial persistence of uniform, rectilinear motion and the manner in which forced deviations occur. The distinction between natural motions and constrained motions is not so clear-cut if we suppose that a body maintains its inertial motion as a result of some connection with the whole universe of bodies.

ABSOLUTE, RELATIVE AND RELATIONAL

Before examining the relativity of motion in detail, a few words on the meanings of some terms are in order. Firstly, let us examine the difference between *absolute* and *relative* quantities. Some characteristics are the same for all observers, such as the number of items in a group. Suppose we are presented with a table, and are asked how many legs it possesses. Our answers will be in agreement (say, four) if we all understand the question in the same way, and are able to examine the table closely. Suppose that we are also presented with an opaque bucket filled with marbles. We count the number of marbles visible in the top layer, and again we all agree on the number (say, twenty). We do not know the total number of marbles in the bucket because only the top layer is visible, yet there are ways of ascertaining the total number (say, one hundred). We could, for instance, tip the marbles out of the bucket and count them. If we are scientific realists we suppose that in the physical world there is a corresponding number of items, four physical table legs, twenty physical top-layer marbles and one-hundred physical marbles in total.

Now, the term *absolute* can be applied to quantities in two ways. Firstly, it can mean that the measured quantity is the same for all observers. Hence, the number of table legs and the number of top-layer marbles may be termed absolute because all observers count the same number. In these cases, we can say that the numbers are *invariant* for observers—they do not vary from observer to observer. Secondly, the term *absolute* could refer to the *total* or *non-arbitrary* value of a quantity. The quantity of four table legs constitutes such an absolute quantity. It is non-arbitrary as well as invariant, whereas the quantity of twenty marbles is invariant but arbitrary—the total number of marbles has not been counted, only those showing at the top of the bucket. Consider body temperature measured with a thermometer. We obtain a reading of, say, thirty-seven degrees centigrade, which is not the absolute body temperature but a measure relative to the temperature at which water freezes, zero degrees centigrade. This zero reference does not mean that freezing water has zero temperature—on the absolute temperature scale, the freezing point of water is about 273 degrees above absolute zero. The absolute or non-arbitrary temperature of the body is then about 310 degrees (37 + 273) above absolute zero. Measures relative to an arbitrary zero point are sometimes called *interval data,* and are contrasted with *ratio data,* or absolute values, measured with respect to an absolute zero. We have, then, distinguished two meanings of the absolute-relative contrast:

1. *Invariant* or *variant:* Do all observers obtain the same measurement (invariant) for a quantity, or do the measurements differ (variant)?

2. *Non-arbitrary* or *arbitrary:* Is a quantity measured with respect to a true zero (non-arbitrary), or relative to an arbitrary but convenient standard ?

With a common substratum for the sense-experiences of many observers, we might hope to obtain quantities that are invariant (not dependent on the special situations of observers) and non-arbitrary (full values, not measured relative to an arbitrary reference). Both kinds of absolute-relative distinction are involved in the problem of motion.

These two absolute-relative meanings are to be distinguished from the *absolute-relational* distinction that we noted in Chapter Six. This distinction referred directly to questions of ontology: are space, time and spacetime to be regarded as actually existing things, as 'substances', or are they certain kinds of relations between physical bodies, events, experiences? Contrasted with relational, 'absolute' means having an actual existence as a substance:

3. *Substance* or *relation:* is something an actual substance or merely a relation between substances? Was Newton justified in ascribing space and time actual existences beyond matter and its changes?

Another distinction we shall meet shortly is the *dynamic-kinematical* contrast, employed by Newton, which takes the dynamic (accelerative) effects associated with forces as indicators of true, absolute motion:

4. *Dynamic* or *kinematical:* is an observed acceleration caused by a real force or is it due to a purely relative motion between the observer and the body?

Finally, it is worth noting that the term *relativistic* refers to the physical theory deriving from Einstein's treatment of relativity, and to the observed effects described by the theory .

THE RELATIVITY OF MOTION

The motions of bodies are always observed *relative* to other bodies. These other bodies act as references, or *frames of reference,* with which we compare motions. As I go for a walk in the countryside, I might estimate my speed to be three miles per hour relative to the path or the landscape. If I walk along the deck of a ship, I will probably consider my motion relative to the deck. In the first case, the surface of the earth is the frame of reference to which I refer my motion, whilst in the second case it is the ship. I could, however, choose alternative frames of reference. As I walk along a path, I could estimate my speed relative to a passing car, or on the ship I could consider my motion relative to the sea, a cloud or a stretch of coast. I could regard myself at rest, and measure the motions of other bodies relative to my frame of reference. If I spin round on a swivel chair, I can interpret my experience of motion in three ways: I am spinning and the universe is at rest; I am at rest and the universe is spinning; or, both the universe and I are spinning, and the combination of spins gives the overall spin. The choice between interpretations is arbitrary, unless there is some criterion for making the choice.

The *relativity of motion* refers, then, to the variance and arbitrariness of the quantities we use to describe motions:

1. *Variance:* measurements of a body's motion vary from observer to observer, depending on the relative states of motion of the observers.

2. *Arbitrariness:* we are unable to recognise an 'absolute zero' of motion, an absolute rest state, and we do not even know if there is one. Therefore, we cannot ascertain absolute (non-arbitrary) values for the quantities that are used to describe a motion.

The two are clearly related. If we had a state of absolute rest available to us as a reference, we would expect our descriptions of motion to agree, for we would be justified in measuring the characteristics of motions relative to this special reference. As it is, however, we have no such special reference. Our standards of rest and motion are arbitrary. We choose a convenient frame of reference and describe motions relative to that frame, but we could equally well choose other frames and obtain different descriptions of the motion. The kinematics of motion provides no criterion for assigning a definite, unique, non-arbitrary state of motion to a body. Depending on the choice of reference frame, we might consider the body to be at rest, in uniform rectilinear motion, in uniform motion round a circular path, or undergoing an accelerative motion along a complex path. All motions are relative as far as the kinematics of motion is concerned, and we may call this fact the *kinematical principle of relativity.*[7]

It is useful to associate a co-ordinate system with bodies used as references for measurements of motion. In astronomy, it is often convenient to use co-ordinate systems having angular measures, similar to the latitude and longitude system for the earth's surface. In classical physics and the special theory of

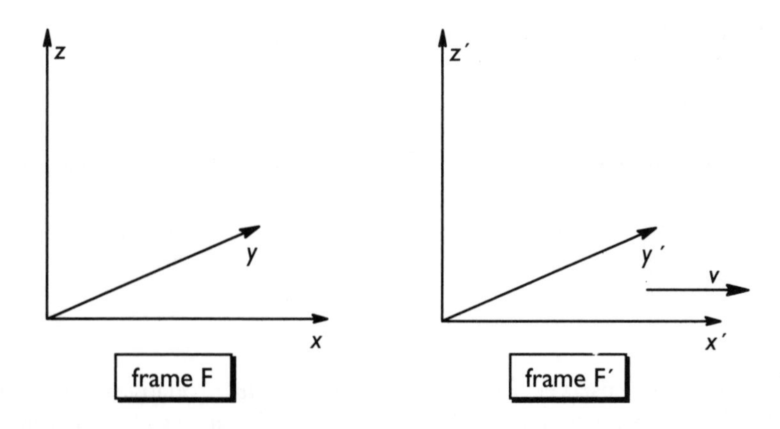

Figure 7.3. Two reference frames F and F′, separating with velocity v.

relativity, the Cartesian or rectangular co-ordinate system is often used: we may picture each frame of reference with a centre or origin, through which the three, perpendicular, spatial axes of the rectangular co-ordinate system pass. The axes provide a calibrated, spatial background, a *relative space,* with respect to which an observer measures the motion of other bodies. There is a plurality of reference frames or relative spaces, one associated with each body. Some are at rest with respect to one another or in uniform relative motion. Together these constitute a group of *inertial frames of reference,* reference frames that have inertial motion relative to one another (rest or uniform rectilinear motion, not accelerated motion).

Figure 7.3. illustrates two frames of reference F and F′ in uniform relative motion, one with the three perpendicular spatial axes, x, y and z, the other with a similar set of axes, x', y', z'. The frame F′ separates from frame F with a uniform velocity v along the x-axis, and the x and x' axes are aligned.

When measurements of the velocity of an object are made, we choose a reference frame and state the velocity of the object relative to the frame. The frame acts as a reference of rest (zero velocity) for our measurements. Suppose we know the velocity of an object measured from one frame of reference, but wish to know the velocity from a second frame of reference in motion relative to the first. How do we go about recalculating the velocity of the object observed from the second frame? How do we convert from the co-ordinate system of one frame of reference to that of another? In classical physics, the velocities along one-dimensional axes are easily recalculated by addition and subtraction, and the equations used to change co-ordinates between frames of reference are referred to as the *Galilean transformations.*

The Galilean transformations for converting co-ordinates between the two reference frames F and F′ depicted above, with the uniform velocity v of F′ along the aligned axes, are:

From frame F to frame F′:	From frame F′ to frame F:
$x' = x - vt$	$x = x' + vt'$
$y' = y$	$y = y'$
$z' = z$	$z = z'$
$t' = t$	$t = t'$

Consider two observers F and G, and an object H, all in relative motion along a line. From F's frame of reference (Figure 7.4.), F is at rest. G is measured to have a velocity of +2 metres per second, and H a velocity of +4 metres per second (a positive sign indicates a motion to the right and a negative sign a motion to the left).

From G's frame (Figure 7.5.), F has a velocity of –2 metres per second (motion to the left). The velocity of H, +2 metres per second (motion to the right), is given by the simple Galilean addition of velocities:

velocity of H in G-frame = velocity of H in F-frame *plus* velocity of F in G-frame,

$$\text{or, } (+2) = (+4) + (-2)$$

From their respective frames of reference, F and G observe H to be in motion, but with different velocities, +4 and +2 metres per second respectively. F and

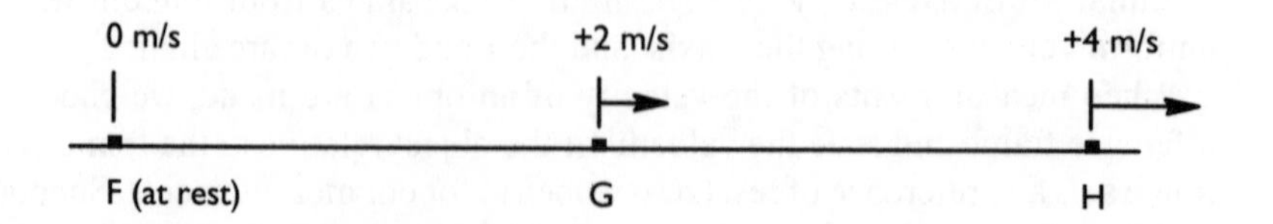

Figure 7.4. The motion in F's frame.

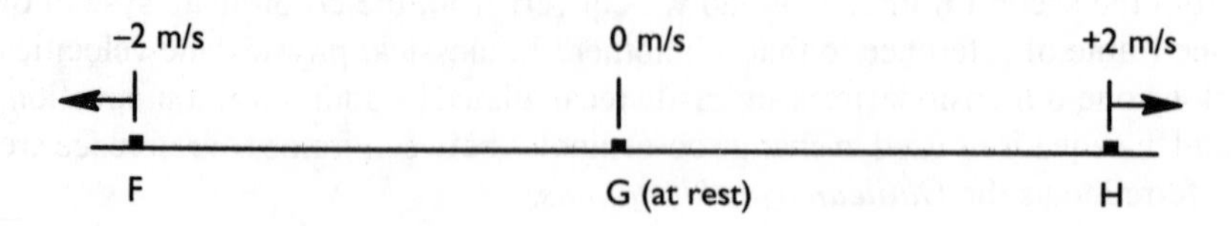

Figure 7.5. The motion in G's frame.

G therefore consider H to cover different path lengths in the same time interval: in one second, F supposes that H moves through 4 metres, while G supposes that H covers a spatial path length of 2 metres.

The following examples provide further illustrations of the dependence of motion descriptions (spatial path, velocity, acceleration) on the choice of reference frame.

1. *Motion of a ball*

It is instructive to consider two-dimensional instances of relative motion, for the introduction of an additional component of motion along a second dimension emphasises the different spatial paths. For example, a ball thrown against a wall will be observed to follow different paths through space, and travel with different velocities, depending on the motion of the observer. Observer F is at rest with the wall, and throws the ball at velocity u, at right angles to the wall. F catches the ball when it bounces back. The path of the ball observed by F is shown in Figure 7.6.(a). Observer G runs parallel with the wall and observes the path shown in Figure 7.6.(b). The ball is thrown at event P, hits the wall at event Q, and is caught by observer F at event R.

Whereas the time interval between P and R is the same for observers F and G (the Newtonian assumption of absolute time), the path length and velocity ascribed to the ball vary. The path length observed by G is longer than the path length observed by F, and, since the ball takes the same time to cover the different path lengths, the observed velocity of the ball must also differ. For observer G, the ball covers the greater distance, and the ball travels at a greater velocity to cover the distance in the same time.

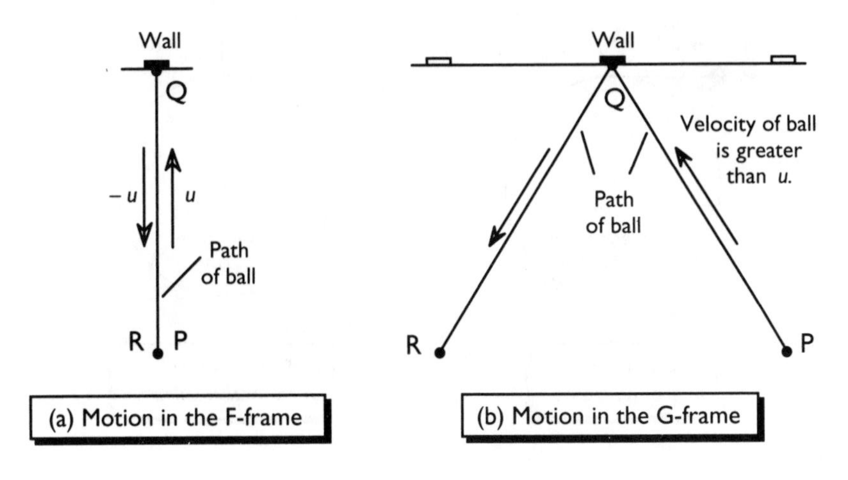

Figure 7.6. The motion of ball B observed from frames at rest with (a) F and (b) G.

2. *Ball released from a roundabout*

To illustrate how a rectilinear motion in one frame can be a curved motion in another, we can note the example of a ball released by an observer R standing on a playground roundabout. In the ground frame of reference, G, the roundabout rotates uniformly. When the ball is released by R at the periphery of the roundabout, it is observed from G to follow a rectilinear path (ignoring gravity and air resistance), tangential to the periphery of the roundabout at the moment of release. In contrast, the observer R at rest with the roundabout observes the ball to follow a curved path.

In frame G, the released ball follows a uniform rectilinear motion, in accordance with Newton's First Law. In frame R, however, it follows a curved path that contravenes Newton's Laws—a freely moving body should exhibit rectilinear, inertial motion. From the perspective of frame G, we can understand the curved path as a projection of R's accelerated circular motion onto the rectilinear motion of the ball. In frame R, we must introduce a force to account for the accelerated, curved motion, if we are to use Newton's Laws. The extra force is called an *inertial force.* If the observer R attempts to walk between the centre of the roundabout and the periphery, a sideways pull ascribable to an inertial force is experienced, and is termed a *Coriolis force.* Observers on earth attribute the deflection of the equatorial trade winds to this type of inertial force, whereas an observer moving with the wind would suppose that the earth is rotating.

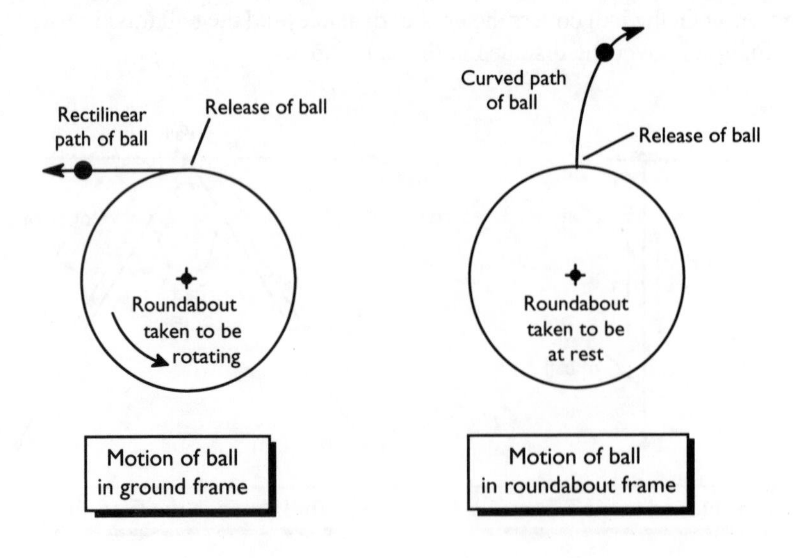

Figure 7.7. The motion of the ball in two frames: ground G, and roundabout R.

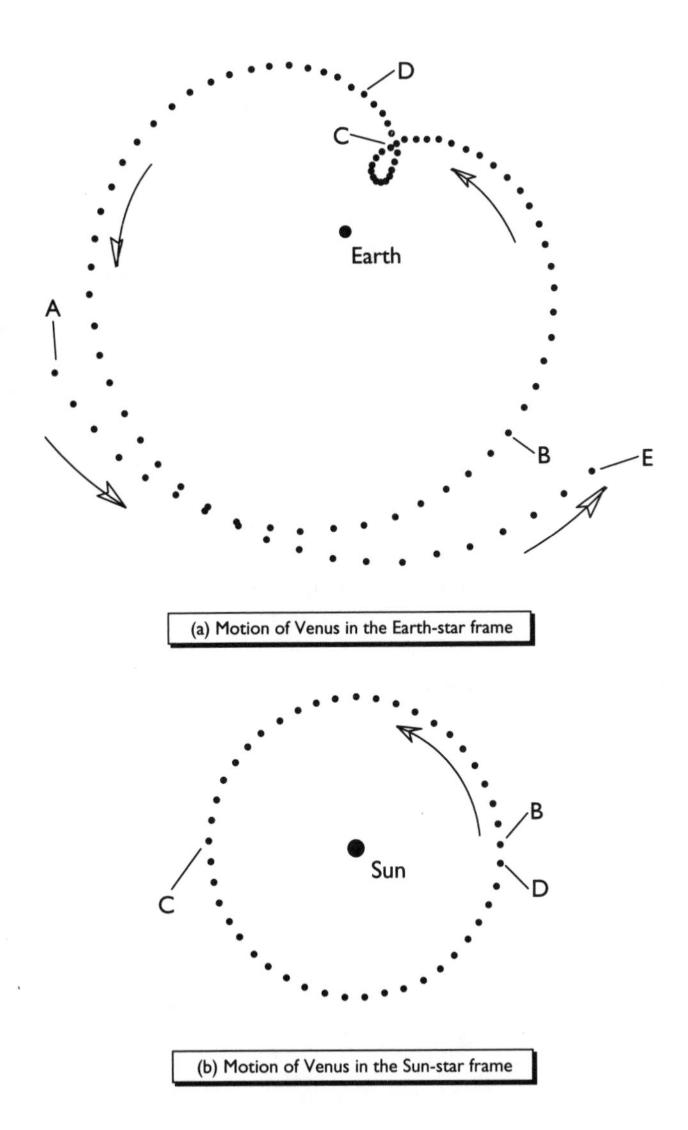

Figure 7.8. The motion of Venus in the plane of the ecliptic, 1991–92, considered (a) from the earth-frame, and (b) from the sun-frame (both are drawn at the same scale). The points show the position of Venus at five-day intervals. In the earth-frame, the small separations between the points in the retrogression loop indicate the lower speed of Venus when it is close to the earth. In diagram (a), the motion from A to E is shown, whereas only part of the motion is shown in diagram (b), from position B to D. In the sun-frame, the motion from B back to B makes up one revolution about the sun, and takes about 225 days (the *sidereal period).* Positions A, B, C, D and E correspond to the following dates:

A – 1st January, 1991; B – 27th March, 1991; C – 15th July, 1991;
D – 2nd November, 1991; E – 15th May, 1992.

3. *Planetary motion*

Striking illustrations of the frame-dependence of motion descriptions are found in astronomy. The motion we ascribe to a planet depends on the frame-of-reference we use. For example, the planetary dance of Venus shifts with the choice of frame, the goddess's variable choreography inviting us to contemplate the mysteries of relativity and the kinematical equality of different perspectives.

From a frame of reference centred on the earth and at rest relative to the stars, the orbit of Venus is an intricate path. The planet is sometimes observed to move in a direction contrary to the normal, prograde sense of the orbital motion, performing the retrogression loops noted before. Over an eight-year period in the earth-frame, Venus traces out its celebrated five-petalled signature (the retrogression loop in Figure 7.8.(a) constitutes one of the five petals).[8]

In a reference frame centred on the sun and at rest relative to the fixed stars, the path of Venus is a near-circular ellipse. Thus, the routes through space, the distances traversed, and the speeds are different in the two descriptions. The motion in the sun-frame is much simpler. Of course, the simplest description would be taken from a frame at rest relative to the planet: zero speed, and zero distance traversed through space.

8. IN SEARCH OF TRUE REST

What are we to make of the many relative descriptions of one motion that are obtained by using different frames of reference? Is just one of the descriptions a true description of the motion, or are all the relative descriptions of equal status? The idea of a common world behind our perceptions, describable by unique and non-arbitrary quantities, will incline us to believe that there is indeed just one correct description, the description of the absolute motion in the substratum. A stress on the actuality of multiple, experiential perspectives may incline us to believe in the equal status of all the relative descriptions of motion. Classical physics took the former route, finding a justification for absolute motions in dynamics. According to Newton, there *are* true, absolute motions and it is absurd to imagine that all relative descriptions of a motion are true.[1] From a realist standpoint, true motions are the motions of objects in the substratum, which our relative observations describe in many relative ways. The substratum is an absolute frame of reference for all motions. Motions are absolute, and moving bodies have definite displacements, velocities and accelerations.

THE CHOICE OF ABSOLUTE FRAME

Where are we to find a frame that is truly at rest, the reference for the measurement of absolute (non-arbitrary) motion? In everyday affairs, it is natural to assume that the ground is at rest, and it is an easy matter to extend this assumption to the contemplation of the heavens. We have seen that in the Aristotelian cosmology the earth was taken to be at rest at the centre of the spherical cosmos, while the planets and fixed stars were carried around on concentric spheres. The mathematical models of planetary motion also took the earth to be at rest. The use of eccentrics and epicycles created additional centres of circular motion, but these mathematical schemes made no claim to be realistic models of the planetary system. The possibility of a mobile earth was considered in ancient thought, but the idea was purely qualitative and was not used to explain irregular planetary motions. In contrast, the mathematical systems of eccentrics and epicycles could be used to obtain reasonably accurate predictions.

A mobile earth is found in the cosmology ascribed to Philolaus of Croton, a Pythagorean of the fifth century B.C. The earth, moon, sun, five planets and the sphere of fixed stars revolve about a fire located at the centre of the cosmos. Another earth, the counter-earth or *antichthon,* lies between the central fire and our earth, and plays a role in eclipses. Discussing these ideas, Aristotle reported a belief that the centre is the most important part of the cosmos, and as such should be occupied by the most precious of things, which is fire, not earth.[2] Another mobile earth is to be found in the system of Aristarchus of Samos (*c.*320–*c.*250 B.C.). Aristarchus seems to have proposed that the sun and the sphere of fixed stars are at rest, while the earth performs an annual, circular orbit around the sun. The east-to-west daily motion of the fixed stars about the immovable earth is replaced by a daily west-to-east rotation of the earth about its polar axis. The idea of a diurnal rotation performed by the earth was also associated with the Pythagorean philosophers Ecphantus and Hicetas (fourth century B.C.), and with Heraclides Ponticus (*c.*388–*c.*315 B.C.). Aristotle, and later, Ptolemy, considered the idea but rejected it. The rapid, daily, west-to-east rotation of the earth appeared unreasonable: if the earth really underwent a daily rotation, surely bodies unattached to the rotating earth would be left behind, and appear to fly westwards like the stars. A new concept of natural and forced motion had yet to develop to give plausibility to the idea of a daily rotation.

The annual and daily motions of the earth were marginal ideas in the ancient world, and had to wait until the sixteenth century before they were revived and developed by Nicolas Copernicus (1473–1543). In his *De revolutionibus orbium caelestium* (1543), Copernicus relates that he decided to take up the hints of Philolaus, Hicetas, Ecphantus and Heraclides on the earth's motion, in spite of the absurdity of the idea. The attempt proved successful and Copernicus placed the earth in annual and diurnal motion. To counter the ancient objection that bodies would be left behind by the earth's rotation, Copernicus argued that the *natural* circular motion of the heavenly bodies is also natural for the spherical earth and the bodies on the earth's surface. The idea carried over into Galileo's conception of circular, inertial motions.

As for the *annual* motion of the earth, Copernicus realised that the retrograde motions of the five planets could be interpreted as parallax effects deriving from the earth's annual motion. The epicyclic convolutions of the Ptolemaic orbits would then be projections of the earth's yearly motion onto the motions of the planets. The withdrawal of the projection placed the centres of the planetary orbits in a cluster near the sun. The sun is *near* the centre and not *at* the centre of the planetary system because Copernicus continued to use epicycles to account for departures from uniform, circular motion. The Ptolemaic system had been, in essence, re-centred near the sun, a move that disclosed for the first time the relative sizes of the planetary orbits. The new system recognised the special role of the sun in the planetary system, a role that had been implicit but unexplored in the Ptolemaic account of the motions of the five planets. Yet Copernicus left the status of the sun uncertain, finding no way of deciding whether it is the sun or the nearby centre of the planetary orbits that is truly at rest. The new system was not generally received as an attempt to describe the actual structure of the planetary system, in spite of Copernicus's realist attitude to the earth's mobility. The anonymous preface to Copernicus's *De revolutionibus* presented the work in an instrumentalist light. The preface, later revealed by Kepler to be the work of Andreas Osiander (1498–1552), a theologian who supervised the printing of the book, explained that the theory was a mathematical device, like the Ptolemaic account, and not a theory that could be demonstrated to be true. Opponents of the earth's mobility could invoke kinematical relativity and argue that it is completely arbitrary whether the earth is said to be moving or at rest. They could also argue that it was presumptuous to suggest that a body as lowly as the earth has circular motion, raising it to the lofty ranks of the celestial bodies. Rather than demeaning the status of human beings, the Copernican displacement of the earth from the cosmic centre elevated humankind into the heavens from the base, corruptible centre of the old cosmology.

The Copernican Revolution was slow to start, but was greatly assisted by Kepler's support and Galileo's controversial advocacy. Kepler revised the nature of the planetary orbits, replacing circular motions with elliptical orbits, and he placed the sun firmly at the centre of the planetary system. The presence of the sun at the centre was not to be regarded as a fortuitous circumstance, but as an indication of the sun's dynamic governance of the system, the sun driving the planetary revolutions from its focal position in the elliptical orbits of the planets. The absolute rest-frame was defined by the stationary, central sun and the stationary fixed stars, the backcloth against which the planets, including the earth, were now considered to trace their motions.

The promotion of the sun to the role of fixed, cosmic centre in astronomy occurred at a time when the sun had become an object of religious veneration in some quarters, through the Renaissance revival of ancient learning. Of relevance were the divine, central fire of Pythagorean cosmology, the solar symbolism of Plato and the Neoplatonic tradition, and the divine eminence ascribed to the sun in Hermetic thought. Both Copernicus and Kepler[3] show the contemporary influence in their discussions of the sun, and the Copernican shift to a heliocentric world-view was interpreted by some as an event of profound religious significance.[4]

The immobile status ascribed to the sun was not to endure for long in the climate of thought encouraged by the Copernican application of kinematical relativity to the Ptolemaic system. The combined Aristotelian/Ptolemaic picture of the universe was disintegrating under the challenge of the Copernican revolution and the evidence of celestial observations. Notable amongst the latter were the appearances of new stars in 1572 and 1604, and various telescopic observations, including sightings of mountains on the moon, sun-spots, comets beyond the moon, and the satellites of Jupiter. These observations undermined the vestigial, Aristotelian ideas of unchanging, heavenly perfection and crystalline spheres, but were not real threats to Ptolemaic astronomy. The telescopic observation of the phases of Venus went against the Ptolemaic system, but was not proof of the validity of the Copernican system. The phases could be reconciled with a planetary system in which the earth was at rest, and Venus revolved around a mobile sun. This was the so-called *Tychonic* system, advanced by Tycho Brahe (1546–1601).

By the end of the seventeenth century, the closed universe of ancient and medieval cosmology, walled in by the sphere of fixed stars, had opened out into an *infinite* universe in which the sun was just one mobile star among many mobile stars. It was no longer believed that change was confined to the earthly realm within the orbit of the moon, and it was even conceivable that in the solar systems, dispersed through endless space, there were planets inhabited by creatures. Medieval geocentricism, and the heliocentricism of Copernicus and Kepler, yielded to a cosmology without a principal centre. In such a universe, humankind could feel humble in the immensity of God's manifest kingdom, or lost and insignificant in a vast, cosmic mechanism.

The revival of ancient philosophies had stimulated the transformation of the closed universe into a universe of infinite space. Particularly influential was the Stoic idea of a spherical cosmos set in an *infinite* void. Also of importance was the infinite void of the Epicurean and Democritean atomisms.[5] Several philosophers drew on the ancient theories to help fashion a new concept of space. These included Bernardino Telesio (1509–88), Francesco Patrizzi (1529–97), Tommaso Campanella (1568–1639), and Pierre Gassendi (1592–1655).[6] The idea of an infinite space filled with innumerable worlds was advanced by Giordano Bruno (1548–1600), who drew inspiration from the unlimited universe discussed by Nicholas of Cusa (1401–64). Behind Bruno's infinite universe can be seen an old Platonic idea turned to use in cosmological speculation, namely *the principle of plenitude,* so-named by the American historian of ideas, Arthur Oncken Lovejoy (1873–1962).[7] According to the principle, the world is made full by the actualisation of all conceptual possibilities or by the complete expression of the Creator's unlimited power and superabundant outflowing into the manifestations of the created world. In the Plotinian scheme, the plenitude is achieved through a procession or emanation down a series of stages, beginning with the overflowing of the One to give the *Nous* and its Intelligible Realm, which in turn emanates the World Soul, and so forth, into the depths of Nature and matter. The movement is not one-way, for the procession down the links of the metaphysical chain is balanced by a return or reversion, a contemplation of the higher stages. Lovejoy notes that a mirror-metaphor was employed by Macrobius (fourth to fifth century A.D.) in his exposition of the Plotinian scheme: "the single radiance [of the One] illumines all and is reflected in each, as a single face might be reflected in many mirrors placed in a series."[8]

For Bruno, only an infinite universe with a plurality of inhabited worlds was a befitting image of the infinite God, an infinite effect of the infinite cause.[9] God would not be so miserly with His infinite power that He would produce a finite universe. However, Bruno drew a distinction between the infinity of God and the infinity of the universe: whereas God is totally infinite, being infinitely and totally in the universe, both in the whole and in each part, the universe itself is not totally infinite, but 'quite infinite', because each part is finite in itself.[10] Bruno deduced the immobility of the universe from its infinity.

With both the earth and sun divested of absolute rest, any theory that entertained absolute motions had to look elsewhere for an absolute reference. The corpuscular philosophy, with its universe of material atoms in constant motion, implied that no material body could provide the reference. Instead, the privilege of absolute rest was bestowed by Newton on space, the space that had come to be regarded as an infinite, incorporeal, homogeneous, immobile receptacle, and which was taken to be a precondition for the existence of material bodies and their motions. It was this space that provided the absolute state of rest in Newton's mechanics. In absolute space, Newton found the metaphysical bedrock on which to rest his mechanics of motion and the theory of gravitation. As we shall see, he believed there were dynamical justifications for his choice. It has also been suggested that Newton's acceptance of space as the absolute background for absolute motions was influenced by religious considerations. If the basis of all is God, it seemed to follow that the mechanical basis would be found in God's representation in the material world. The material sun no longer provided an appropriate symbol for the divine presence in and governance of the world. Immaterial space, on the other hand, could not be dislodged so easily, and there were precedents for associating space with God. In Newton's later writings the religious angle on space is pronounced: God and space share the attributes of omnipresence.

> He is not eternity and infinity, but eternal and infinite; he is not duration or space, but he endures and is present. He endures forever, and is everywhere present; and, by existing always and everywhere, he constitutes duration and space.[11]

It has been suggested that Newton's thought on absolute space owes much to the ideas of the Cambridge Platonist, Henry More (1614–87).[12] More developed his theology of space in response to the Cartesian philosophy of spirit and body, and found support in Neoplatonic and Kabbalistic ideas that linked space with God's omnipresence.[13] To avoid the Cartesian dualism of unextended spirit and extended matter, More supposed that spirit, as well as matter, has extension. More thought that extension was necessary for existence, and that extensionless mathematical points could not exist. In consequence, he rejected the view of the Cartesian "Nullibists" who banished spirit from the realm of extended matter.[14] According to More, matter is not the only extended substance: spirit and God are also extended. More noted that the attributes of God, described by the "metaphysicians", also belong to space. The attributes include:

> one, simple, immobile, eternal, perfect, independent, existing by itself, subsisting through itself, incorruptible, necessary, immense, uncreated, uncircumscribed, incomprehensible, omnipresent, incorporeal, permeating and embracing all things, essential being, actual being, pure actuality.[15]

Space is real and divine, and motion in this real, divine void is an absolute, not the relative motion of Descartes' plenum. More does not go so far as to say that space is God, but that space is "a certain rather confused and vague representation of the divine essence or essential presence".[16]

> That spiritual object, which we call space, is only a passing shadow, which represents for us, in the weak light of our intellect, the true and universal nature of the continuous divine presence, till we are able to perceive it directly with open eyes and at a nearer distance.[17]

For More, God's omnipresence lay in His infinite extension. More's position on the relationship between divine omnipresence and space seems to have been a considerable innovation. In the scholastic explanation of omnipresence, God is said to be ubiquitous through His *total,* simultaneous presence at *every* part of space, not through an infinite extension over infinite space as More argued. Edward Grant provides some useful notes on the idea, referring to it as the "whole in every part" doctrine.[18] In the Middle Ages, it was common to suppose that spiritual substances, whether God, angels or souls, occupied a body through a complete presence in each part of the body, a mode of occupation that maintains the indivisibility of the spiritual substance if the body is divided. The presence of the spiritual whole in the part also accounts for the activity and perceptions of the soul in all parts of the body.[19] Grant notes that the idea can be traced to the Plotinian discussion of the soul. According to Plotinus, the soul is at once both divisible and indivisible:

> ... its divisibility lies in its presence at every point of the recipient, but it is indivisible as dwelling entire in the total and entire in any part.[20]

Parts that are wholes make unified activity possible—isolated parts would be unaware of one another and the whole would lack unity.

The idea was transmitted to medieval Christian thinkers through the formulations of St Augustine (by way of Peter Lombard's *Sentences)* and St John of Damascus.[21] It was applied to the omnipresence of God in the world, as well as to the presence of the soul in the body.

More opposed the idea of a spiritual substance wholly in every part, supposing instead that a spirit is an extended, immaterial substance that is able to expand or contract to fill a body. More's philosophy retained the Cartesian dualism between spirit and matter, but brought the two closer together by ascribing spirit with extension.

For Newton, space was not only an expression of the divine omnipresence, but also of the divine omniscience, which follows from God's immediate presence at all things in space. Newton's famous statement that space is God's sense organ ('sensory' or 'sensorium') in the *Opticks,* is an analogy that expresses the faculty of omniscience through omnipresence.[22] In the Newtonian scheme, the existence of a privileged observer, the omniscient and omnipresent God, gives religious credence to the idea of a privileged rest frame, absolute space. With his concept of absolute space, Newton ascribes to God a knowledge of the true, absolute motions of objects, rather than the apparent, relative motions presented to us by our little sense-organs.

In the religious background to the notion of absolute space, we may discern the ancient theme of divine fixity in the midst of transformation. True rest is to be found only in God. In the Philolaic cosmology, the 'still point of the turning world' was a central fire, the house of Zeus, and in the heliocentric cosmology, the fixed sun-throne became the proper seat of divinity. By the time of Newton, the idea of a fixed cosmic centre was losing credibility, and the perfect rest of divinity was transferred to the receptacle of space. Yet the new emblem of divine repose in the universe shared with its predecessors a common background of light theology, the association of space with light and divinity. In our familiar experience, light and space are likely to be associated: we experience a luminous spatiality of objects, and perceptual space may be illumined by dispersion or reflection: a shaft of light in a dusty room, a rainbow in a cloud of rain, a radiant sky at dawn.[23] The mystical association of light and space seems to be equally natural, and was expressed in Neoplatonic thought and elsewhere.[24] Our discussion of universal experiences may suggest to us why space, light, divinity and fixity are liable to be associated with one another in mystically-influenced, physical conceptions of the world. The stable, luminous spatiality of universal experience would constitute a supreme state of fixity, a tenseless permanence of motion that is not itself in motion. For More, Newton and others, infinite three-dimensional space took on the role of fixed, divine, everlasting background for the transforming material content. In the same century, the mystically-inspired Thomas Traherne concluded that infinite space was insufficient to hold the plenitude of God's treasures. As we shall see later, the full plenitude of the universe was not to be limited to the infinity of countless planetary systems in infinite space, as it was for Bruno, or to the infinite space of More, or to the infinite spatio-temporality of eternity, for the infinite expression of God in a part could make even the finite infinite.

ABSOLUTE SPACE

Absolute space plays an important role in underpinning Newtonian mechanics for it provides the special frame of reference for absolute motions, both uniform rectilinear motions (First Law) and motions accelerated from the ideal by forces (Second Law). Absolute space defines a state of absolute rest, providing a fixed background in which objects are absolutely at rest, or move with an absolute velocity or absolute acceleration, in accordance with the Laws of Motion. Newton seems to have maintained that the centre of mass of the solar system was at rest in absolute space, for his universal gravitational theory implied that the sun is subject to gravitational accelerations and has a small motion. He did not, however, extend this consideration to the gravitational interactions of the solar system with the fixed stars.

There is a problem with absolute space: it displays no observable features, and therefore cannot be used as a reference to make absolute observations of motions. We observe bodies in motion relative to other bodies, not relative to an absolute, featureless space. Our knowledge of motion is always relative. In the *Principia,* Newton acknowledged that:

> It is indeed a matter of great difficulty to discover, and effectually to distinguish, the true motions of particular bodies from the apparent; because the parts of that immovable space, in which those motions are performed, do by no means come under the observation of our senses.[25]

However, Newton believed that the matter was not entirely hopeless, arguing that there are criteria for distinguishing between true, absolute motions and apparent, relative motions. According to Newton, it is the *dynamics* of a motion, the study of forces and their effects, that may help us ascertain the true or relative nature of the motion. The magnitudes of dynamical effects are the same for all frames of reference: they are invariant, and, in this sense, absolute. Nowadays we would qualify Newton's views by pointing out that it is only the accelerative *effects* of forces that can be used, as forces themselves are not observed.

Newton seems to implicate absolute space in the persistence of the inertial motions of bodies: a force is required to accelerate a body out of its absolute uniform rectilinear motion through absolute space, and it is the consequent accelerative effects that tell us that an absolute motion is taking place. It is almost as if absolute space maintains a body in its uniform, rectilinear motion, whilst forces cause the body to deviate from this inertial motion. To demonstrate the dynamical criterion, Newton focused attention on the special case of circular motion, a motion that exhibits dynamical effects. True, absolute, circular motions are caused by impressed forces; apparent, relative, circular motions may be produced without the action of impressed forces.

> The effects which distinguish absolute from relative motion are, the forces of receding from the axis of circular motion. For there are no such forces in a circular motion purely relative, but in a true and absolute circular motion, they are greater or less, according to the quantity of the motion.[26]

Newton illustrated the dynamical effects of absolute, circular motion with his famous *rotating bucket* thought-experiment, and with a *two-globe* thought-experiment. We shall consider the latter example. Two globes are attached by a cord (Figure 8.1.). We wish to decide whether the system is stationary or rotating. If absolute, circular motion is taking place, the globes will attempt to move apart to maintain rectilinear motion, but the cord constrains them into a circular motion and tension forces arise in the cord. The constraining force is called a *centripetal* force, accelerating the globes from rectilinear motion into the circular motion about a centre (centripetal, 'moving towards the centre'). The reaction force in the cord is called a *centrifugal* force (centrifugal, 'fleeing from the centre'), the resistance of the globes to deflection from rectilinear motion. The action of forces, shown by the stretching of the rope, is taken to indicate *absolute* circular motion. The magnitude of the tension provides a measure of the degree of circular motion. When no tension is present in the cord, we are able to conclude (according to Newton) that the system has no absolute circular motion, and any circular motion we might ascribe to it is merely an apparent, relative motion.

Applying the dynamical criterion to the earth, we can decide that the earth undergoes a real, absolute, diurnal rotation because it exhibits dynamical effects—an equatorial bulge, and a slightly lower gravitational acceleration at the equator compared with the poles.

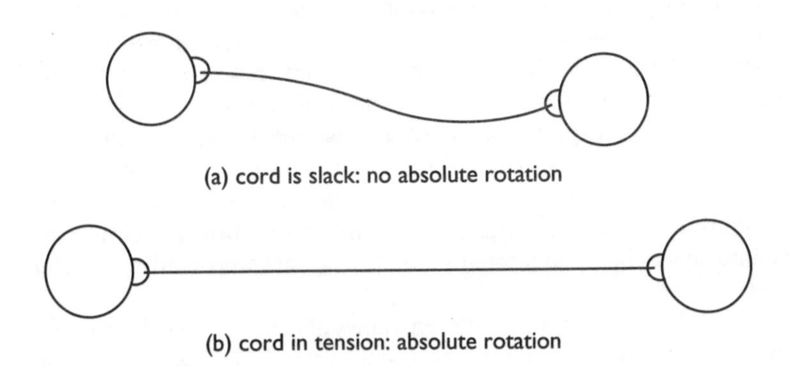

Figure 8.1. Two globes attached by a cord. (a) No rotation: cord is slack. (b) Rotation: tension in the cord, perhaps exhibited as a stretching. Newton interpreted the tension as an indication that the globes and cord are truly rotating through absolute space.

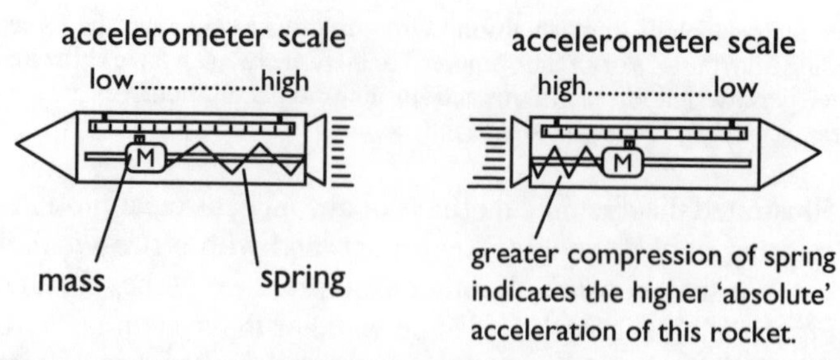

Figure 8.2. Two rockets accelerating apart. The spring-accelerometers measure the absolute acceleration of each rocket, but yield no information about their absolute velocities. Only the *relative* velocity of separation can be measured.

The importance given by Newton to finding true determinations of absolute motions is indicated at the end of his scholium on absolute space, time and motion in the *Principia,* where he states:

> But how we are to obtain the true motions from their causes, effects, and apparent differences, and the converse, shall be explained more at large in the following treatise. For to this end it was that I composed it.[27]

Yet the promise was not fulfilled. The criterion of accelerative effects indicates absolute accelerations of bodies, but not their absolute velocities. Consider two rockets that move apart along a straight path, with a uniform relative acceleration. Each rocket contains a mass on a spring that acts as a device for measuring absolute acceleration, an accelerometer—the compression of the spring gives a dynamical indication of the rocket's absolute acceleration (Figure 8.2.) Although we can assign an absolute acceleration to each rocket, indicated by the degree of compression of its accelerometer spring, we cannot gauge the *absolute* instantaneous velocity of the rockets. All we know is the *relative* instantaneous velocity of separation. Nor can dynamical criteria be used to distinguish between reference frames in uniform rectilinear motion, for there are no accelerative effects to consider, no deviation from inertial motion. In the rotating globe experiment, we cannot ascribe an absolute, instantaneous speed to the globes because the whole system may have a uniform, rectilinear motion in addition to the uniform, circular motion. We have no way of ascertaining whether the system is in uniform rectilinear motion through absolute space, because inertial motion is not accompanied by accelerative effects.

Our inability to distinguish between frames of reference in uniform rectilinear motion constitutes the principle of relativity in classical dynamics. Newton gave expression to it in the fifth of the six corollaries presented with his three laws of motion in the *Principia.*

> The motions of bodies included in a given space are the same among themselves, whether that space is at rest, or moves uniformly forwards in a right line without any circular motion.[28]

The complete arbitrariness of motion-descriptions in kinematical relativity is replaced by a principle of relativity in which the descriptions of uniform velocity (inertial motions) continue to be arbitrary and relative, but in which accelerations are now definable as absolute through the appearance of dynamical accelerative effects. This form of relativity has been called *Newtonian, classical, dynamical* or *Galilean*[29] *relativity,* to distinguish it from kinematical relativity and the relativity of Einstein's theories. Mechanical experiments cannot be used to resolve the relative velocity between bodies into the component absolute velocities of the bodies, but can resolve a relative acceleration into the component absolute accelerations of the bodies, for the latter are revealed by the accelerative effects exhibited by each accelerating body.

Since dynamics provided a criterion for attributing absolute accelerations to bodies, the general idea of absolute motions in an absolute space seemed to follow. Velocities and paths of bodies are to be regarded as absolute, even though their absolute values cannot be determined experimentally, and in practice have to be treated as relative.

Before we move on to look at the critical reaction to the idea of absolute space, we shall summarise the understanding of motion and matter in the Newtonian synthesis:

1. *Absolute Motion.* Motion is absolute, consisting of changes of position in the absolute space container. Absolute motion is true motion; relative motion is apparent. All of Newton's laws of motion are valid when applied to motions in the absolute frame, but are not generally true when the motions are treated as purely relative (inertial forces may need to be introduced—see the *roundabout* example in Chapter Seven).

2. *Relativity of inertial motions.* There is one type of *relative* motion to which Newton's laws of motions are directly applicable. Newton's laws are valid in *inertial* frames of reference (no absolute accelerations and forces). The classical principle of relativity implies that absolute velocities and path descriptions cannot be determined through mechanical experiments.

3. *Matter.* A material body occupies a region or volume of absolute space.[30] Matter is distinct from the space that contains it, although it is implicit in Newton's dynamical criterion for absolute acceleration that absolute space plays a role in the inertial properties of matter. Matter is characterised by geometric-kinematic qualities and by inertial mass. It is supposed that

> mechanical explanations, invoking the contact of material bodies, will be sufficient to explain all natural phenomena, even those effects that show no obvious intervening mechanisms, such as the apparent action-at-a-distance of the force described in Newton's Universal Law of Gravitation.

Relative motion was well-established in classical science, but the form it took was not rigorously examined and lived side-by-side with the old tendency to set up a special rest frame. Points One and Two above exist side-by-side with some awkwardness, the first supporting the idea of absolute space, the second detracting from it. Relative motion and absolute space were not happy bedfellows in the Newtonian world-view.

THE COSMIC FRAME

The idea of absolute motions in absolute space gained widespread acceptance among scientists, and remained largely unchallenged in the following centuries, although a number of thinkers were critical, notably Huygens, Leibniz, Berkeley and Mach. Huygens was not convinced by Newton's idea of absolute space, and was unable to conceive how immaterial space could be ascribed a state of motion, whether one of absolute rest or uniform velocity. Initially, Huygens was attracted by the dynamical criterion of accelerative effects in circular motion, but eventually satisfied himself that dynamical effects provide no justification for the idea of absolute motions.[31] In 1715–16 Leibniz engaged in a famous correspondence with Samuel Clarke (1675–29), a theologian and friend of Newton. Leibniz criticised some of Newton's theological and philosophical ideas, including the idea of an absolute space and time distinct from anything else. Leibniz took a relational approach, supposing that space and time are nothing more than the ordering of objects—space is the order of co-existent things and time is the order of successive things. Space and time are relations, and not actual substances themselves. But Leibniz could find no way of countering the dynamical argument for absolute space, and notwithstanding his relational theory of space and time, he seems to have accepted the reality of absolute motions: Leibniz believed that the change in motion of a body is absolute when the *cause* of the change lies in the body.[32]

Berkeley in the eighteenth century, and Mach in the nineteenth century, rejected the idea of absolute space, and in both cases the rejection stemmed from empirically-oriented philosophical positions, suspicious of ideas that are not directly related to experience. As motion is never observed relative to an absolute space, it follows that the idea of absolute space should be dropped, and motion be viewed as relative to observed bodies. Berkeley argued that absolute motion can be treated as a motion relative to the heaven of fixed stars, an idea that anticipated the arguments of Mach in *The Science of Mechanics*

(1883). Mach's thinking reflects a late nineteenth-century strand of positivism in the philosophy of science, and in the philosophy of mechanics in particular, also expressed in the works of G. R. Kirchhoff (1824–87), William Kingdon Clifford (1845–79) and Karl Pearson (1857–1936). In an illustrative passage, Pearson argued that it is futile to invoke the things-in-themselves to explain the continuity of groups of sensations that we call objects:

> It is idle to postulate shadowy unknowables behind the real world of sense-impression in which we live. So far as they affect us and our conduct they are sense-impressions; what they may be beyond is fantasy, not fact; if indeed it be wise to assume a *beyond,* to postulate that the surface of sense-impressions which shuts us in, must of necessity shut something beyond out.[33]

Mach's positivism is similar to Berkeley's empirico-idealist immaterialism in its denial of physical entities that are not experienced directly, such as forces, mass, atoms and absolute space. The terms and laws of scientific theory are to be regarded as theoretical constructs that help us to organise sensations in a simple manner, but have no reality in themselves. *Mass* and *force* are terms useful for correlating perceptions of the accelerations of bodies, but absolute time and absolute space are rejected as metaphysical speculations, unjustified by experience. Mach supposed that rotational motion is not absolute: it occurs relative to the rest of the observed universe, and it is this relative motion with the rest of the universe that is to be associated with dynamical effects, not a motion in absolute space. In a strictly positivist approach, it is merely the association of accelerative effects with the motion relative to the universe that is considered. The frame of the 'fixed stars' replaces the unobservable absolute space. If we depart from a strict positivism and are open to considering unseen causes, we shall be interested in how accelerative effects, such as the Earth's equatorial bulge, arise from rotations relative to the rest of the matter in the universe. Why, in other words, does a body follow uniform, rectilinear motion relative to the rest of the matter in the universe, and resist changes to this relative rectilinear motion? What is the nature of the relationship between bodies throughout the universe, a relationship that seems to underlie the mechanical behaviour of bodies?

It is clear that the relationship is connected in some way with gravitational phenomena, for there is a remarkable co-incidence in classical physics, nowadays referred to as the *equivalence of inertial and gravitational mass*. The equivalence is mysterious in classical physics but becomes more intelligible if we suppose that inertial motion, inertial mass and gravitation are linked. The equivalence is this: the inertial mass m_i (the measure of resistance of a body to disturbance from uniform rectilinear motion relative to the fixed stars) is proportional to the measure of the body's gravitational attraction to other bodies, the gravitational mass, m_g (the mass in Newton's universal law of gravitation).

Newton's 2nd Law of Motion: $\mathbf{F} = m_i \mathbf{a}$

Law of Universal Gravitation: $\mathbf{F} = m_g M_g \frac{G}{\mathbf{R}^2}$

where G = gravitational constant,
M_g = gravitational mass of other body,
$\mathbf{R}$ = separation between bodies.

Equivalence of inertial and gravitational mass:

m_i is proportional to m_g
(a numerical equality, if suitable units are chosen).

If this proportionality failed, the famous observation associated with Galileo would not hold: bodies of different inertial mass would *not* take the same time to fall to the ground. The classical understanding of gravitation shed no light on the connection between the mechanical behaviour of a body and the universe as a whole, and there has been much debate over the contribution made by modern treatments of cosmic gravitation (based on Einstein's General Theory of Relativity) to the clarification of the matter. Einstein was stimulated by Mach's ideas, and his approach to gravitation linked inertial mass with gravitational mass by exploiting the similarity between the accelerations ascribed to gravitational force and inertial forces. The precise relationship between Mach's ideas and the general theory of relativity remains undecided,[34] as does the debate between substance (space or spacetime as actualities) and relational theories (space or spacetime as relations between physical bodies).[35]

We shall return to Einstein's general theory in the next chapter. For the moment let us attempt to summarise how Mach's criticism of Newton's absolute space has left the question of absolute motion in an absolute substratum. In the previous section, we saw that Newton's dynamical criterion was only good for discriminating absolute accelerations, and told us nothing about the absolute velocities of bodies. These accelerations were 'absolute' in the sense that observers with all kinds of relative motion could observe the accelerative effects manifested in a body and agree on a single acceleration of the body, by applying the dynamical criterion. These accelerations were invariant. It does not follow, however, that the accelerations are 'absolute' in the sense of being describable by non-arbitrary measures of acceleration, and being the actual attributes of substratal bodies.[36] Mach's views made this clear by linking dynamical effects to the relative motion between a body and the large-scale distribution of matter in the universe. Dynamical effects indicated a motion relative to the totality of other bodies, not the non-arbitrary motion of a body in the absolute substratum.

Newton's 'absolute' acceleration is better termed a *dynamical* acceleration, to distinguish it from the completely arbitrary accelerations of kinematical relativity. The dynamical criterion seems to tell us about accelerative motion relative to the totality of matter in the universe, not about absolute accelerations in the elusive absolute space. It is not a criterion to find the unique, definitive, non-arbitrary acceleration of a body, but is a criterion to find the accelerative motion of a body relative to the remainder of the universe. To bring this out more clearly, we could imagine that the whole material universe is accelerating uniformly through Newton's absolute space, say in a straight line or in a uniform circular rotation (the idea of such a motion would, of course, be rejected from the standpoint of a relational philosophy of space). A Newtonian physicist might argue that dynamical effects indicative of an absolute acceleration should manifest throughout the universe, since the universe of matter is undergoing an absolute acceleration through absolute space. The absence of such effects means that the fixed stars are at rest in absolute space. A Machian, on the other hand, might counter by arguing that dynamical effects would not appear, because dynamical effects arise solely through motions relative to the large-scale matter distribution in the universe, not through motions relative to an absolute space. Absolute space has been divested of its implicit role in the inertial behaviour of bodies.

If dynamical phenomena in mechanical experiments cannot reveal absolute motions, even truly absolute accelerations (as opposed to dynamical accelerations relative to the rest of the universe), we may wonder whether there are any phenomena at all that indicate absolute accelerations, absolute velocities and absolute paths. In the nineteenth century, developments in the physics of electromagnetism and optics raised the hope that the absolute rest frame would be detected. This hope was not realised, and a revolution in physical thought ensued. Albert Einstein's Special Theory of Relativity (1905) and its extension in the form of the General Theory of Relativity (1915) to cover gravitational interactions brought about a profound revision of the treatment of relative motion, and showed that the Galilean composition of velocities is only approximately true, accurate when relative velocities are low compared with the speed of light.

ABSOLUTE AETHER

The possibility of determining absolute motions using non-mechanical means arose with the growing interest in aether theories. The existence of unseen aethers—special, subtle types of matter that act as media for the propagation of influences between gross bodies—had long been a subject of speculation in physical discussions of light, electricity, magnetism and heat. The idea of the aether took on new life in the nineteenth century as a result of developments in the study of light and electromagnetism. The wave theory of light had come into favour through the efforts of Thomas Young (1773–1829), who was convinced that a wave theory of light was superior to particle theories. He found support for his belief in certain phenomena exhibited by light that are reminiscent of the interaction of water waves. Crests of intersecting wave patterns on a water surface combine *(superpose)* to give higher crests, while troughs combine to give deeper troughs, and crests and troughs cancel each other to give a smooth surface. In the case of light, bands of varying brightness are obtained when light beams are mixed under certain conditions, and these bands are reminiscent of wave superpositions. Young termed the effect *interference,* and interpreted it as evidence that light is an undulation in a medium, the luminiferous ('light-bearing') aether.

There was, however, one optical phenomenon, called *polarisation,* that seemed to stand in the way of the wave theory of light. Young found a solution by supposing that the vibrations of light waves take place in planes at right angles to the direction of transmission. This so-called *transverse* vibration contrasts with sound waves in air, which consist of vibrations of the air medium in the direction of propagation, or *longitudinal* vibrations. Augustin Fresnel (1788–1827), who developed the mathematical treatment of the wave theory, realised that a medium capable of supporting transverse waves must resist distortions to its structure, and in this respect is like an elastic solid. In consequence, a number of efforts were made to model the luminiferous aether in terms of theoretical elastic solids, with properties in accord with the laws of classical mechanics. But the aether was also ascribed fluid properties to account for the ability of the planets to move through the medium without encountering any noticeable resistance.

Another major development in nineteenth century physics occurred when a close relationship between electricity and magnetism—both known separately in various forms since ancient times—was demonstrated. Influenced by German nature philosophy and its unified view of nature, H. C. Ørsted (1777–1851) sought a connection between electric and magnetic phenomena, and in 1820 found that an electric current affects a compass needle. This confirmed earlier suspicions that electric and magnetic effects are related. In fact, magnetic effects are associated with electric charges in motion. Faraday interpreted electromagnetic effects using a field theory: the space surrounding bodies is filled with a medium, an electromagnetic aether, which carries the magnetic effects of the electric current. Faraday's electromagnetic aether consisted of lines or tubes connecting opposite electric charges and opposite magnetic poles, an idea that had been suggested by the lines assumed by iron filings scattered in the vicinity of a magnet. Attraction consisted of a shortening of the field tubes between opposite charges or poles, whilst repulsion followed from tubes pushing sideways against one another. Faraday was also occupied with the endeavour to unify the phenomena of nature, and in 1846 he suggested that light might consist of vibrations of the field tubes that connect particles. Faraday's approach was taken up by Maxwell, who provided a mathematical treatment of the field concept. Maxwell devised a mechanical model in which Faraday's lines of force were treated as rotating tubes of fluid, exhibiting centrifugal effects of sideways expansion and lengthways contraction. Layers of small spherical particles surrounded the tubes, to allow them to rotate in the same sense. Maxwell considered the manner in which disturbances were propagated through the system, and found that the propagation was similar to light-wave transmission. In addition, a mathematical constant, c, which appears in the description of electric force and in the equation for the rate of propagation of disturbances in Maxwell's model, was found to be suspiciously close to the known velocity of light (approximately 300,000,000 metres per second, or 186,000 miles per second). This suggested to Maxwell that light is an electromagnetic disturbance, and that the luminiferous aether and the electromagnetic field aether were one and the same.

Maxwell refrained from elaborating the mechanical aether model, and concentrated his efforts on developing the mathematical treatment. Other physicists, however, were keen to find models that could provide explanations of the mathematical descriptions, using material analogies and the classical laws of mechanics. This was not a fruitful enterprise because an unusual and contradictory combination of mechanical properties was required of the hypothetical material aether to account for the physics of light and electromagnetism.

In the drive to unify all phenomena, it was even suggested that particles of matter consisted of vortices or whirlpools in the aether, and that gravitational force would also be explicable in terms of the aether. The aether promised to be the *arche* of physics, the unifying basis of force and matter.

In classical physics, it was recognised that mechanical experiments are unable to distinguish between states of relative, uniform, rectilinear motion, a realisation that is expressed in the classical principle of relativity. Physics, however, is not confined to the obviously mechanical phenomena, and the emergence of the electromagnetic-luminiferous aether in the nineteenth century revived interest in the experimental determination of absolute motions. The aether, as the medium of electromagnetic propagation, appeared to be an ideal candidate for the role of privileged frame of reference, providing a medium through which light waves propagate and in which material bodies are at rest or in motion. As a result of the earth's motion through the aether, we might expect to find an aether wind or drift flowing through the earth, a wind that changes its direction as the earth rotates daily and orbits annually. No drift could be detected, a result that suggested to some that the earth dragged a portion of the aether along with it and was therefore at rest with the aether in its immediate vicinity. The idea was difficult to support in the face of stellar aberration, a phenomenon discovered in 1725 by the astronomer James Bradley (1693–1762). Stars show small elliptical changes in position, owing to changes in the earth's velocity during the annual orbit round the sun. Assuming a wave theory of light, the stellar aberration effect would require the aether in the earth's vicinity to be at rest and undisturbed, unless special aether motions are invoked, the 'convected' aether of George Stokes (1819–1903). Furthermore, the results of an experiment conducted by A. H. L. Fizeau (1819–96) in 1851 on the dragging effect of a water stream on light could be interpreted as confirmation that the aether was not dragged by a moving material body. It was therefore tempting to suppose that the aether was truly at rest, and that this stagnant or stationary aether provided an absolute state of rest and a basis for absolute motions. It was hoped that more accurate optical-electromagnetic experiments would reveal the earth's absolute motion through the stationary aether.

The hope, however, was ill-founded. Magnetic effects, we have noted, are associated with electric charges in motion, with an *electric current.* The supporter of the absolute aether theory would argue that this motion, generative of magnetic effects, is the motion of electrical charges through the absolute rest-frame of the aether. In practice, however, an observer finds that electromagnetic effects depend on the state of motion of the charge relative to the observer's reference frame, and not on the state of motion of the charge relative to the hypothesised absolute rest-frame provided by the aether. If we are at rest relative to the electric charges, we observe only electrical effects and no magnetic effects, but magnetic effects appear when relative motion takes place. Thus, some observers will observe magnetic effects and some will not, depending on their state of motion relative to the charge. Electromagnetic effects, like spatial paths, velocities and accelerations, are not invariant between all frames of reference, but depend on the state of relative motion of the observer and the charge. The famous Michelson-Morley experiment, conducted in the 1880s, showed no variations in the velocity of light relative to the Earth's orbital motion through space round the sun, suggesting again that there are no optical-electromagnetic criteria for distinguishing absolute from relative motions.

One way of retaining the aether, suggested independently by G. Fitzgerald (1851–1901) and H. Lorentz (1853–1928), was to suppose that objects, in motion through the aether, physically contract in the direction of motion. The contraction affects the measurements of electromagnetic effects, resulting in contrasting observations of electric and magnetic fields from reference frames in relative motion. There is only one true description of motions and electromagnetic effects, and that is from the rest frame of the absolute aether. Apparent observations from moving reference frames would have to be corrected to obtain the true description. In the case of electromagnetic phenomena, the apparent observations are obtained because the measuring instruments are contracted as they move through the absolute aether. The velocity of light is actually different for observers in motion relative to the absolute aether, but the observers will all measure the same velocity owing to the contraction of measuring instruments in the direction of motion. The physics conspires to hide the absolute state of motion. The contraction was conceivable on the assumption that electromagnetic forces are involved in the material composition of the instruments, holding the constituent molecules together. Electromagnetic experiments could not be used to find the rest frame of the aether, and absolute space remained as elusive as ever.

It was at this stage that Einstein produced an alternative interpretation. This involved the abandonment of the aether as an absolute frame, and the declaration of a new absolute, namely the invariance of the speed of light between frames in relative motion. This invariance or constancy was *not* to be interpreted as an artefact of the measurement process, resulting from the contraction of measuring instruments in motion through an absolute aether.

9. ABSOLUTE SPACETIME

We have seen that in classical science the true motions of objects in the physical world were elusive. The motions of bodies are always observed *relative* to other bodies, and none of the phenomena studied in classical physics, whether classed as mechanical, gravitational or electromagnetic, prove to be of any help in distinguishing actual substratal motions from relative motions. It is true that Newton's dynamical criterion distinguished a special class of accelerations invariant for all observers, but these so-called 'absolute' accelerations could be regarded as accelerations relative to the universe at large. Although motions in absolute space could not be determined, the idea of an absolute substratum containing physical objects with absolute motions was generally accepted by scientists.

However, Einstein's insights into relativity have swept away the ideas of absolute time and absolute space/aether, and we must therefore reconsider the idea of substratal objects with definite attributes of motion. Before considering Einstein's re-evaluation of relative motion, and Minkowski's subsequent idea of a relativistic, absolute world, it will be useful to tighten up our usage of the word *observation,* and distinguish it from *perception.*

OBSERVATION AND PERCEPTION

In discussions of relativistic theory, the term *observer* is frequently used. The observer is said to *observe* various events, such as the emission of a light pulse or the contraction of a length. In relativistic theory, an observer is a *measurer.* The observer takes measurements of distances and time intervals using measuring devices. The observer need not be a person, and could, for instance, be a computer which operates measuring devices, and records and processes the data collected by the devices.

The instrumentalist, extreme empiricist or positivist regards science as the study of the relationships between these measurements, whilst the scientific realist believes that the measurements describe a physical substratum in some way. If we follow the realist path and assume that there is an underlying physical world whose characteristics we measure, then *observation* refers to the process of gathering measurements, and using them to build a picture or representation of the physical substratum and its objects. The process involves the gathering of data using measuring instruments, the processing of the data according to some tacitly assumed or explicitly recognised theory of measurement, and an interpretation of what the information reveals about the structure of the world. Thus, when a realist says that an observer *observes* an object and its motions, it is an *indirect* knowledge of the object that is meant, an observation constructed from measurements and measurement theory. Einstein appreciated the importance of defining how measurements of lengths and time intervals are conducted, as we shall see in the discussion of *relative simultaneity.*

Observation needs to be contrasted with universal experience and perceptual experience. We have entertained the possibility of substratal content revealed in universal mystical experiences. These experiences would constitute a *direct* knowing of the underlying world, independent of any measuring devices or interpretation, although it seems that interpretation very often occurs during and after the experience. We also have to distinguish perception from observation. Perception, we usually suppose, is dependent on a transmission of information, on sensory processes and on some unconscious, interpretative processes. In a representative theory, the perceptual experience is regarded as a representation of the external world. We have, therefore, three terms to distinguish:

1. *Observation:* in a realist theory, indirect knowledge of the substratum, obtained through measurements and interpretation. Observation tells us about the structure of the physical world, beneath the variations that relative perceptions introduce.

2. *Universal experience:* direct experience of the substratum, not mediated by sense-perception or measuring instruments.

3. *Perception:* in realist theory, sense-representations of the substratum, mediated by the sense-organs, incorporating some implicit interpretation.

Within the study of relativistic physics, the distinction between *observing* and *seeing* was not fully appreciated for many years. What is observed is *not* what is seen. An oft-cited example is that of a cube passing an observer at a velocity approaching the velocity of light. The observer *observes* or *measures* the object, finding that it is contracted along its line of motion—this is a relativistic effect. However, the observer would *see* a rotation of the object—this is a consequence of the visual process, which involves the transmission of light from the moving cube to the eyes of the observer.[1]

THE SPECIAL THEORY OF RELATIVITY

Let us now consider Einstein's revision of classical relativity theory, including the idea of physical time. At the heart of the Special Theory is a revised principle of relativity called Einstein's *special principle of relativity* or the *Relativity Postulate.* The principle is expressed in a number of ways, but a common version asserts that:

> The same laws of physics hold in every inertial frame of reference.

Einstein's principle extends the classical principle of relativity by stating that a uniform, rectilinear motion cannot be established as absolute by electromagnetic or mechanical means. It is accepted that optical-electromagnetic effects, as well as dynamical effects, provide no way of defining an absolute motion. An observer is unable to determine a state of absolute, uniform, rectilinear motion by conducting experiments using optical and electromagnetic phenomena. All the laws of physics, not just the laws of mechanics, hold in every inertial frame, and therefore departures from the laws cannot be used to distinguish absolute from relative velocities.

To the Relativity Postulate is added a second postulate, the *Light Postulate,* which again has more than one form of expression. The following version has been called *the invariance of the speed of light:*

> The velocity of light in empty space is the same in all inertial frames of reference, whatever the state of motion of the light source.

The two postulates are related. According to the first, the laws of electromagnetism must have the same form in every inertial frame of reference. Electromagnetic phenomena cannot be used to distinguish one inertial frame from another. Now, the velocity of light in free space, *c,* appears in the equations of electromagnetism as a constant, and as the laws of electromagnetism are the same in every inertial reference frame, it follows that the velocity of light in empty space will also be the same in every inertial reference frame. Einstein courageously took the velocity of light in free space to be invariant between inertial reference frames, contradicting the classical principle of relativity. It follows that the Galilean transformations of classical mechanics have to be replaced by new transformations between co-ordinate systems, the Lorentz transformations, originally introduced by Lorentz to account for the null results of aether-drag experiments. For the reference frames F and F′ illustrated in Chapter Seven (Figure 7.3.), these are:

From frame F to frame F′:

$$x' = \gamma\,(x - vt)$$
$$y' = y$$
$$z' = z$$
$$t' = \gamma\,(t - \frac{vx}{c^2})$$

From frame F′ to frame F:

$$x = \gamma\,(x' + vt')$$
$$y = y'$$
$$z = z'$$
$$t = \gamma\,(t' + \frac{vx'}{c^2})$$

where $\gamma = \dfrac{c}{\sqrt{(c^2 - v^2)}}$ and v is the velocity of F′ measured from F.

As Einstein realised, the invariance of the speed of light upsets the classical notions of absolute time and the absolute simultaneity of events. The transformation equation for the time co-ordinates is no longer the Galilean equality $t = t'$, and there is no longer a temporal order of events that is the same for all observers. The temporal interval between the same two events differs when measured from frames of reference in relative motion.

The velocity of light in free space acts as a maximum limit for the propagation of signals or changes and is approximately 3×10^8 metres per second in free space (the value is lower when the propagation takes place through a medium). Bodies may be observed to approach the velocity of light, but will never be observed to reach it. Nowadays there is ample experimental support for the invariance of c. It is a very strange result, for it clashes with the commonsense (classical) view of relative motion, with its straightforward vector addition of velocities. The classical laws of motion are only approximately valid, giving an adequate description when relative velocities are low compared with the velocity of light.

To illustrate the peculiar nature of the Light Postulate, consider two observers F and G in rockets that move apart in a uniform rectilinear motion, with relative velocity v. F sends a light pulse, and measures it to have a velocity of c in the direction of G's receding rocket. G measures the velocity of the pulse and discovers it be c, not the value of $(c - v)$ expected using Galilean velocity addition. The relative motion of the observers makes no contribution to the measured velocity of the light pulse. The velocity of light is independent of the velocity of the observer.

There are a number of results derivable from the invariance of c that conflict with pre-relativistic expectations, and one of the most dramatic is the effect known as *time dilation*. Consider the example of relative motion in two dimensions described in Chapter Seven, used to illustrate the kinematical relativity of spatial path and velocity in classical physics: the motion of a ball considered by two observers F and G in relative motion (Figure 7.6.). Before the advent of the special theory of relativity and the Light Postulate, it might have seemed reasonable to treat a light pulse in the same manner as the ball,

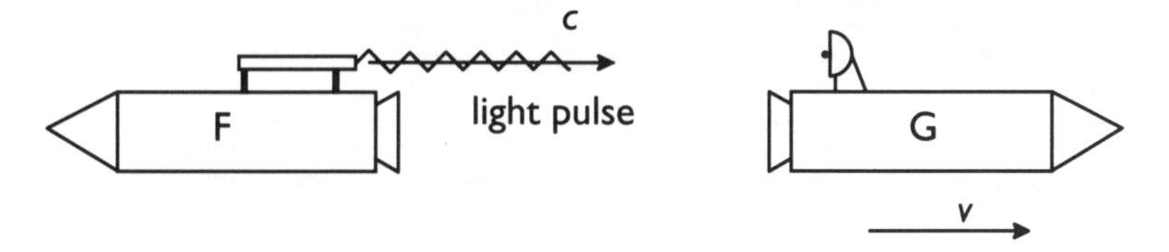

Figure 9.1. G also measures velocity of light pulse to be c, not $c - v$.

replacing the wall with a mirror and putting $u = c$, the velocity of light. F holds a light source that emits a pulse or photon of light (event P). The photon travels to the mirror, is reflected at the mirror (event Q), and is received by F (event R). By analogy with the classical treatment of the ball, we would expect the velocity of light to be greater in the G-frame, for it covers a greater path length in the same time (Newtonian assumption of absolute time).

Now, in the relativistic treatment, the path length of the light pulse again differs between the frames of reference, but the Light Postulate tells us that the velocity of light is the same, *c,* in both frames. The light pulse takes *longer* to traverse the path from event *P* to Q in G's frame of reference. This is because:

1. The light path is observed to be longer in G's frame *(kinematical relativity of spatial path length).*

2. The velocity of the light pulse in its direction of propagation in G's frame is the same as in F's frame *(Einstein's Light Postulate):* $c_F = c_G = c.$

The idea of an absolute frame (and the one true spatial path) has been rejected in special relativity, and all the relative path descriptions are taken as equally valid. There is, however, a quantity that *is* absolute across all the relative frames, namely the invariant velocity of light. It is this combination of relative, spatial light-paths with an invariant light velocity that leads to the surprises of special relativity, such as the relativity of time intervals and lengths of bodies.

The time intervals observed between the events P and Q are different in the F and G frames, with the greater time interval observed in the G-frame. This difference is termed *time dilation,* a 'dilated' or 'expanded' time interval.

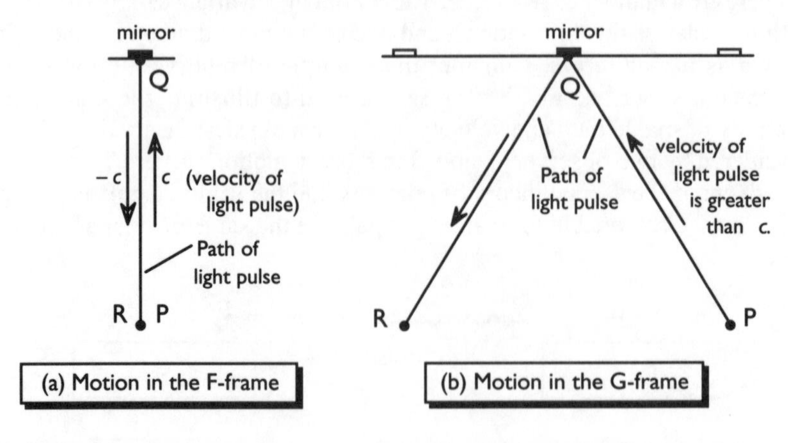

Figure 9.2. Classical case, with pulse of light equivalent to the ball in Figure 7.6.

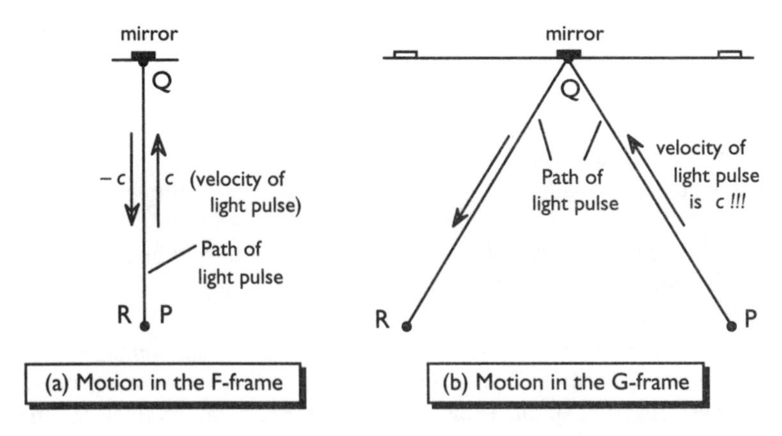

Figure 9.3. Relativistic case: light has the same velocity in frames F and G.

It is important to recognise that time dilation is a truly reciprocal effect. We could set up an identical light source and mirror (in effect, a light-pulse clock) at rest in the G-frame. Now F observes the longer light-path and greater time-interval between the emission of the pulse and its return. Time dilation is a reciprocal effect.

It may be wondered how the experiment would be described by an observer at rest with the light pulse. The situation is hypothetical because in the special theory of relativity, it is not possible for a material body to achieve the speed of light, and an observer cannot attain a state of rest with a photon. Experiment confirms the Light Postulate—light in free space always has a velocity *c* relative to the observer. At the age of sixteen, Einstein puzzled over the form of a light-beam observed from a frame at rest with the beam: the idea of a light wave at rest with an observer seemed contradictory to both experience and Maxwell's equations of electromagnetism, and it seemed to Einstein that the laws of physics for the observer should be the same as the laws in the earth's rest frame.[2] In this intuition lay the seeds of the special theory of relativity, which Einstein presented ten years later in 1905.

The time interval between two events connected by a light transmission (such as the events P and Q in the example above) is usually said to be zero in the light-frame.[3] All the temporal states of the photon can be taken to be simultaneous, at least according to the revised concept of simultaneity used in relativistic theory,[4] to be discussed shortly. The nature of things that travel at the maximum, invariant velocity (such as light and other electromagnetic radiations) is not clear. Should an entity with the maximum, invariant velocity be regarded as a particle of matter with temporal states and its own frame of reference? The motion of such a particle constitutes an actual transportation of matter from place to place. Or is it more accurate to interpret the entity as a propagation of *changes* in the frames of real observers, as a limiting speed of efficient causation? The invariance of the velocity would incline me to the latter alternative.

Besides time dilation, there is another relativistic effect following from the Light Postulate: *Lorentz contraction* is the observed length contraction of an object in its direction. Suppose F and G hold metre rulers, aligned along their line of relative motion. F will measure G's ruler to be shorter than F's own ruler. Again the effect is reciprocal: G measures F's ruler to be shorter in the direction of relative motion. Reciprocity is a basic consequence of the postulates of Special Relativity.

Relativistic effects are not the consequence of observers' relative perceptions. They are not optical illusions or artefacts of the perceptual processes. The effects—different spatial separations and temporal intervals between the same events measured by observers in relative motion—are *observed,* rather than perceived. They are deduced from measurements by applying the postulates of special relativity.

Clearly we cannot talk of absolute lengths and absolute time intervals any more, and the idea of an absolute substratum with definite spatial separations and temporal intervals between events has to be abandoned. The notion of a single, common receptacle, housing objects and providing an arena for their motions, is replaced by the idea of a plurality of *relative spaces* (frames of reference), each observer associated with a relative space. Discussing the concept of space in a popular exposition of relativistic theory, Einstein suggested that a consideration of containers in relative motion, each enclosing a space, leads one to apportion a space to each container, and thereby entertain a multiplicity of spaces in relative motion.

> Before one has become aware of this complication [a relative space associated with each object in motion], space appears as an unbounded medium or container in which material objects swim around. But it must now be remembered that there is an infinite number of spaces, which are in motion with respect to each other. The concept of space as something existing objectively and independent of things belongs to pre-scientific thought, but not so the idea of the existence of an infinite number of spaces in motion relatively to each other. This latter idea is indeed logically unavoidable, but is far from having played a considerable rôle even in scientific thought.[5]

Einstein has replaced the idea of absolute motions in absolute space (one true description of motions) with the idea of relative motions in a plurality of relative spaces (many equally valid but different descriptions of the motions of bodies, from inertial frames of equal status). Not only are spatial paths and velocities found to differ by observers in relative motion (as in classical mechanics): in relativistic physics, the time intervals observed between the same events, and the lengths of objects in the line of relative motion, are also different.

MINKOWSKI'S ABSOLUTE SPACETIME

The absolute space of classical science was sundered by Einstein's postulates into a multiplicity of relative spaces of equal status. From these observer-frames in relative motion, such basic features as the time interval between events and the length of an object could be measured to differ. The idea of a common, underlying physical world with definite, unique attributes was under threat. Yet a synthesis of relative spaces into a new absolute substratum was soon to emerge, a physical world of events separated by intervals that are invariant for the multiplicity of observers, whatever their states of motion. This new absolute world was not a three-dimensional space like the ill-fated absolute space of classical science, but a four-dimensional continuum in which space and time were combined in a special way.

Before the advent of the special theory of relativity, there had been moves to forge closer links between space and time. For example, the mathematician and astronomer William Rowan Hamilton (1805–65) was convinced that space and time are "indissolubly linked". Like Ørsted, Hamilton was influenced by the *Naturphilosophie* and its stress on the unity of nature. He pondered

> how the One of Time, of Space the Three,
> Might in the Chain of Symbol girdled be.[6]

The chain was to be mathematics, with an algebra of time and a geometry of space, and his mathematical discovery, the *quaternions*—complex numbers generalised to four dimensions—was to be the tool for demonstrating the union of time and space.

However, it was the special theory of relativity that provided a strong motive for linking space and time. The discovery that lengths, time intervals and simultaneities can vary, depending on the frame of reference from which they are measured, threatens the notion of an absolute substratum, an underlying physical world that is the same for every observer. It was soon noticed, however, that a *kind* of absolute world could be formulated by combining space and time in a special way. The absolute picture of the world returned in a new guise, a special form of spacetime that encapsulates Einstein's version of relativity theory. It was the mathematician Hermann Minkowski (1864–1909) who saw that the amalgamation of space and time would provide a new invariant for the common, absolute reality behind the relativity of observers:

> Henceforth space by itself, and time by itself, are doomed to fade away into mere shadows, and only a kind of union of the two will preserve an independent reality.[7]

Spatial separations alone and temporal intervals alone provide inadequate forms of physical description for the "independent reality" because their values vary from observer to observer, depending on the observer's state of motion. They are not absolutes, not invariants. They cannot be regarded as characteristics of an absolute substratum. However, it is possible to construct a mathematical quantity, a combination of spatial and temporal values that is invariant for all observers, whatever their states of motion. The spatial separation and temporal interval between events vary from observer to observer, but a combination of them in the quantity known as the *invariant interval* ($\Delta\tau$) is the same for all observers. The square of the invariant interval is given by the square of the temporal interval minus the square of the spatial separation. For three space dimensions, the invariant interval is given by the equation:

$$(\text{invariant interval})^2 = \Delta\tau^2 = c^2\,\Delta t^2 - (\Delta x^2 + \Delta y^2 + \Delta z^2),$$

or for just one spatial dimension, by

$$(\text{invariant interval})^2 = \Delta\tau^2 = c^2\,\Delta t^2 - \Delta x^2$$

Quantities such as the energy and momentum of an object are also found to differ when observed from inertial frames of reference in relative motion. Again a mathematical quantity, combining energy and momentum, can be constructed that is invariant between frames of reference.

We have seen that in classical physics the spatial path between events varies from frame to frame, but the time interval is invariant. It is therefore impossible to construct an interval combining space and time that is invariant for all frames of reference in classical physics. The time interval cannot adjust to compensate for differences in the spatial separation. Newtonian absolute time is aloof from the relativity of spatial separation between frames in relative motion. There is no equivalent to the relativistic invariant interval in the classical formulation, combining space and time into a unique interval between events, and it is therefore sometimes stated that space and time are not brought together in any profound sense in classical physics.

The invariant interval, unlike the spatial separation and temporal interval, is absolute (invariant) for all observers. The invariant interval would therefore seem to be the measure appropriate to an absolute substratum. It is this idea that forms the basis of Minkowski's approach to relativity. The underlying world is a four-dimensional continuum, called *spacetime,* in which the separation between things is given by the invariant interval. Two things at points in the four-dimensional world are separated by a 'distance', the invariant interval, which can be resolved into pairs of space-separation and time-interval values, to suit the requirements of any reference frame. This is analogous to the way in which a length can be resolved into sets of three length components (length, breadth and height), depending on the orientation of the rectangular co-ordinate system.

It is important to recognise that the absolute spacetime in which the invariant interval is the measure of distance does not have the three familiar space dimensions (x, y, and z) combined with the one spatialized time dimension (ct), in contrast to the time-distance graphs and Newtonian spacetime discussed in Chapter Six. This is because the form of the equation for the invariant interval is reminiscent of, *but not identical to,* the equation that expresses distances in Euclidean three-dimensional space as combinations of the three distance components (Δx, Δy, Δz) along three independent axes x, y, and z, of the rectangular co-ordinate system. The equation is based on the theorem of Pythagoras for the sides of a right-angled triangle, and is:

$$(\text{distance})^2 = \Delta x^2 + \Delta y^2 + \Delta z^2$$

The formula for the invariant interval is clearly different in one respect. The squares of the spatial separations are subtracted from the square of the time interval, not added to the time interval, and the four-dimensional space is therefore termed *semi-Euclidean,* and not Euclidean. To give the invariant interval equation the form of the distance equation in Euclidean space, we have to eliminate the minus sign, which can be accomplished, as Minkowski realised, by substituting t with a new variable s:

$$s = \sqrt{(-1)}\, ct, \quad \text{or } s = ict \quad \text{(where } i \text{ is the square root of } -1\text{).}$$

The invariant interval can then be written as

$$\Delta\tau^2 = \Delta s^2 + \Delta x^2 + \Delta y^2 + \Delta z^2,$$

which has the required form for a separation in Euclidean space. The Minkowski spacetime therefore has the three familiar space dimensions (x, y, z) and one *imaginary* spatialized time dimension (s). The dimension is termed imaginary because mathematicians term the square roots of negative numbers *imaginary* to distinguish them from the *real* numbers, numbers which do not involve the roots of negative numbers. *Real* and *imaginary* are algebraic terms, and do not refer to the existence or non-existence of things.

Alternatively, we could have made the minus sign disappear by substituting three imaginary spatial variables, in which case the spacetime would combine the familiar, spatialized time dimension (ct) with three imaginary space dimensions (ix, iy, iz).

Minkowski spacetime, with its mix of algebraically real and imaginary dimensions, provides an absolute substratum, absolute because it is the same for every observer. The absolute spacetime world is resolvable for each observer into co-ordinate axes of real space (distance measurements) and real spatialized time (time measurements), and the relative space-separations and time-intervals thus obtained are not generally invariant from one observer to another. Each point in the spacetime is called a *worldpoint,* and a body with duration, such as a point in three-dimensional space, consists of a sequence of such worldpoints, a *worldline.* We used this terminology in our discussion of Newtonian spacetime. The worldpoint is also called a *point-event,* to stress that the *point* is a location in space and an *event* in time.

Absolute Minkowski spacetime is rather different from the Newtonian spacetime we considered earlier. It involves an imaginary time dimension, or, alternatively, three imaginary space dimensions, not the real spatialized time dimension of the time-distance graphs or the Newtonian spacetime diagrams. When Minkowski spacetime is represented diagrammatically to illustrate relativistic effects, it is the real t dimension that is drawn, not the imaginary s dimension. In fact, the s dimension plays no further role in relativity theory. Many spacetime diagrams with t dimensions are required to represent the single, absolute Minkowski spacetime with its s dimension, for each diagram represents one of the relative frames into which the unitary Minkowski spacetime is resolved. To highlight the point, we shall refer to these oft-encountered, relative representations of unitary Minkowski spacetime as *real-time diagrams,* spacetime diagrams with an algebraically real time-dimension. The worldpoints have co-ordinates (t, x, y, z) in the real-time diagrams, in contrast to the (s, x, y, z) co-ordinates in Minkowski spacetime. Although real-time diagrams are not exact representations of Minkowski spacetime (distances between worldpoints in real-time diagrams are not invariant intervals), the diagrams are very useful for showing how space separations, time intervals and simultaneity are not absolute in the special theory of relativity. Each real-time diagram represents the world measured from one particular frame of reference.

Let us examine a couple of these real-time diagrams, each of which represents the same region of a Minkowski spacetime with one space dimension and one imaginary time dimension. The two real-time diagrams are resolutions of the Minkowski spacetime into spacetime diagrams with real time axes, one for observer F and one for observer G, who move with a relative velocity of half the speed of light, ½ c. The observers pass each other at event O, which we shall make the origin of the real-time diagrams.

The worldlines of observers F and G consist of sequences of worldpoint states of F and G. In the real-time diagram for F's frame, the worldline of F forms the perpendicular time axis, ct_F. This time axis is peculiar to F and is called the *local time* of F. Likewise, G has a local time of its own, defined by G's worldline, ct_G. There is no absolute time ct anymore. Instead there is a multiplicity of individual local times, consisting of the worldlines of things. The continuity of each thing, the sequence of worldpoint states, defines each local time. There is no common time for all continuing substances. But frames at rest with one another will have their time-axes aligned. When there is relative motion, the worldlines are at angles and the local times are different.

For convenience, the spatialized time-axes are usually scaled by the factor c. The worldlines of a pulse of light, velocity c, show as lines at forty-five degrees to the axes, owing to the scaling factor. If the scaling factor were not used, the light worldline would be almost indistinguishable from the space axis (see Figure 9.5.). No worldline can have a shallower gradient than the light-worldlines, since light is ascribed the maximum possible velocity for a transmission. Note that the observers have their own space co-ordinate axes, x_F and x_G, instead of the common absolute space-axis of Newtonian space. When a frame of reference is considered to be at rest, the co-ordinate system consists of time and space axes drawn at right angles to each other. Axes of frames in relative motion to the rest frame are not at right angles to each other. It follows from the definition of simultaneity in relativistic physics (to be considered in the next section) that the space axis of the moving reference frame is tilted in the rest-frame in such a way that the light-worldline bisects the angle between the space and time axes.

From a frame considered to be at rest, the 2-D co-ordinate system of a moving reference frame consists of a diamond lattice (see Figure 9.6.). Note the different calibration of the two sets of axes in any one diagram. In the case of the moving reference frame, the units of time and distance are displaced further along the axes from the origin, in accordance with the equation describing the

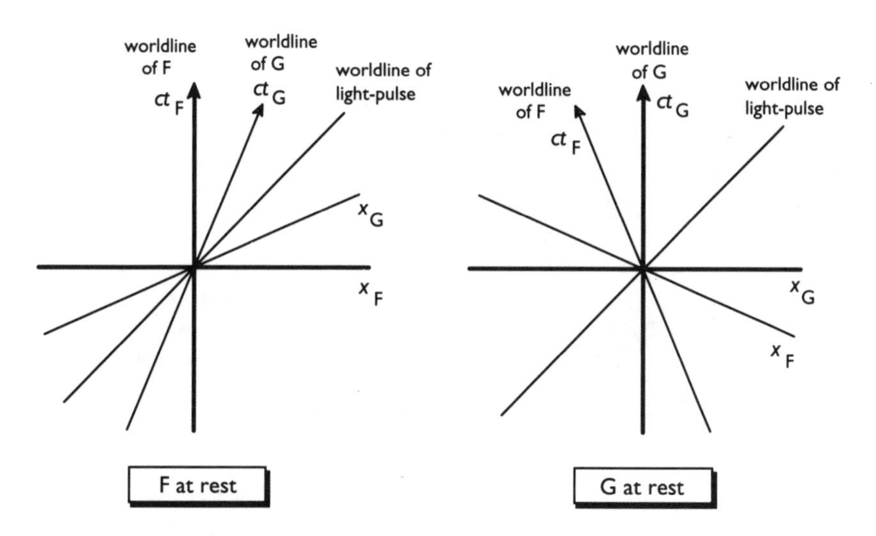

Figure 9.4. Real-time diagrams for observers F and G in relative uniform motion.

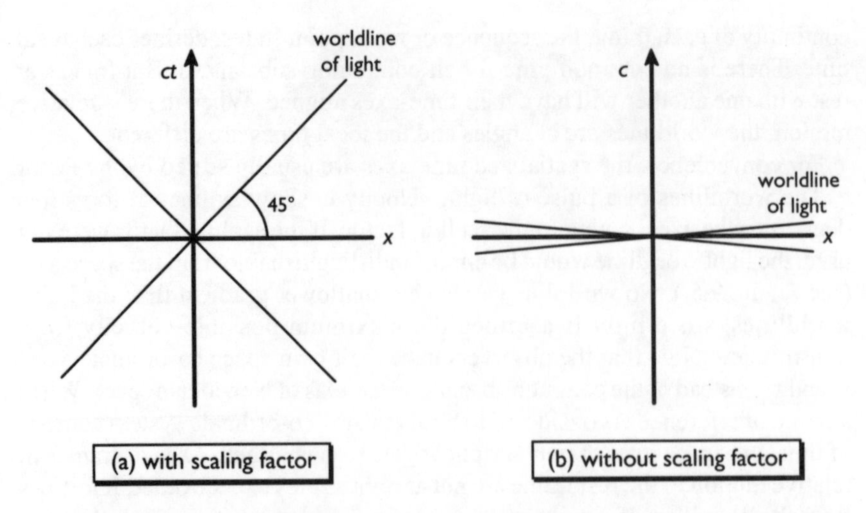

Figure 9.5. Real-time diagrams (a) with, and (b) without, the scaling factor c applied to the time axis t. In fact, the slope of the light worldlines in diagram (b) has been exaggerated to make them distinguishable from the space axis.

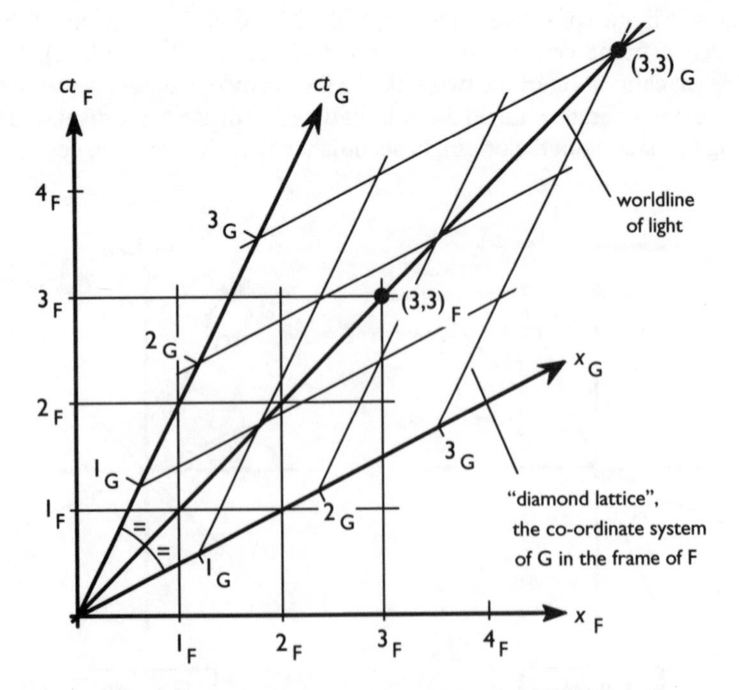

Figure 9.6. The diagram shows part of Figure 9.4 (a) in detail, with the co-ordinate system of G superimposed on the co-ordinate system of F. The light worldline bisects the angle between the time and space axes.

invariant interval. The Lorentz equations of special relativity are used to convert co-ordinates from one system to the other.

THE RELATIVITY OF SIMULTANEITY

How, then, is simultaneity defined in special relativity? Let us first consider the nature of simultaneity more generally. In everyday life we have a notion that some events happen at the same time. At its most direct and basic, the notion refers to the concurrence of events in the same experience. Feelings, sounds, objects, that occur together in one experiential moment are experientially simultaneous.[8] It is a phenomenological simultaneity. This experiential concurrence is probably the origin of the idea of simultaneity, the togetherness of events in the experiential now. Experiential simultaneity is *relative* in the following sense: two things that occur together in my experiential moment, such as two sounds, may not occur together in your experiential moment. This is the relativity of *experiential* or *perceptual* simultaneity, and is to be distinguished from the relativity of *physical* or *observational* simultaneity considered in special relativity.

In the course of imagining the world beyond immediate sensory experience, people evolved an intuitive theory of time in which distant events could be placed in a single, temporal order. The theory became more subtle when it was realised that the speeds of signals (sound, light, and so forth) conveying information from distant events are finite and have to be taken into account in the construction of a temporal order. Events that are simultaneous experientially may not be simultaneous in the physical world, owing to the different speeds of signal propagation or the different distances between the events and the perceiver. For instance, the difference between the speed of sound and light shows in the pause between the flash and the boom of a lightning stroke. And if we see a star exploding in the sky, we do not suppose that the physical explosion of the star is simultaneous with our visual experience of it. Taking into account the finite speed of light signals, we realise that the explosion in the physical world happened thousands or millions of years before our perception of it. There is a time-lag between the physical event and the perception, owing to the finite velocity of light. Each perceptual moment is a compilation of events from a span of physical times.[9]

Because the velocity of light is so great, it was often assumed to be infinite, providing an instantaneous transmission of signals and an instant knowledge of simultaneous events. In everyday matters, we tend to interpret the world in this way, until a disparity between signals from the same event reminds us otherwise, such as the flash and bang of a starting pistol that are experientially out of step with each other. In scientific contexts, however, the finiteness of the velocity of light came to be accepted by the close of the seventeenth century,

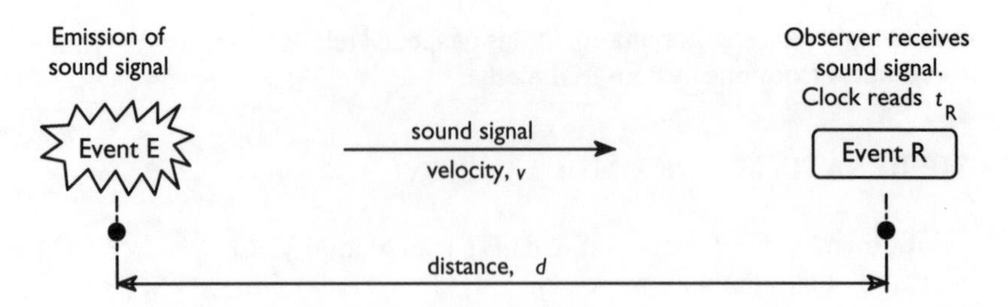

Figure 9.7. Emission and reception of sound signal.

suggested by Galileo, and measured by Ole Rømer (1644–1710) in 1676. Thereafter, the distinction between experiential simultaneity and the simultaneity of events in the physical world was open to recognition. Acknowledging this distinction between *experiential simultaneity* and *physical simultaneity,* we are obliged to take into account the velocity of physical signals when we work out the temporal order of events. This may involve a consideration of the speed of nerve signals and perceptual processing, in addition to the speed of the signals that reach our sense organs. Suppose that a sound signal is emitted (event E) from a starting pistol located at a measured distance d from an observer (Figure 9.7.). The observer notes that the signal is received (event R) when the observer's clock reads time t_R. Taking the velocity of sound to be v, the observer calculates that the emission E occurred at a time

$$t_R - \frac{d}{v}.$$

Having calculated the travel times of signals, an observer can work out a temporal sequence of events in the physical world. Some events are said to be simultaneous with others. If these events could emit signals with an infinite velocity, they would also be experientially simultaneous, but as the signals are finite we have to work out their physical simultaneity through a knowledge of the signal speeds and the distances the signals have travelled.

Now the special theory of relativity tells us that the velocity of light is invariant for observers. We may therefore choose to use light signals to define the physical simultaneity of events, since we can take the velocity of the signals to be an absolute. The lengths of objects and their distances from an observer are to be measured using light signals—measure the time taken by a light signal to reach the object and return to the observer, and calculate the distance using c. The observer synchronises distant clocks by sending light signals. The clocks register the time of arrival of the signals, and the observer checks that the readings agree with the expected readings, calculated from a knowledge of the invariant velocity of light and the distances to the clocks. Einstein followed this route, examining how observers are able to define a physical simultaneity of events, given the finite and invariant velocity of light signals. It follows from the light-signal approach to observation and simultaneity that observers in relative motion *disagree* over the simultaneity of events—physical simultaneity is relative (variant).

Let us consider an example. Suppose I stand in the middle of a railway carriage at each end of which a flash gun is positioned. I perceive the guns to flash in the same experiential moment (event C), and because I have decided they are equidistant from me, I deduce that the guns flashed at the same physical time. The experiential simultaneity of the flashes in my perceptions is matched by a physical simultaneity of the flash-gun emissions (events A and B in Figure 9.8.).[10] Now suppose that the carriage moves along a track relative to an observer on a station platform. Since the velocity of light is invariant for frames in relative motion, the second observer (on the platform) decides that the events A and B are not simultaneous. This is because the train has moved for the second observer, and the light from the flash gun at the rear of the carriage has to traverse a greater distance than the light from the other gun. The motion of the train lengthens the rearward spatial path length to the middle of the carriage, and shortens the forward path length, in the relative space of the observer (Figure 9.9). Since the two flashes arrive at the middle of the carriage together, they were not emitted at the same time—same light-velocities (Light Postulate), different path lengths, hence different times of emission.

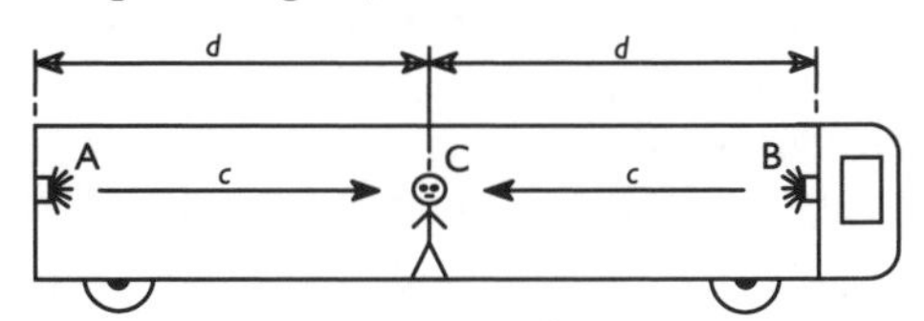

Figure 9.8. Physical simultaneity of flash-gun emissions A and B in the railway-carriage frame. Events A and B are equidistant from the observer.

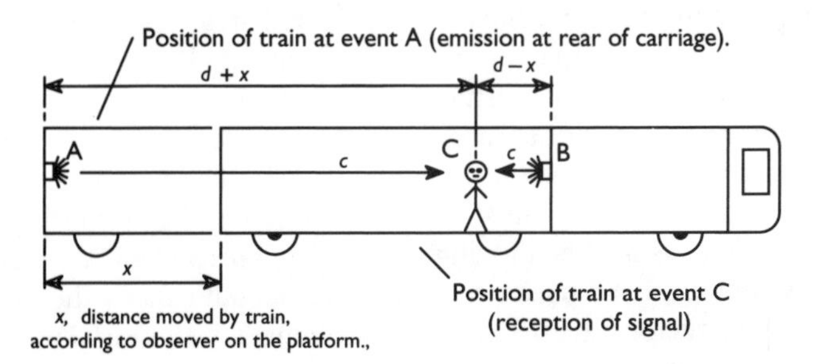

Figure 9.9. Flash-gun emissions A and B are not simultaneous for the observer on the platform, who observes the train to move through a distance x between the flash A and the reception C. The light from A traverses a longer path $(d + x)$ than the light from B, $(d - x)$. As the two flashes arrive at C together and travel at the same velocity c, the flash from A must set out earlier.

Thus, if we employ a definition of simultaneity that assigns distance and time co-ordinates to distant events using the finite, invariant velocity of electromagnetic signals as a yardstick, observers in relative motion will place some events in a different temporal order. One observer may order an event A before an event B; another observer may measure A and B as simultaneous; another places B before A. The invariance of light combines with the different spatial paths observed from frames in relative motion to undermine the idea of absolute, physical simultaneity. There is, instead, a relative physical simultaneity for each observer, defined by distance and time measurements using the finite, invariant velocity of light. Each set of relative, simultaneous events for an observer, each relative Now, can be used to define a spatial cross-section of the observer's spacetime picture of the world.

The real-time diagrams illustrate well the relativity of physical simultaneity. As we have noted, it is this idea of simultaneity that defines the space axes in time-distance (or spacetime) diagrams. A space axis is a locus of point-events that an observer takes to be simultaneous with the observer's own point-event. In the real-time diagram of one observer, the space axis of a frame in relative motion is tilted with respect to the observer's perpendicular time and space axes. All events on the tilted space axis are simultaneous for the moving frame, and events on each line parallel to the tilted space axis are also cross-sections of simultaneity. For instance, in the spacetime illustrated in Figure 9.10., observer F takes events P and Q to be simultaneous, whereas observer G takes events Q and R to be simultaneous.

Let us consider briefly how the relative nature of physical simultaneity in special relativity is related to Lorentz contraction. Observers in relative motion use different time axes (worldlines), and different space axes (cross-sections of physical simultaneity, defined using the light-signalling approach). Measurements of time intervals and spatial separations along these different time and space axes give different values. Figure 9.11. illustrates Lorentz contraction. A ruler in spacetime is represented by the shaded area. The ruler is at rest in the frame of observer F, and in motion in the frame of observer G. F measures the ruler to be one metre long using light signals, from O to P. However, G measures the ruler to be shorter than one metre, measuring from O to Q. Note that in the diagram, the distance OP is shorter than the distance OQ, but observer G's axes are calibrated differently, its units being extended from P's point-of-view. Hence G measures the moving ruler to be *shorter* than one metre. The example is depicted from observer F's rest-frame, but exactly the same kind of geometry and reciprocal effects would be obtained by taking G to be at rest. G observes F's ruler to be contracted, and F observes G's ruler to be contracted. Time dilation can be illustrated in a similar fashion, with real-time diagrams showing how observers' time and space axes divide and measure spacetime differently.[11]

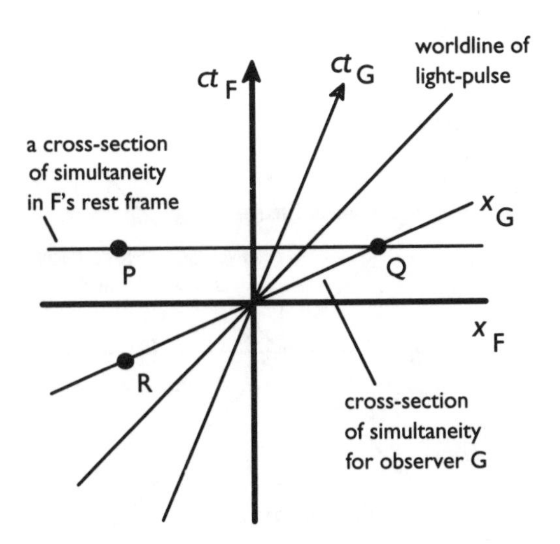

Figure 9.10. Events P and Q are simultaneous for observer F, whilst events Q and R are simultaneous for observer G.

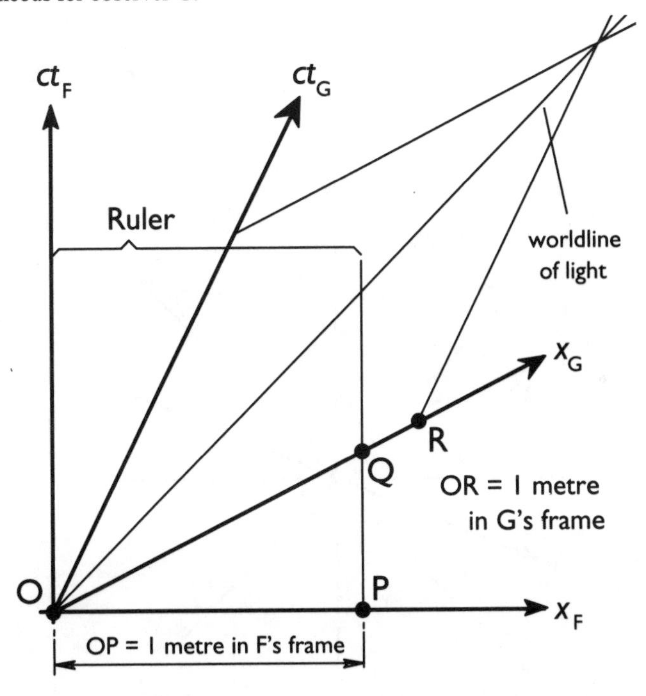

Figure 9.11. Lorentz contraction—observers in relative motion use different space axes (cross-sections of simultaneity, x_F and x_G) to measure the length of an object, and obtain different values. F observes the ruler (cross-section OP) to be one metre long. G observes ruler (cross-section OQ) to be less than one metre long (OQ is shorter than OR).

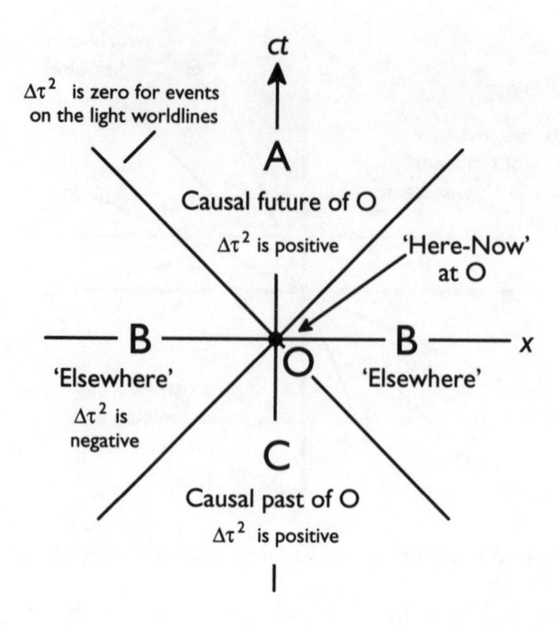

Figure 9.12. Three regions of 2-D spacetime, (1+1)D. Each region has different causal relations with an event at the origin O.

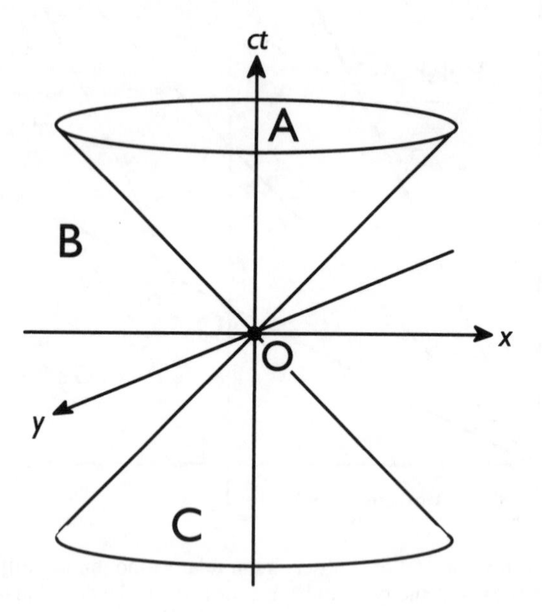

Figure 9.13. The light cone divides 3-D spacetime, (2 + 1)D, into three regions.

CAUSALITY IN RELATIVISTIC SPACETIME

In relativistic physics, the maximum speed at which a change can be transmitted is *c*, or 3×10^8 metres per second. The consequences of a change in one place cannot be developed through the environment at a speed greater than *c*. The limiting velocity is held to apply to the propagation of changes in the fields of all the known forces of nature. For instance, it is thought that neither electromagnetic signals, such as light, nor gravitational signals, such as gravitational waves, can propagate at a speed greater than *c*. The worldlines of limiting-velocity signals divide the real-time diagram into three types of region, labelled A, B and C in Figure 9.12. Events in these three regions have different causal relationships (efficient causation) with an event at the origin O of the real-time diagram. The sign of the square of the invariant interval ($\Delta\tau^2$) between the origin and events in each region is shown in the diagram. In a three-dimensional spacetime, (2+1)D, the worldlines of light form a cone, the *light-cone*, with circular cross-sections (Figure 9.13.). In the four-dimensional case, the cross-sections are spherical.

Because changes cannot be transmitted at a speed greater than *c*, the event O can be a cause (through the transmission of effects) only for events in region A. Likewise, only events in region C can be causes, by way of transmitted effects, at the event O. Consequently, region A is called the causal *future* of event O, and region C the causal *past* of O. No event in the regions labelled B can be efficient causes or effects of event O, because the spatial separation is greater than the temporal interval. No worldline of a signal can connect O with an event in region B—no transmissive, causal connection is possible. Region B has been termed *Elsewhere,* for some observers will suppose an event in B to come before O, while others will observe it to occur after O, as we noted in the discussion of relative simultaneity. It is only events in this Elsewhere region that observers with different states of motion at O would place in different temporal orderings (and the scaling factor *c* of the time-axis exaggerates the size of the Elsewhere region).

The Present or Now, a spatial cross-section of simultaneity, is no longer well-defined—observers employ different cross-sections of simultaneity, depending on their states of motion. The relative Nows are of little importance on their own in the causal structure of spacetime, for they have become part of a greater region of spacetime, the Elsewhere region. They are, however, useful for explaining the connection between relativistic effects, such as time dilation and Lorentz contraction, and the way observers conceptually slice spacetime into cross-sections of simultaneity to measure spatial separations and time intervals. In contrast, each universal Now (a world-wide instant) of classical science was of great importance, taken to be a physical reality, being one, absolute temporal state of the universe, determining the subsequent universal state and determined by the previous universal state. In relativistic physics, the simple, layered causal structure of Nows has been replaced by causal structures of intersecting 'light-cones'. The idea of the Now is best restricted to the centre of each diagram, the Here-Now coincidence of events at the origin, with the rest of the cross-section of simultaneity included in the Elsewhere region, neither causal Past, causal Future, nor Here-Now.

We can now understand more clearly the feature of relativistic spacetime that fuelled the debate on the reality of Becoming, noted in Chapter Six. There are no universal Nows, no Nows that are absolute for all observers. Instead there are relative Nows, relative cross-sections of simultaneity. If we have regarded the flow of time as a succession of absolute Nows, one causal state of the universe giving rise to and replaced by the next, then the abolition of absolute simultaneity may be interpreted as a sign that the physical world is not in flux. Kurt Gödel outlined the argument:

> Change becomes possible only through the lapse of time. The existence of an objective lapse of time, however, means (or, at least, is equivalent to the fact) that reality consists of an infinity of layers of "now" which come into existence successively. But, if simultaneity is something relative in the sense just explained, reality cannot be split up into such layers in an objectively determined way. Each observer has his own set of "nows", and none of these various systems of layers can claim the prerogative of representing the objective lapse of time.[12]

Gödel took this as support for the views of Parmenides, Kant and other "idealists": flux is not an objective fact, but "an illusion or an appearance due to our special mode of perception".[13] Milic Capek's response, we have seen, was to argue that Becoming is not to be associated with the passage of universal Nows, an idea that he considered a relic from classical conceptions of the world.

10. THE PHYSICS OF THE LARGE

Following the success of the special theory, Einstein proceeded to work on a theory capable of accommodating gravitational phenomena. In the present chapter, we shall look at this *general* theory, and our chief concern will be the notion of *curved* spacetime and its interpretation—is curvature simply a mathematical device or an actual curvature of substratal spacetime? Indeed, we shall have to consider the actuality of spacetime itself, with or without curvature, for the Minkowski absolute spacetime world is not easily reconciled with the idea of an experiential substratum of objects that partly *resemble* the objects of our sense-experiences.

THE GENERAL THEORY OF RELATIVITY

In Einstein's general theory of relativity, the relativistic treatment was broadened to cover the *gravitational attraction* between bodies, a phenomenon which the special theory had not taken into account. The first step towards the general theory is the recognition that accelerations attributable to gravitational forces in one frame can be attributed to inertial forces in another. We touched on this equivalence in Chapter Eight when considering Mach's Principle and the proportionality between gravitational and inertial masses. Einstein's *postulate of equivalence* maintained that gravitational and inertial forces are of the same nature. To illustrate the equivalence we can use the example of the lift or vessel that falls freely towards the earth. An observer in the vessel floats freely as the vessel drops towards the earth—see Figure 10.1.(a).

There is no relative acceleration towards the floor of the vessel, no weight, and the observer in the lift can imagine that gravitational force is absent. The observer might imagine that the vessel is in some distant region of space, far removed from the gravitational field of a star or planet, and is therefore an inertial frame, free from external forces—Figure 10.1.(b). To an observer on the earth, the vessel and the occupant fall towards the earth with the same gravitational acceleration in the earth's field, which accounts for the lack of relative acceleration observed within the vessel. The lack of a relative acceleration between the vessel and its contents is attributed in classical physics to the co-incidental proportionality between gravitational mass and inertial mass: objects experience the same gravitational acceleration, whatever their inertial mass. When a relative acceleration *is* encountered, the proportionality means that the acceleration can be attributed to the action of either gravitational or inertial forces.

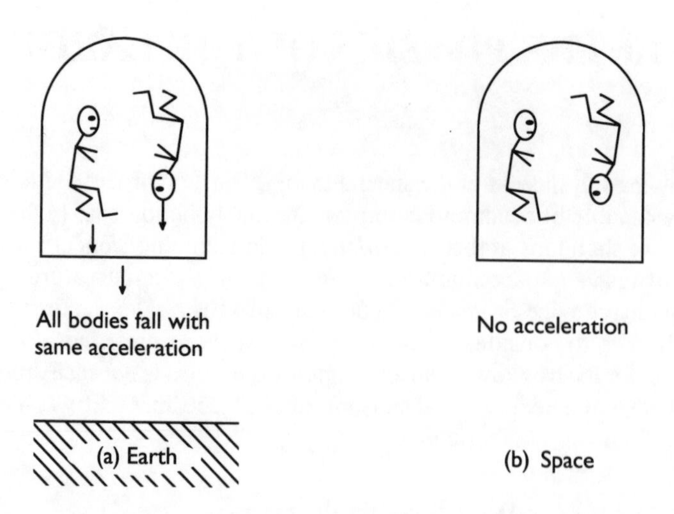

Figure 10.1. Free-floating contents in a vessel. Two possible interpretations by the observer: (a) free-fall in earth's gravitational field; (b) vessel floating in space, far from strong gravitational fields.

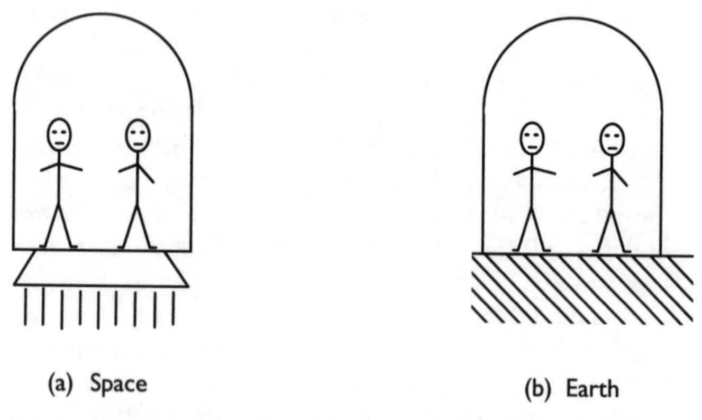

Figure 10.2. Accelerative effects within a vessel. Two possible interpretations by the observer: (a) vessel is accelerated by rockets; (b) vessel is at rest in a gravitational field.

Consider an observer inside a vessel far from any large concentrations of matter. The vessel is accelerated by rockets and the observer notices some accelerative effects, such as a push against the floor or an accelerometer reading. The observer can attribute these effects to inertial forces created by the rocket thrust, which disturb the observer's *uniform* rectilinear inertial motion—see Figure 10.2.(a). Alternatively, the observer could imagine that the vessel is standing at rest on a planet and that the push against the floor is a gravitational force, a weight.[1] In classical physics, the similarity between inertial forces and gravitational forces is attributed to the co-incidental equivalence of inertial and gravitational masses. However, according to Einstein, there is only one kind of mass, and gravitation has the status of an inertial force, that is, a relative force arising from the relative, accelerated motion of the observer's frame.

Now, we have said that the observer in free-fall towards the earth does not observe any accelerative effects and can suppose that no accelerating gravitational field is present. This is not quite true: a subtle accelerative effect can be detected with sensitive measuring instruments.

Contents in the vessel undergo a small acceleration towards one another in one direction, and a small separating acceleration in a direction at right angles to the first. The observer on earth attributes this effect to the non-uniformity of the earth's gravitational field over the volume of the lift. The earth's field is radial, attracting matter towards the centre of the earth, and particles are drawn together as they move radially towards the centre. In addition, the strength of the earth's gravitational field falls off with the distance from the earth, and a particle further from the earth has a smaller acceleration than one closer to the earth. These relative accelerations in the vessel, attributable to non-uniform

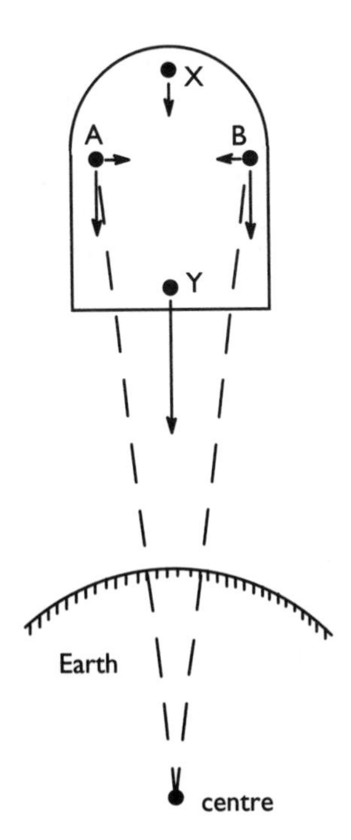

Figure 10.3. Relative accelerations between particles in the free-fall vessel, owing to a non-uniform gravitational field. A and B move together, and X and Y separate (Y is subject to a greater pull, being closer to the earth).

gravitational fields, are called *tidal effects*, after the water tides on the earth's surface.

The pre-Einsteinian observer detects these relative accelerations in the vessel and decides that a non-uniform gravitational field must be present (alternative (a) in Figure 10.1.). If the vessel were vanishingly small, there would be no field variation across it and we could treat it as a true inertial frame, free from gravitational forces. The gravitational field can be made to disappear locally, in a very small region in which tidal effects are negligible, by a judicious choice of moving frame.

The next step towards understanding the general theory of relativity is to remember that an acceleration is represented in a time-distance graph or spacetime diagram by a *curved* line. In contrast, a straight line represents a motion with constant velocity. We can represent the motions of two particles with a relative acceleration by using two real-time diagrams (Figure 10.4.). In the reference frame of one particle F, the other particle is represented as a curved worldline W_G, and vice versa.

By shifting the frame of reference (kinematical relativity), the accelerated motion can be turned into a uniform rectilinear motion or a state of rest: the curved line becomes a straight line. Similarly, gravitational accelerations (excluding the tidal effects) can be interpreted as relative inertial accelerations, showing as curved lines which can be straightened by a suitable choice of reference frame. However, the gravitational tidal effects cannot be eliminated in this way, but require the introduction of an *additional* curvature.

Einstein's great insight in the general theory of relativity was to suppose that the tidal, relative accelerations between particles in non-uniform gravitational fields can be treated in the spacetime representation as an *extra* curvature of the worldlines, in fact, as a curvature of spacetime itself. Instead of the flat

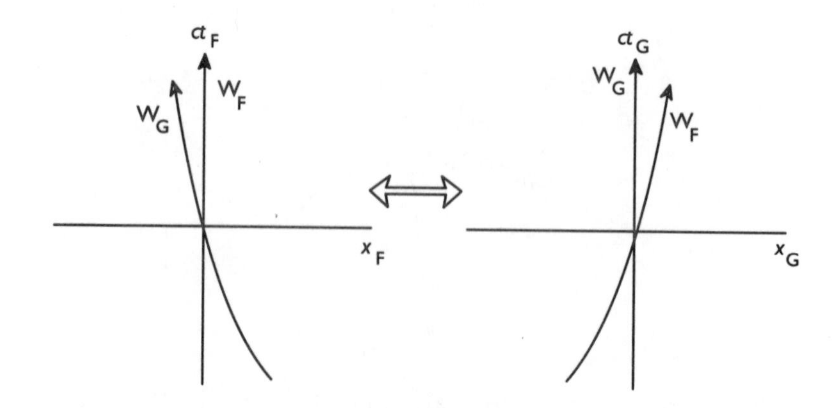

Figure 10.4. Accelerations as curved worldlines in spacetime.

spacetime of special relativity, we have a curved spacetime, and the degree of curvature of a spacetime region is determined by the distribution of matter and radiation in the region. The curvature of spacetime replaces the non-uniform gravitational fields around concentrations of matter and radiation. In this way, gravitational acceleration and inertial acceleration become fully identified as the curvature of worldlines in curved spacetime.

Matter and space are thus more closely related in General Relativity than in the classical view or in the special theory of relativity. In the classical view, space was the receptacle of material objects and was implicitly connected with the inertial properties of matter.[2] But in General Relativity, matter and radiation have the role of determining the curvature of space, which in turn is responsible for the local relative accelerations that were previously attributed to the action of a gravitational force between material bodies. Kinematic qualities, dynamics, and the gravitational force introduced by Newton, all reduce to the curved spacetime geometry in the presence of matter and radiation. Gravitational force acting in three-dimensional space is replaced by the local curvature of four-dimensional spacetime, a curvature that is dependent on the matter-radiation distribution. In an address in 1920, Einstein made the point that the idea of an *absolute* aether was discarded in relativistic theory, but a non-material aether of sorts lives on. This is the spacetime of general relativity, which "is itself devoid of *all* mechanical and kinematical qualities, but helps to determine mechanical (and electromagnetic) events."[3] The curvature of the 'spacetime aether' of general relativity is determined by the presence of matter and radiation, and in turn lies behind the effects we have called gravitational. Whereas Newton's absolute space was *implicitly* involved in the inertial behaviour of matter, Einstein's aether, a modern *lapis aethereus,*[4] has an *explicit* role in the inertial/gravitational accelerations of bodies.

In Einstein's theory, matter and spacetime remain distinct entities, reflecting a dichotomy between electromagnetism and gravitation, "two realities which are completely separated from each other conceptually",[5] but which are nonetheless causally connected. Einstein looked forward to the combination of the two in a unified physics, an enterprise that has gained momentum in recent years with promises of a complete unification of forces in curved spacetime theories. Some interpreters, notably Arthur Stanley Eddington (1882–1944), took the intimate connection between matter and space in the general theory as an indication that matter itself is essentially spacetime curvature, a "disturbance in the gravitational field" rather than the cause of the disturbance.[6] Instead of postulating two distinct but causally-connected substances, space and matter, why not regard matter-radiation as spacetime curvatures or singularities in space? The unification is comparable with the nineteenth-century idea of matter consisting of the aether *arche,* with its vortices or squirt-atoms, but now the primal substance has become spacetime. Eddington pointed out[7] that the idea was anticipated by W. K. Clifford, who had suggested that matter in motion consists of a propagating curvature of space, and that matter and motion are therefore reducible to extension. Although the general theory of relativity constitutes a step forward in the ancient program of geometrification, with its interpretation of gravitational forces as geometrical curvature, the full geometrification of nature must wait until matter has been absorbed into geometry. There is the promise that all the forces of nature will eventually be unified in a geometric theory, a possibility that we shall have cause to note in Chapter Thirteen. A full geometrification would not, of course, constitute a complete understanding of nature, as our discussion of experience and the mind-body problem has highlighted: kinematics and dynamics may be absorbed into geometry, but the astructural qualities are not reducible to geometry. In our experiential approach, the geometry mapped out by physics is only the structural framework of the experiential substratum, the skeleton of experience.

CURVED SPACETIME

It is difficult to grasp what *curvature* of space or spacetime means. We tend to think of space as an emptiness, as an absence of objects, a void, and it is not immediately obvious how an absence or a nothingness can be curved. In our familiar experiences, curvature is ascribed to an object of sense-perception, and refers to the shape of the whole object or a specific part. A circle, for instance, is said to be curved, and the curvature of a circle decreases as the radius increases. When there is no curvature, a line is said to be *straight,* and a surface without curvature is called *flat.* The idea that space might be curved arose in the nineteenth century, when mathematicians began to consider alternatives to flat, Euclidean geometry. The parallel postulate[8] of Euclidean geometry had long been under suspicion, and attempts to prove the postulate had all failed. By discarding the parallel postulate, Janos Bolyai (1802–60) arrived at a non-Euclidean geometry in the 1820s and the German mathematician Carl Friedrich Gauss (1777–1855) also made inroads into the subject, but was reticent to publish his novel ideas. The other major figure involved in the birth of non-Euclidean geometry was the Russian mathematician Nikolai Lobachevsky (1792–1856).

Of particular relevance to general relativity is the geometry of *curved surfaces.* Gauss, and then G. F. B. Riemann (1826–66), provided the mathematical treatment that Einstein was to apply in the general theory.[9] It was Riemann's suggestion that geometry can be extended into curved, non-Euclidean, higher-dimensional spaces that made possible the development of general relativity. Since the advent of general relativity and the discovery of experimental support for the theory, many physicists have supposed that space is non-Euclidean, but experiments so far have not been sufficiently accurate to detect any departures from flatness. Over small distances, relative to separations at the cosmic scale, it is fair to approximate space as flat.

Gauss studied the geometry of surfaces and was surprised to discover that curvature is an internal or *intrinsic* property of a surface. He termed this the *theorema egregrium,* the 'extraordinary theorem'. An intrinsic property is one that is confined to the surface and needs no reference to the space outside the surface. All measurements of the property take place within the surface. Thus, a measurement of the distance between points on the Earth's surface with a tape measure yields intrinsic data, but the measurement of the curvature of the Earth's shadow on the moon during a lunar eclipse would be extrinsic because reference has been made to something outside the surface of the Earth. Gauss discovered that the curvature of a surface, and its geometry in general, can be determined from measurements taken solely within the surface.

For instance, on a flat surface (zero curvature) the sum of the angles of a triangle is 180 degrees, but the sum for a triangle on the surface of a sphere is always greater than 180 degrees. The surface of a sphere is an example of *positive* curvature. In surfaces that have negative curvature, such as the saddle depicted in Figure 10.5., the sum of the triangle's angles is less than 180 degrees. The measurement of angles therefore provides a means of working out a surface's geometry. In a flat space, light rays that set out parallel, remain so, whilst in a positively-curved space they converge and in a negatively-curved space they diverge.

Riemann extended Gauss's treatment of two-dimensional surfaces to three- and higher dimensional surfaces, and showed that zero-curvature Euclidean geometry and the negative-curvature, non-Euclidean geometry of Bolyai, Lobachevsky and Gauss were special instances of a more general geometrical theory, which also encompasses a positive curvature geometry.

The idea of curved, three-dimensional space is an extension of the observation that two-dimensional surfaces can be curved in three-dimensional space. The mathematical treatment of curved, three-dimensional space or four-dimensional spacetime is an extrapolation of the familiar geometry of 2-D

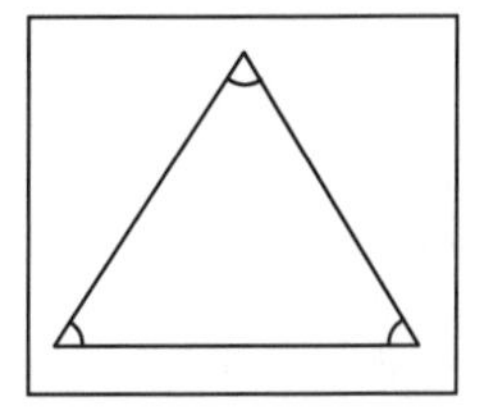

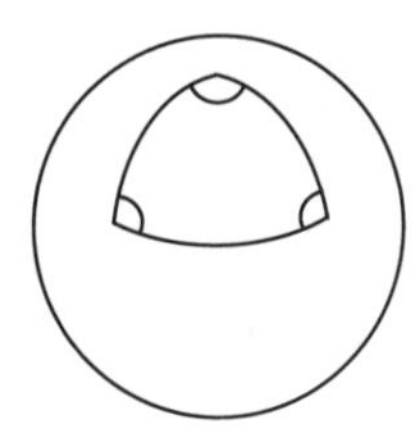

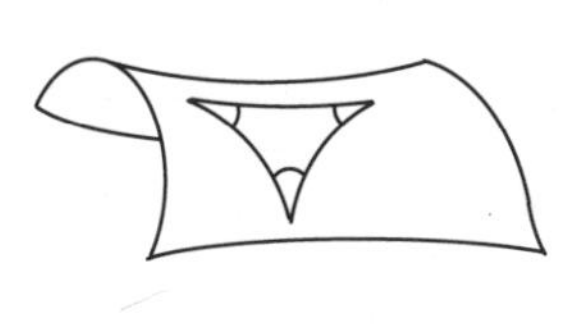

Figure 10.5. Triangles in the surfaces of a plane, sphere and saddle—flat, positive, negative curvature respectively.

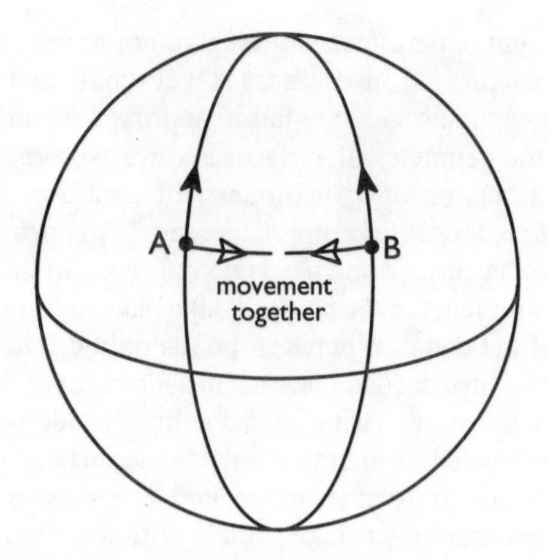

Figure 10.6. Travellers A and B on the earth's surface discover they are moving together.

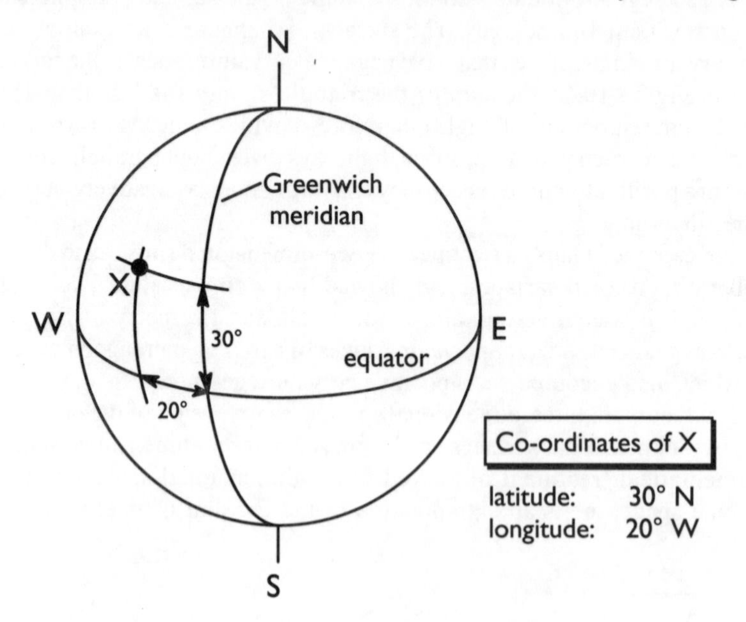

Figure 10.7. Latitude and longitude.

surfaces into higher dimensions. The curvature of two-dimensional surfaces is often used in introductory discussions of general relativity to illustrate, by analogy, the curvature of spacetime. The analogy of the sphere and its surface is widely used in this context. For instance, unaware that the Earth is approximately spherical, two travellers may set off along parallel paths on the surface of the Earth, only to discover that they move closer and closer together and eventually meet (Figure 10.6). This can be understood if the surface of the Earth is curved. Parallel lines on a positively-curved surface meet. In the analogy, the two travellers argue that a tidal force has pulled them together across the flat earth, just as physicists supposed that a gravitational force was responsible for tidal effects. Now if the travellers measure the intrinsic geometry of the terrain they will find that it is curved and that the force of attraction they have posited is an expression of the curvature of the surface.[10]

The surface of a sphere is a two-dimensional space that encloses a three-dimensional space—any point on the surface can be described with just two co-ordinates. For the earth, these co-ordinates are the terrestrial latitude and longitude, angular distances measured from the great circles of the equator and Greenwich meridian respectively (Figure 10.7.).

When the curvature of three-dimensional space is considered, the analogy with the three-dimensional (3-D) sphere and its two-dimensional (2-D) surface is often employed. The geometry is of the positive-curvature type described by Riemann. We are invited to conceive of a three-dimensional space that is the *surface* of a four-dimensional sphere, a 4-D hypersphere. We cannot imagine the four-dimensional sphere directly, but the analogy provides a way of thinking about curved space. The familiar two-dimensional surface of a three-dimensional sphere is called a *two-sphere,* a two-dimensional surface embedded in a three-dimensional, Euclidean space. By analogy, a four-dimensional hypersphere has a three-dimensional surface called a *three-sphere.* The three-sphere has three-dimensions, three co-ordinates defining the position of a point on the surface. The three-sphere is embedded in a four-dimensional, 'flat' (not curved) space. Table 10.1. summarises the two- and three-spheres and also shows the *one-sphere,* which is simply the boundary line of a circle.

	1-sphere, S^1	2-sphere, S^2	3-sphere, S^3
Dimensions of the flat Euclidean space that embeds the ... -sphere.	two (a 2-space)	three (a 3-space)	four (a 4-space)
The ... -sphere is the surface of a ...	circle	sphere	4-D hypersphere

Table 10.1. Surfaces of spheres in two-, three- and four-dimensional spaces.

If the geometry of the universe is described in terms of higher-dimensional surfaces, we may wonder whether any reality is to be ascribed to the embedding dimension of the surfaces. If, for instance, we were to treat space as the three-dimensional surface (three-sphere) of a four-dimensional hypersphere, would we suppose that there is an actual, extra dimension in the physical world that embeds the curvature of the surface, or is the fourth spatial dimension of the hypersphere simply a mathematical device with no physical reality? In general relativity, is the curvature of spacetime to be regarded as an actual curvature of substratal spacetime, in an extra dimension, or is the curvature to be interpreted instrumentally as a purely mathematical curvature, with no physical significance but useful for constructing a theory that makes accurate predictions?

To illustrate these alternatives, consider the analogy of the Earth's curvature. In charting the Earth's surface, a cartographer might construct a three-dimensional globe, a sphere on which the features of the Earth's surface are shown to scale. The distances measured between points on the globe are directly proportional to the corresponding distances over the Earth's surface. The cartographer might also construct two-dimensional charts of the Earth's surface. But the representation of the Earth's curved surface on the flat surface of a map entails some distortion. Depending on the method of projection, shapes of surface-features, directions and areas will be distorted. For instance, the common Mercator's projection greatly exaggerates the size of areas near the poles, stretching the areas in an east-west direction.

The globe map has an extra dimension compared with the chart map, for the two-dimensional surface of the globe is embedded or 'immersed' in a three-dimensional space—it is the surface of a sphere. The embedding dimension of the globe corresponds to a physical reality: the Earth's surface is really the surface of a three-dimensional spheroid. The globe represents the earth fairly accurately, whilst the flat maps are convenient but flawed two-dimensional representations of a three-dimensional actuality. We can, however, construct the three-dimensional globe from the distorted map representations if we know the method of projection.[11]

In the case of the Earth, we can move below and above the surface, into the embedding third dimension, making extrinsic as well as intrinsic measurements. However, in the case of the 3-sphere surface of a 4-D hypersphere, there is no possibility of movement out of the three-dimensional surface. All measurements are intrinsic, taken within the three-dimensional surface. And just as we can construct flat maps of the earth, projecting the three-dimensional curvature onto two-dimensional, flat surfaces, so we can disregard the embedding fourth dimension of the three-sphere and concern ourselves with only the intrinsic geometry of the three-sphere. The phrase *curvature of space* is not meant to imply that three-dimensional space is actually embedded in a real, existing higher-dimensional space that can accommodate curvature. The embedding dimension of space or spacetime curvature in General Relativity is not usually taken to be a physical actuality, although popular expositions sometimes give the impression that it is an actually existing space dimension. In contrast, textbooks on general relativity may warn the reader that curvature in an embedding dimension is not be interpreted as an actual curvature in a real, extra dimension. The dimension is "fictitious"[12] or "superfluous"[13] and "we must resist any temptation"[14] to think of the curvature of worldlines associated with tidal, relative accelerations as actually immersed in an extra spatial dimension. It is "regrettable" and "unfortunate" that the mathematicians' curvature terminology has been used in discussions of the general theory, for "the property of being non-Euclidean is an intrinsic property which has nothing to do with immersion"[15] in a higher-dimensional space.

The practical physicist can quite happily get on with the business of general relativity without reference to the embedding dimension because the surface geometry is intrinsic. The positivist rejects talk of an actual, four-dimensional spacetime, never mind actual curvatures in an extra, fifth spatial dimension: the theory is a mathematical means of linking sense-perceptions, and mathematical curvature discussed in the theory is not to be confused with the curvature we meet in our perceptions. The realist, however, is not able to dismiss the matter so easily.

Perhaps the idea of a truly-existing embedding dimension for curved spacetime is not a total fantasy or a mathematical expedient. For the moment, however, the interpretation of spacetime and curved spacetime remains uncertain. If we do take a physical realist attitude to spacetime curvature, the substratum may be viewed as five-dimensional, (3+1+1)D: three space dimensions, one spatialized time dimension, and one embedding dimension for the curvature of the other dimensions. For the experientialist, the curvature may be considered a curvature of luminous, spacetime structures, a characteristic similar to the spatial curvature we encounter in our sense-perceptions, but extending into higher dimensions.

THE SHAPE OF THE COSMOS

Of greater interest to the physicist is another uncertainty: the nature of the overall intrinsic geometry of the universe. General relativity, as a theory of gravitation, finds application in cosmology, the study of the large-scale structure of the universe. Soon after Einstein published his theory of General Relativity in 1915, a number of spacetime models of the universe were constructed. A curved spacetime was proposed by Einstein in 1917—the spatial cross-sections of the Einstein universe are three-spheres of constant diameter. With its constant diameter, the Einstein universe is static, not expanding or contracting, a feature that required the introduction of an extra term into Einstein's equations, the famous *cosmological constant.* The axis provides an overall time dimension for the universe, a cosmic time, and is not curved.

We cannot picture the Einstein universe itself, but a lower dimensional analogue can be depicted. Taking a universe with one space, one time and one embedding dimension, (1+1+1)D, we obtain a cylinder—the curvature of space wraps the two-dimensional spacetime round the time axis, and the spatial section consists of the circumference of a circle, a one-sphere.

Space in the Einstein universe is described as 'finite and unbounded', for space has been wrapped round onto itself to form the 3-D hypersurface (three-sphere) of a 4-D sphere, which is finite but has no boundaries in the surface. In this model, then, finiteness of space returned to cosmological theory, having been absent since the fall of the spherical, Aristotelian universe. In theory, a traveller who sets off into space in one direction will return to the place of departure after circumnavigating the closed universe.

Einstein took the universe to be in static equilibrium, with no expansion or contraction. However, in 1922, A. A. Friedman (1888–1925) produced solutions to Einstein's cosmological equations that described a universe evolving with time, and in 1929 Edwin Hubble (1889–1953) presented observational

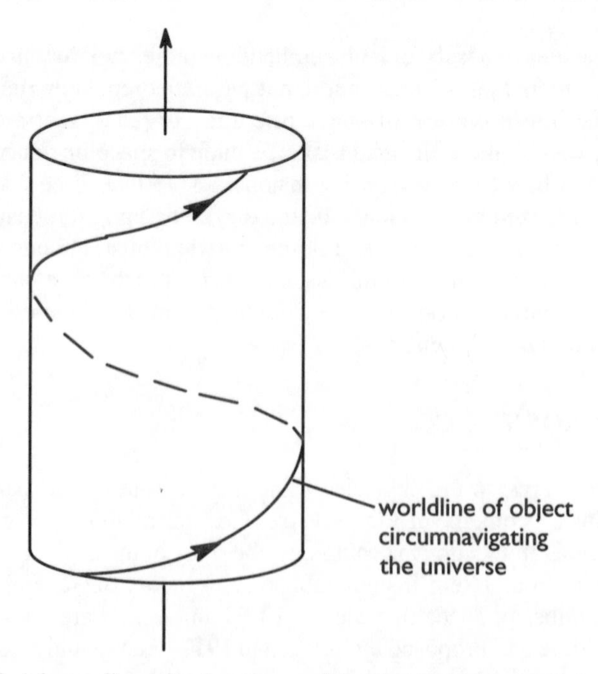

Figure 10.8. A lower dimensional analogue of the Einstein universe, (1+1+1)D. Circumnavigations of space show as a spiraling worldline.

evidence that the universe is actually expanding. Hubble studied the recession of groups of galaxies away from our local group, a motion that is deduced from the measurements of redshifts of light radiation emitted from stars in these groups. The redshift of light, analogous to the Doppler effect in acoustics,[16] is most commonly interpreted as an indicator of recession, of the universe expanding. Hubble deduced that groups of galaxies are moving away from one another with a speed of recession that is proportional to the distance that separates them. Hubble's Law embodies this relationship:

$$v = \mathrm{H}\,D$$

where v is the velocity of recession;
D is the distance between groups;
H is the Hubble constant, a constant of proportionality estimated to be about $1/(1.8 \times 10^{10}\,\text{years})$

The expansion of the universe is sometimes compared with the inflation of a balloon. Imagine little buttons attached to the surface of a balloon, each button representing a group of galaxies. As the balloon inflates, the distance between the buttons increases. The greater the distance between the buttons, the greater is the speed at which they recede from one another. The buttons themselves do not expand, only the rubber surface that separates them. Similarly, there is no increase in separation between galaxies within a group. The expansion only applies at the cosmic scale of distances, between groups and larger distances.[17] The recession of groups of galaxies is not a movement *through* space, but an *expansion* of space between the groups, just as the button-separations on the balloon increase through a swelling of the rubber and not a movement of the buttons across the rubber. We normally think of expansions taking place from a centre. In the case of the balloon, we can take each button to be an intrinsic centre (within the surface of the balloon) from which all the other buttons recede, or we could move out of the surface and consider the centre of the balloon as the single, extrinsic centre. Likewise, in the cosmic expansion, each galactic cluster can be regarded as the centre of expansion, and no place within the expanding space has the special privilege of being the sole location from which the expansion started. And because the embedding dimension of the curved space is not considered, the extrinsic centre in the embedding space is not regarded as a centre of expansion. Such a centre would be outside our familiar three-dimensional space. It is currently estimated that the expansion would have begun about fifteen billion (15,000,000,000) years ago. Physicists have attempted to trace the physical history of the universe back to within a fraction of a second after the starting-event, the Big Bang.

When considered in terms of spacetime, the cosmic expansion corresponds to a space that expands along the time dimension. If we introduce expansion to the static Einstein universe, the radii of the 3-spheres are no longer constant, but increase along the time axis. The radius increases in diameter from a point or a minimum radius, corresponding to the Big Bang. Because gravitation has a decelerating effect on the expansion, a curving-in of spacetime would be expected, and the Friedman solutions provide a number of idealised spacetime curvatures that correspond to the global deceleration. The derivation of the solutions is based on assumption that matter, at the very large-scale of the cosmos, is distributed uniformly throughout the universe *(homogeneity)* and that an observer finds the universe to be similar in all directions *(isotropy)*. Which of the solutions, if any, is appropriate to our universe depends on whether there is sufficient matter and radiation in the universe to curve spacetime into a closed geometry. Three basic possibilities are presented in the Friedman solutions for the expanding, homogeneous, isotropic universe:

1. The *open* universe: there is insufficient matter and radiation to close the universe, which keeps expanding forever. The open Friedman universe has spatial cross-sections of negative curvature. These cross-sections consist of *3-pseudospheres,* also called *3-hyperboloids.* The pseudosphere is the negative-curvature equivalent of the positive-curvature sphere, both having constant curvature. The pseudosphere belongs to the hyperbolic, non-Euclidean geometry of Gauss, Bolyai and Lobachevsky, and was deduced by E. Beltrami (1835–1900).

2. The *closed* universe: the matter and radiation density is sufficiently great to close the universe. The expansion slows down, stops and is followed by a contraction, with a 'Big Crunch' marking the final stage. The spacetime curvature is *closed* spatially and temporally. The spatial cross-sections of the closed spacetime have positive curvature and are 3-spheres, with increasing and then decreasing radii. The geometry is of the non-Euclidean, elliptical type first considered by Riemann.

3. The *flat* or *critical* universe: the matter and radiation density is at a critical value. This is the intermediate solution, poised between the open and closed universes. Expansion only just continues forever. The spatial cross-sections of the curved spacetime universe consist of flat 3-spaces (flat three-dimensional space). As a Euclidean space of constant zero-curvature, it is intermediate between the non-Euclidean hyperbolic and elliptical geometries of the open and closed universes.

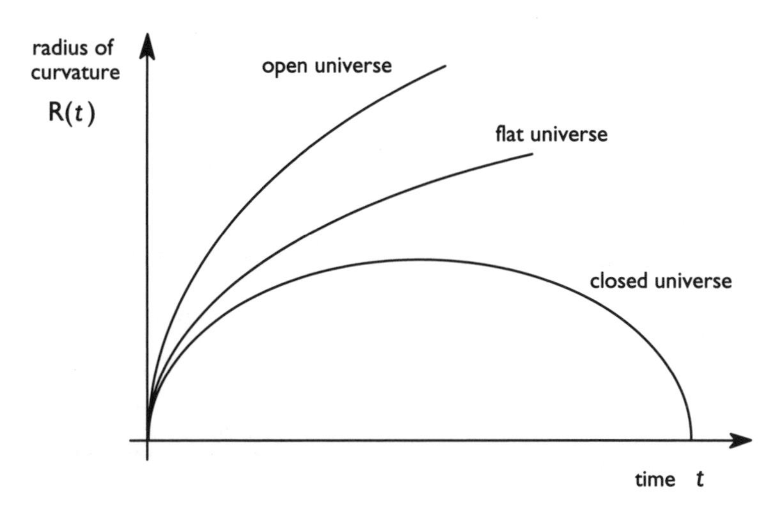

Figure 10.9. Variation of radius of curvature R(t) with time, for open, closed, and flat universes.

The three solutions can be illustrated in a graph that shows the change of the radius of curvature R of the universe as a function of time t (Figure 10.9.).

The closed spacetime solution can be depicted for the (1+1+1)D spacetime. Instead of the 2-D spacetime wrapped round a cylinder (Figure 10.8, the lower-dimensional analogue of the Einstein universe), the 2-D spacetime is wrapped onto the surface of a sphere (Figure 10.10.). The spatial cross-sections of the spacetime are closed one-dimensional spaces (circles or 1-spheres). Both space and time dimensions are closed—the universe is properly finite.

The time dimension of the closed universe can be made open by supposing that the expansion and contraction make up only one cycle in a series of many cycles, which may or may not begin with an initial cycle and end with a final cycle. A Big Bang follows the Big Crunch, and the universe is reborn. In the spacetime-view, the universe consists of the hypersurface of a sequence of hypersphere-like shapes. It is like a temporally-open cylinder universe pinched along the overall time dimension into a string of beads. This form of spacetime is called an *oscillating universe* (see Figures 10.11. and 10.12.).

One attraction of the infinitely oscillating universe is that each cycle may be given the role of cause for the following cycle—the Big Bang is not a mysterious starting-point of the spacetime geometry, but is merely a place of maximum contraction located between each phase of the spacetime universe's cyclic development. The physics that would describe the changeover between cycles is not well understood at the moment, for quantum effects would be important and a satisfactory combination of gravitational theory and quantum theory has yet to be achieved. The problem of the maximum contraction state,

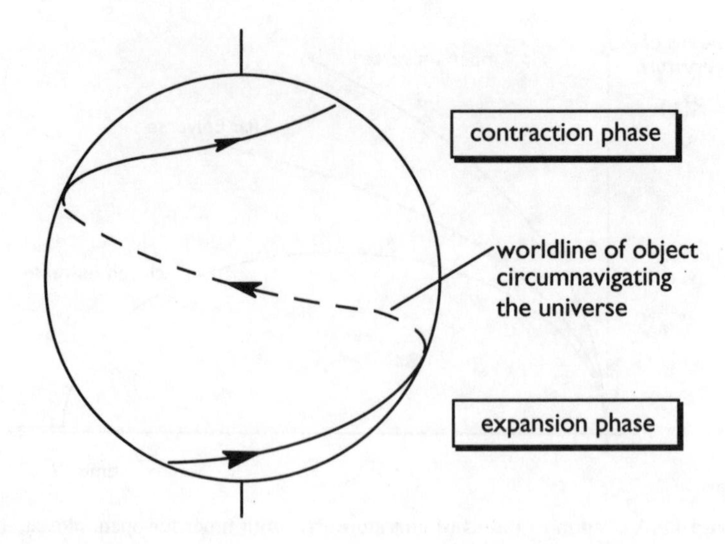

Figure 10.10. The closed (1+1+1)D spacetime, a lower-dimensional analogue of the closed universe (3+1+1)D. Circumnavigations of the space show as spiral loops with increasing, then decreasing, radii.

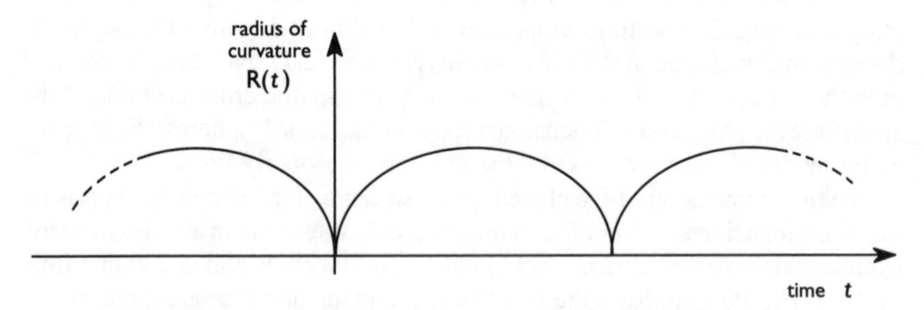

Figure 10.11. Variation of radius of curvature R(t) for the oscillating universe.

the *singularity,* which also appears in the physics of black holes, has puzzled physicists for some time—in general relativity, unmodified by quantum considerations, the contraction of the universe is unopposed, leading to an infinitely dense and curved singularity. The oscillating model would require some intervention in the gravitational collapse, enabling a re-expansion to occur. For one cycle to be the physical cause of the next, some structure would have to survive the minimum-radius neck between the cycles.

Expanding models of the universe have been popular in recent years, but it is not yet known whether there is sufficient matter and radiation in the universe to bring about a contraction. Recent speculation has focused on the idea of *dark matter,* unobserved forms of matter that could be present in sufficient quantities to close the universe. Alternatives to the expanding universe have been suggested, such as the steady-state model.

Traditional religious cosmologies provide different accounts of the spatio-temporal structure of the world. Some cosmologies suggest a single beginning and a single end to the universe, a creation and a destruction, such as the Zoroastrian and Christian accounts. Others describe a cyclic universe consisting of an infinite number of periods of existence, separated by creations and destructions. This is a common idea in Indian thought, each cosmic period or sub-period being termed a *kalpa.* It is also found in the cosmology of the Stoics, who supposed that the world comes to an end in a great fire *(ecpyrosis).* It is clearly unwise to draw any physical inferences from the religious or mythical cosmologies for they may embody ideas that do not derive from experiential insights into the structure of the substratum, but come from other sources or may be purely symbolic. For instance, the cyclic cosmologies may simply reflect an ancient concern with the periodicity of life, the cycles of growth and decay, death and rebirth, reflected in the cycles of the seasons, agriculture and human generations,[18] and may have no connection with the oscillating cosmologies of modern physical theory, other than through a vague analogy. Similarly, the widespread emphasis on the sphere, and the popularity of spherical cosmologies in pre-scientific thought, may simply reflect the appearance of the sky to a central observer, the celestial sphere. We shall have to wait for scientific developments to determine the geometry of spacetime.[19] This caution, however, is not meant to exclude unconventional sources of cosmological information. It is conceivable that the structure of the substratum is knowable

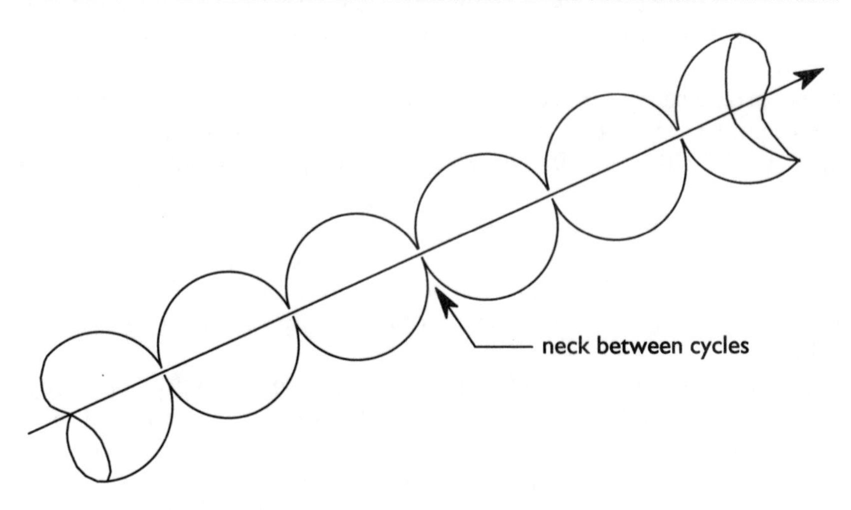

Figure 10.12. Lower dimensional analogue of the oscillating universe.

directly, although it might be difficult for experiencers to interpret what is experienced, unless they happen to be conversant with higher-dimensional geometry and are able to relate their experiences to mathematical forms of description.

THE STATUS OF ABSOLUTE SPACETIME

Spacetime diagrams provide helpful insights into the meaning of special relativity, and the idea of curved spacetime has far-reaching applications in the physics of gravity and cosmology. Yet the ontological status of spacetime is open to debate. Spacetime is a very useful concept, but does spacetime actually exist? If it is valid to ascribe spacetime an actual existence, how are we to conceive of this existence—as a physical or experiential structure underlying our perceptions, or as some kind of mathematical realm that regulates our perceptions?

In the discussion of the spacetime concept in Chapter Six, we noted that physicists and philosophers have disputed whether spatialized time is an actuality or is merely a convenient diagrammatic means of illustrating physics. In the latter view, relativistic spacetime is simply a tool for illustrating the mathematical relationships between frames of reference. It is pointed out that Minkowski spacetime is no true union of space and time—time cannot be regarded as a fourth space dimension, for a minus sign distinguishes time from space in the equation of the invariant interval. The absolute Minkowski world, in which the invariant interval between events applies to all frames of reference, is not a spacetime consisting of the familiar space dimensions and time dimension, but is one in which an imaginary time-axis (s) replaces the familiar time-axis (t) in order to dispose of the minus sign in the invariant interval equation (alternatively, three algebraically imaginary space-axes to replace the three familiar space-axes). It is common nowadays for this point to be emphasised, unlike in the early days of relativity when spacetime, squeezed into the mathematical form of Euclidean geometry, was received enthusiastically as an absolute world. The absolute Minkowski spacetime world is not the spacetime that has been represented in the real-time diagrams, which are diagrams for specific frames of reference and do not show invariant intervals between events directly. They are not pictures of Minkowski spacetime and its imaginary s-axis.

It is not surprising that we use the real-time diagrams to depict particular frames, and do not try to represent Minkowski spacetime directly. In absolute Minkowski spacetime, the length between worldpoints is the invariant interval, $\Delta\tau$, the square of which can be zero or negative, as well as positive, even though the space-separation and time-interval have actual, positive magnitudes. For instance, two worldpoints that have a very great space separation and time interval between them, will have an invariant interval of zero if the two points lie on the worldline of a light beam. The invariant interval will be the square root of a negative number if the space-separation is greater than the time-interval. In Minkowski spacetime, these two points have no separation in the first case, and are separated by an imaginary interval in the second case. We cannot usefully draw absolute Minkowski spacetime to depict events, with its imaginary s axis, real, zero and imaginary invariant intervals, but have to be content with the real-time diagrams that use the real t axis and do not depict the invariant interval directly.

It had been hoped that Minkowski spacetime would provide an absolute world underneath the relativity of length, duration and simultaneity for observers, but the structure of events in this absolute world turned out to be very peculiar. The Minkowski spacetime, with its invariant-interval separations between events, does not seem to provide us with the kind of substratum we would have expected from our survey of universal experiences, which suggested substratal objects that resemble the objects of our transient experience. Absolute Minkowski spacetime is not an attractive candidate for the role of substratum, and it is a complete mystery how it could be linked with our experiential fluxes. How are we to relate absolute Minkowski spacetime and its invariant-interval separations with the perceptual world of transient, spatial objects? In Chapter Six, we could make some headway in connecting transient experience with a spacetime having real time and real space dimensions. Absolute Minkowski spacetime is a different matter, with its strange organisation of events.

It is tempting to agree with the modern attitude to the Minkowski unification of space and time: absolute Minkowski spacetime is an expression of the mathematical relationships between the various space separations and time intervals measured from different reference frames, and the introduction of imaginary time ($s = ict$) is a mathematical expedient to make the spatialized time variable look like a Euclidean spatial variable in the equations. Absolute Minkowski spacetime expresses a mathematical relationship that connects the relative observations of frames in relative motion.

Let us summarise how the investigation of substratal spatio-temporal features has proceeded in Part II. In postulating a substratum for transient experience, we might have expected it to be described by definite, unique, non-arbitrary, invariant quantities. Some quantities are absolute for all observers, such as the number of legs possessed by a particular table. The causal relationships between events might also be expected to be absolute (invariant), the same for all observers. However, the quantities describing motion are notoriously relative. The classical response to the relativity of motion was a world of absolute motions in an absolute space or aether, a space that in theory was plausible but in practice was mysteriously elusive. The experimental successes of relativistic theory have suggested that the classical version of the absolute world was unsound. Instead, special relativity has given us a multiplicity of relative spaces of equal status, between which measured lengths and durations vary with the relative motion of the frames. This constitutes an additional relativity of geometric-kinematic qualities, on top of the relativity of spatial paths and velocities that we met in classical physics.

It is not, however, a relativity that is avoidable by taking one of the many relative frames to be the true, absolute frame, the frame of the physical world behind our relative sense-perceptions. This step has been abandoned in relativistic theory—the relative frames are *observationally* relative, not merely *perceptually* relative, and thus each has claims to physical actuality in a realist interpretation of physical theory. It is true that a relativistic absolute world can be constructed, namely Minkowski spacetime. This is not a special frame of the world, but an absolute substratum of events resolvable into the various relative frames of observers. However, absolute Minkowski spacetime, with its invariant intervals, is not a four-dimensional world in which events and objects are ordered in a manner comparable with the ordering in perceptual experiences and in universal mystical experiences.

What, then, has happened to the physical world of traditional scientific and representative realism, with its familiar geometric-kinematic qualities of lengths and durations? It was this underlying physical world that we infused with characteristics excluded by the conceptual parsimony of the early atomists and reductionists, such as the quality of luminosity and the experiences of feeling and knowing. The idea of an experiential substratum, which absorbs the structural world of physical science into a more generously furnished substratum, was put forward to bridge the mind-body divide, and intimations of its actuality could be found in some unusual experiential states. Must we now abandon the notion of an experiential substratum having a geometric structure of real space separations and real spatialized time intervals?

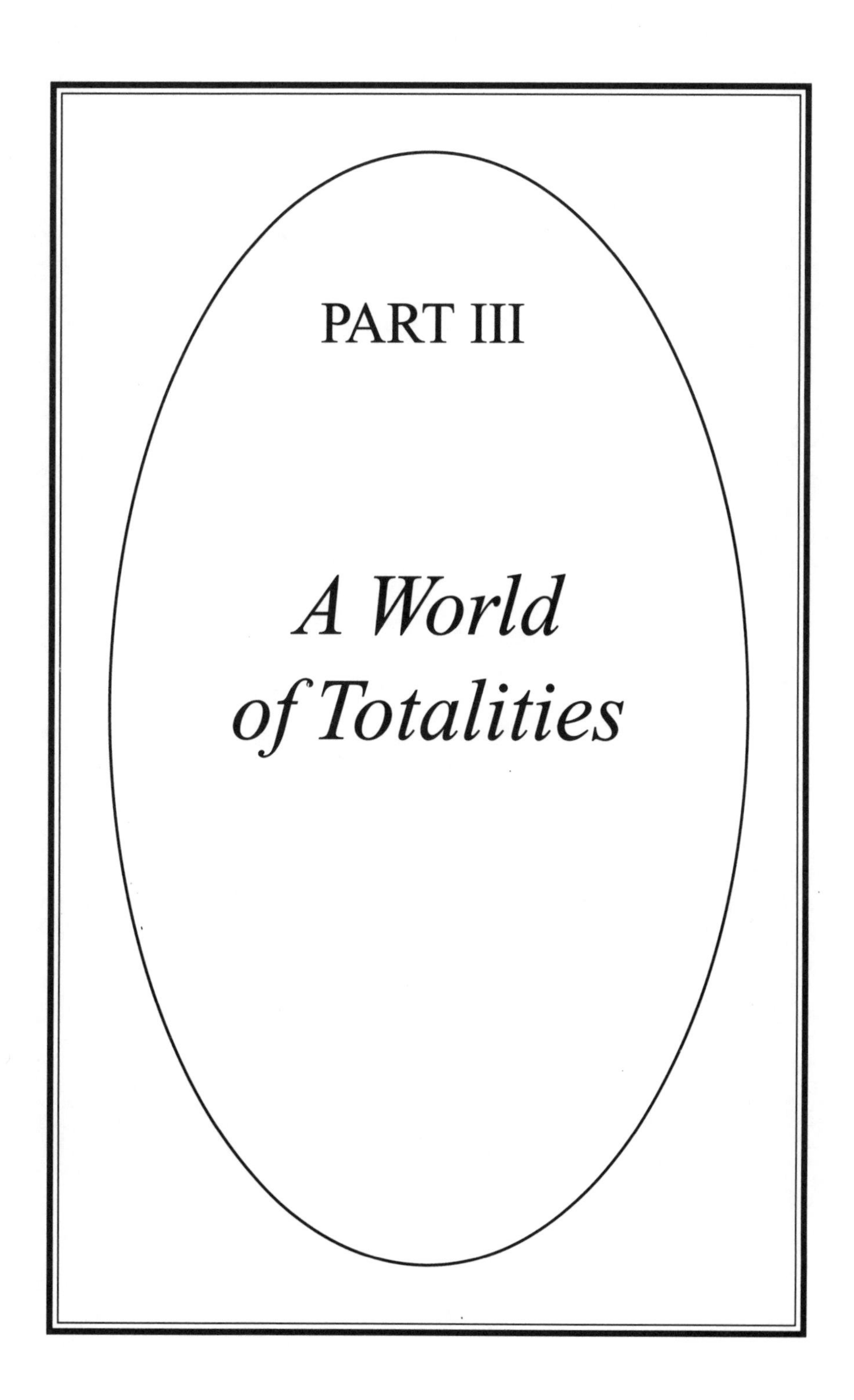

PART III

A World of Totalities

11. RELATIVE SPACETIME

We have seen that the Minkowski-type spacetime provides an absolute spacetime world: the 'distances' between events are the same for all observers. However, these 'distances'—the so-called invariant intervals—are not the familiar space separations and spatialized time intervals, but mathematically derived invariants that may involve imaginary numbers. We could leave the matter here, and give up any attempt to retain the familiar geometric structures and spatio-temporal relations of objects. Alternatively, we could retain the familiar structures and spatio-temporality, but abandon the idea of an *absolute* substratum, one that is exactly the same for all observers. This step would sever the conceptual knot with which we attempt to bind together our relative frames into a realist notion of a single whole. In order to preserve real spatial and temporal separations as fundamental characteristics of spacetime, we can explore the possibility that the substratum consists of *relative spacetimes,* different spacetimes for observers in relative motion. In so doing, we shall be considering seriously the passing association that is sometimes made between Einstein's special theory of relativity and the monadology of Leibniz.[1]

Leibniz, we have noted before, rejected Newton's absolute space and argued for a relational theory of space and time. In addition to this relationalism, and not unconnected with it, was Leibniz's unusual metaphysical system, a philosophy of monads. Leibniz maintained that there is no one, singular state of the world, but a plurality of complete perceptions of the universe from unique points-of-view. These perceptions are independent of one another and differ according to their perspective, but are harmonised with one another, each expressing the world from its particular point-of-view. At first sight, the monadology may strike one as a very odd system, but on reflection the idea can be seen to express a plurality that accords with the plurality of ordinary experiences. Furthermore, the monadological idea of 'perceptual' perspectives accords well with the experiential ontology we have followed here. In this chapter, we consider the idea of a substratum of relative spacetimes, and place it in the context of Leibniz's pre-relativistic monadology and some related historical notions.

SPACETIME PERSPECTIVES

The student of relativistic physics may be struck by a vague but suggestive affinity between Einstein's special theory and the monadology of Leibniz. The invariance of the velocity of light for observers, whatever their states of motion, is a perplexing idea, and is all the more curious because experiments suggest that it is true. Furthermore, it follows that there are different spatial separations and temporal intervals between the same events for observers in relative motion. Now, in Leibniz's monadology there are multiple versions of the world that differ in perspective, and these differing monadic perspectives may serve as an analogy for the different spatio-temporal observations made by relativistic observers. The idea has been expressed by Aloys Wenzl:

> One could say, that the observers of various moving systems are like Leibniz's monads and that Leibniz's idea of a pre-established harmony finds an analogy in the theory of relativity: Just as the world is mirrored differently in each monad and yet the sights of all monads are related to each other and translatable into each other, so also does the "absolute" four-dimensional world-continuum appear in different values of spatial and temporal measurements to every observer imprisoned (as he is) in his own system, yet all sights are transformable into each other.[2]

Let us consider how we can turn the analogy into a realist interpretation of relativistic theory and spacetime. A way forward is suggested by the manner in which a spacetime depiction of events is shown diagrammatically, not as an absolute Minkowski spacetime diagram with an imaginary time-axis, but as a number of real-time diagrams into which the Minkowski spacetime resolves for each observer in relative motion. Each real-time diagram has one algebraically real time axis and three algebraically real space axes, and shows real spatial, temporal and spacetime separations between events. A diagram is required for each observer in relative motion, for the space and time separations between events are different for each observer. Thus, instead of one diagram that is suitable for all observers, there are many diagrams, each of which shows the same events and causal relationships, and the same velocity of light, but also different spatial and temporal separations between events.

The next step is to suppose that the plurality of spacetime diagrams represents the actual composition of the substratum: drop the idea of a single, experiential spacetime substratum, and suppose that there are many experiential spacetime substrata, each containing the same events but with different space separations and time intervals between the events. We no longer suppose that there is a single, absolute experiential spacetime, but a multiplicity of *relative spacetimes* that provide a substratum for our diverse, partial experiences and our different substratal observations. This move is analogous to the shift in the space-concept described by Einstein,[3] namely the multiplication of spaces from one absolute space to a plurality of relative spaces, or from one absolute aether to a plurality of relative aethers. The great tapestry becomes many great tapestries, all exhibiting the same events. We replace one absolute spacetime (invariant-interval separations) by a multiplicity of relative spacetimes (real space separations and real time intervals). All these spacetimes are structurally identical to one another, apart from their different accounts of relative motion, including different separations between the constituent worldpoints. They have identical events with identical causal relations, but different space, time and spacetime intervals. Mathematical transformations link the different space and time separations found in the relative spacetimes—the Lorentz transformations apply in the flat spacetime of special relativity.

Because each relative spacetime is one complete version of the universe in its entire spatio-temporal extent, it may be appropriate to call it a *Totality*. The substratum consists of whole parts, relative spacetimes that are total experiences. The description 'total' needs qualification: each relative spacetime is a Totality in the sense that each is a whole spatio-temporal cosmos, but each is not the total substratum, which includes all the Totalities.

How many spacetime Totalities would exist in the substratum? The problem of relative motion led us to the idea of relative spacetimes. Relative motions between bodies appear in spacetime as geometrical relationships between worldlines, the sequences of worldpoints of the bodies. It is tempting, then, to suppose that there is one Totality, one unique version of spacetime, for each worldpoint state of a particle in motion—there are as many Totalities as there are worldpoints. Each worldpoint would be associated with the origin or centre of one Totality, and would be found off-centre in all the other Totalities. This may be a fair assumption for the curved-spacetime universes of General Relativity, in which inertial frames apply only locally. In this case, the number

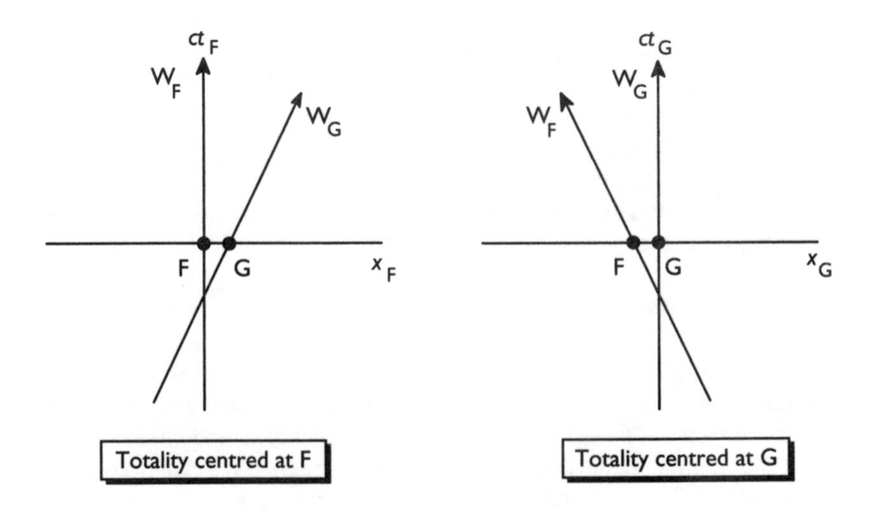

Figure 11.1. Each real-time diagram corresponds to a distinct spacetime Totality. Here the *flat* spacetimes of special relativity are represented, but the actual Totalities would presumably have the *curved* spacetime structures discussed in the general theory of relativity.

of Totalities in the underlying basis would be equal to the number of world-points in any one Totality, and the number could be infinite if spacetime is spatially or temporally open.

Each worldline in one spacetime Totality consists of a sequence of world-points and therefore corresponds to a group of Totalities in the substratum. It may be useful to refer to such groups of Totalities as *worldline-groups.* In the case of composite objects, whose states are made up of particles from a number of worldlines, several worldline-groups of Totalities would be involved.

Interpreting the Totalities in the experientialist framework, we can say that the basis that underlies all our transient experiences consists of a plurality of luminous, spacetime experiences, which are identical to one another except for the special, experiential vantage-point from the centre and the depiction of relative motions, including the magnitudes of worldpoint separations in the geometric spacetime structure. The worldpoint therefore takes on a special meaning: it corresponds to a centre round which a total, substratal experience is organised. It is a *centre-of-experience.* If worldpoints are taken to be states of particles that build up the structural patterns of spacetime, it follows that a particle is a sequence of centres-of-experience. In Chapter Thirteen, the interpretation of the particle as a centre-of-experience will be developed further.

In Chapter Four, we examined universal mystical experiences in the hope that they would yield some clues about the characteristics of underlying experience. The question was raised whether all universal experiences are identical. The supposition that there is a plurality of underlying spacetimes would imply that universal mystical experiences could not be absolutely identical in structure, for each experiential Totality is organised from a particular centre, and is thus a particular spacetime perspective. There is no single substratal experience of the world that individuals could report. Each universal mystical experience draws upon a unique Totality, or a worldline-group of Totalities if a succession of Totalities contributes to the experience. Yet the Totalities are all-encompassing and identical, apart from perspectives and worldpoint separations, and it is therefore still valid to regard each experience as universal.

Descriptions of universal mystical experience suggest that the experience is organised from a centre, and in this respect is similar to our ordinary transient experiences. In the latter, we see the spatial arrangement of things from a particular point-of-view. Phenomenologically, each is at the centre of the universe, and it is not possible for us to imagine a spatial arrangement of items without taking some spatial position in relation to the items. We cannot conceive of a spatially-delocalized, perspective-free experience, all-pervading with no special, central vantage-point or particular perspective. This is not to say that there could not be some special kind of experience that is not organised from a centre, just as we could not be sure that geometric qualities must always be accompanied by colour qualities. That we have not had a certain experience and cannot envisage what it would be like does not mean that such an experience is impossible. The four-dimensional space of spacetime is an instance of this: we have entertained the notion that spacetime may be an experiential actuality, but we strain without success to imagine an actual four-dimensional array within normal, transient experience, and resort to lower-dimensional analogies. We have taken transient experience to be closely related to spacetime experience, so it is tempting to suppose that the plural Totality-experiences share with transient experiences the characteristic of central vantage-points, centres-of-experience. In fact, the same temptation arises over the question of plurality: our trains of experience involve a *multiplicity* of perspectives. Thus, an underlying basis that is both plural and experienced from centres is in keeping with the nature of everyday experience.

THE MONADOLOGY OF LEIBNIZ

Before developing the structure of plural, relative spacetimes any further, it will be useful to compare the idea of relative spacetimes with Leibniz's monads and consider some earlier ideas that have affinities. The general notion of a plurality of omniscient, universal 'minds' is traceable in one form or other to early times, occurring under various guises in the organic and vitalistic philosophies of nature and in religious/mystical contexts. But its most famous incorporation into a system of Western philosophy occurs in the metaphysics of Leibniz.

Leibniz invoked the relational theory of time (time as the order of successive phenomena) at a late stage in his philosophical career, during his correspondence with Clarke in 1716. Yet the relational theory ties in well with the monadology. Each monad (Greek *monas,* 'one', 'unit') is a soul or mind, which in the course of its development has within itself perceptions of the world from a succession of unique points-of-view. The temporality of a monad consists of the succession from state to state. Time is the order of things that cannot co-exist, namely the successive states of the self-actualising monads. Flux derives from the tendency of a monad to change from one state to the next, this tendency being called *appetition.* The causal development of the individual substance and the idea of relational time are therefore closely linked, but not as closely as substance and time in relativistic spacetime. Here the worldline of a body defines a *local* time that is peculiar to the body, whilst the times of the monads are synchronised. Leibnizian time is relational, but not relativistic.

Leibniz says that the states of monads are nothing but perceptions, which are "the representation in the simple of the compound"[4] or "the inner state of the monad representing external things".[5] Each perception—the inner state of the monad—embraces everything in the world, indeed, is everything in the world of that monad. Each monadic state has a different world-perspective, from the unique point-of-view of the state, and the perceived world is none other than a representation of all the other monads. But ordinarily, our perceptions are very limited, and are marked by varying degrees of confusion. This seems to take Leibniz to a noteworthy distinction: as I have understood his theory, he discriminates between *unconscious* and *conscious* perceptions. There are the distinct, full perceptions of the monad, which are largely unconscious, depending on the level of development of the monad, and there are the 'little perceptions' or *apperceptions,* which are the ordinary, conscious perceptions of most monads. Perception is the *inner* nature of the monad, whilst monads considered *externally* (that is, perceived in the inner state of other monads) are the "true atoms of nature and, in a word, the elements of things".[6] The representation of other monads in the inner state of a monad constitutes the materiality of Leibniz's system. The represented monads are point-like, indivisible, extensionless and shapeless. The distinction between clear perceptions and little perceptions may correspond to the difference between substratal experiences and partial, transient experiences. The Leibnizian point-of-view would correspond to the centre-of-experience of a Totality. But the different perspectives of the Totalities involve more than a difference in vantage-point, for the relativistic insight tells us that separations between events are different. Like the monad, the Totality can be viewed as an atom in its 'external' aspect, represented as a worldpoint particle-state within another Totality. Leibniz uses a mirror-metaphor to bring across the idea of the monad:

> ... every monad is a mirror that is alive or endowed with inner activity, is representative of the universe from its point of view, and is as much regulated as the universe itself.[7]

The monads are living mirrors, reflecting both the structure and orderly regulation of the universe.

Leibniz's monads are uncreated and indestructible, for "they mirror an indestructible universe".[8] The continuity of a monad's states suggests that states continue beyond the death of the organismic body, with which every monad must be associated, and Leibniz says that it would require a miracle to end the succession. A monad is therefore

> never despoiled of all its organs all together; in animals there is often metamorphosis, but never metempsychosis, nor transmigration of souls.[9]

According to Leibniz, there is transformation, without absolute birth or death.

> And what we call *generation* is a development and a growth, while what we call *death* is an envelopment and a diminution.[10]

Expressed in the language of spacetime, the worldline, as a succession of worldpoints linked by continuity, is always associated with a body of worldpoints, a sheath of worldlines. The worldtube-body of an organism may contract at times, but is never completely shed to reveal a single worldline.

Leibniz's organicism is essentially three-tiered. In order of increasing complexity, there are first the *bare monads,* which have no psychological processes such as memory. A lump of rock, for example, would be an aggregate of such bare monads. Then there are the monads called *animal souls* and the monads called *rational souls,* both of which have psychological processes. Human beings fall into the category of rational souls, which have greater mental capabilities than animal souls. Organisms consist of a ruling or dominant monad, with representations of subservient monads forming the body of the organism. In one sense, the dominant monad is the soul of the body, but we could also take a Plotinian line and argue that a monad or soul in its inner aspect, as a whole perception of the universe, houses the body, and all other bodies, within itself. We have noted that varying degrees of confusion are associated with monads. Conscious perceptions of the world are not total. The varying degrees of consciousness and complexity of organisms lead to an explanation of the commonly applied distinction between things that are conscious and living against those which are inanimate and material. The latter are to be seen as highly unconscious minds, which, lacking both a clear apperception of the world and a developed body of subservient monads with which to act, are limited and passive in their interactions. Physics and chemistry, according to this view, constitute psychologies of very dull, passive minds.

Being indestructible, a monad endures as long as the universe exists, so a very large number of phases of body-growth and diminution would take place in the course of a monad's history. Yet Leibniz is not too consistent in outlining the evolutionary possibilities of a monad in the organic hierarchy, for he maintains that there is a fixed number of monads in the system, yet also countenances some degree of evolution through endless time. Endless evolution and limited numbers of participants in a hierarchical scheme do not go together very well, for the necessary supply of lower-level monads is likely to become exhausted if there is a general advancement.[11] A related problem was encountered in the Indian systems that envisaged an advance up the 'chain of being' through rebirth. In these systems, the number of participants in the universe is not fixed, for individual liberation *(moksa)* from the cycle of rebirth takes participants out of the system of rebirth. In spacetime terms, the world we are considering is temporally open in the future direction (no ultimate end), possibly open in the past direction, and may undergo oscillations (infinite cycles of creation and destruction).[12] An individual worldline would presumably come to an end with the final liberation *(parinirvana* in Buddhist terminology).

Now, if beings are gradually disappearing from the world through liberation, a question arises: what prevents the depletion of participants from bringing the universe to an end? One approach would be to argue that new individual beings are created, replenishing the supply. This would mean that the worldline of an experiencing being has a beginning as well as an end. But the common view, in Buddhism and Jainism at least, seems to have been that experiencing beings have an infinite past, although the historical Buddha made a point of keeping silent on this type of question. In the Jain organicism, the problem is addressed with the notion of an *infinite* reservoir of 'plant souls', a source that provides a never-ending supply of souls to replace those that have moved up the evolutionary ladder towards liberation. The reservoir consists of microscopic globules of soul-aggregates, called *nigodas*, or group-souls, which are densely packed throughout space. These group-souls, which occupy the bottom level of the Jain classification of life-forms, are held to possess various life processes, such as respiration and nutrition, and to suffer "exquisite" pains. It is a sort of *prima materia* out of which souls awaken to commence the long journey towards liberation.[13]

It is not clear how Leibniz arrived at his theory of monads. Leibniz was critical of Benedict de Spinoza's (1632–77) doctrine of the one substance, one thing that can exist on its own. For Spinoza, the one substance was both the whole of reality and God. In contrast, Leibniz posited a plurality of simple substances, the monads. Perhaps it was the plurality within apperception, the many states of an individual's transient experience, and the multiplicity of individuals, that suggested the notion of plural monads.[14] We commonly suppose that there is a plurality of experiencing individuals. The monadology seems peculiar because it goes beyond the commonsense view, by making each of the plurality of experiences into an all-inclusive whole.

The idea of a simple substance consisting of perceptions and their changes also provided Leibniz with a solution to the mind-body problem created by the mechanical philosophy: "... *perception* and that which depends on it *cannot be explained mechanically,* that is to say with figures and motions."[15] The mechanism of a machine, with its impinging parts, cannot explain a perception. The explanation "must therefore be sought in a simple substance, and not in a compound or in a machine."[16] The monadology is also connected with Leibniz's interests in the fields of logic and linguistics. For Leibniz, relational statements are really statements about the inherent properties of a substance. Each individual substance has a *complete concept,* a concept that includes all its characteristics throughout its temporal development.

Leibniz's monadology is a system of plurality and flux. The monads consist of transient perceptual states. Both the clear substratal perceptions and the partial apperceptions are characterised by Becoming. Our Totality hypothesis therefore differs from the Leibnizian monadology in a significant respect: each

Totality is a whole spacetime experience, complete in itself, displaying all events in all successive states. As I understand Leibniz's monadology, each state of a monad is just the spatial perspective of the states of contemporary monads, and Leibniz's monads are subject to change, one state being replaced by the next. Each of these universal three-dimensional perspectives has the past and future states implicit in it, since "every state of a simple substance is a natural consequence of its preceding state, so that the present state of it is big with the future".[17] With sufficient knowledge of the laws of transformation, one could work out all past and future states of a monad by inspecting any one state. But in the theory developed here, each unit is a whole spacetime, not a three-dimensional, spatial cross-section of simultaneity. The whole of spatialized time is contained in one experience. These spacetime units are tenselessly permanent, unlike the fleeting states of a Leibnizian monad. The concept of a monad as a succession of transforming three-dimensional states is replaced by the notion of the tenselessly permanent world-group of Totalities, a collection of spacetime units related by their association with a common worldline, the line of continuity or identity of an experiencing being.

The monadology, with its plurality of units in flux, is an attractive philosophy for those who wish to preserve the distinctness of the individual and the reality of Becoming. It provides a significant, pluralist alternative to the absolutist strain of thought that tends to subsume the individual in a single, timeless whole. The urge to defend the individual self against the absolutism of Hegel and his successors, including the absolute idealism of Green and Bradley in England, was expressed in the personal idealism of the late nineteenth century and early twentieth century. We have already mentioned one of the leading personal idealists, J. E. McTaggart. In contrast to Leibniz's monads, the members of McTaggart's community of selves are not in flux, for McTaggart, as we have noted, denied the reality of time. Other notable personal idealists of the period included G. H. Howison (1834–1916), J. Ward (1843–1925) and A. S. Pringle-Pattison (1856–1931). Leibniz's monadology was a source of inspiration for the personal idealists, as was the philosophy of R. H. Lotze (1817–81), which followed the monadology by entertaining a plurality of spirits in flux, linked by a pre-established harmony. The Leibnizian monadology exerted a significant influence on Whitehead's philosophy of organism. Both philosophies have in common the ideas of multiple, perceptual perspectives and a universe in flux. Interestingly, Whitehead rejected 'simple location', the idea that a piece of matter is located in one particular spatial region, independent of any other region.

> In a certain sense, everything is everywhere at all times. For every location involves an aspect of itself in every other location. Thus every spatio-temporal standpoint mirrors the world.[18]

In Chapter Thirteen we shall have cause to replace the idea of 'simple location', typified by the mechanical philosophy, with a holistic notion of *multiple location.*

ROOTS OF PLURALISTIC IDEALISM

Notions of a plurality of universal minds, perceptions or experiences antedate Leibniz's monadology, and are to be found in one form or other in the traditions of several cultures. The historical roots of pluralistic idealism are diverse and often intertwined. A stimulus towards pluralism is likely to have been the various beliefs and speculations about souls. A plurality of human beings suggests a plurality of souls, and the idea can be extended to include the plurality seen in nature, including the multiplicity of animals, plants and minerals (hence panpsychism and animism). Related to panpsychism is the organic stream of thought, in which the whole is likened to a living organism, consisting of living, interrelated parts. Organistic thought is to be found in Plato's philosophy, Stoicism, and Neoplatonism, and was widespread in India and China.[19] There is also a mystical background to pluralistic idealism. Of importance in the West is Plotinus' mystical philosophy of various levels of manifestation and return—at the summit of the scheme is the One, followed by a level of multiplicity, the intelligible order of *Nous.*

W. T. Stace[20] describes a form of mysticism that he calls *mystical monadism:* these are expressions of mystical experience or theory in which the individual self is not fully obliterated during the togetherness of mystical union. He regards mystical monadism as "a minority mystical tradition" that is in opposition to the "major mystical tradition" in which union is thought to submerge the individual completely.[21] Stace cites the Jewish philosopher Martin Buber (1878–1965) as an exponent of mystical monadism and suggests that the Jewish mystical tradition is inclined towards it.[22] However, in distinguishing between mystical monadism and mystical absolutism as alternatives, care must be taken, for it seems that there are various kinds and stages of trans-sensate mystical experience.[23] In the Plotinian system, for instance, there is the mystical experience at the level of *Nous,* which is plural. There is a union at this level, with seer and seen identified, but the multiplicity of things and their distinctness remain. From the level of *Nous,* union with the One may follow, which is singular. The individual souls are, in their higher reaches, cosmic intelligences—"each of us is an Intellectual Cosmos"[24]—but above the complex plurality of the cosmic intelligences is the simple.[25]

Pluralities of consciousness are to be found in some ancient Indian systems, which contain elements of archaic nature philosophy. Stace[26] cites the Jain and Samkhya-Yoga philosophies as further instances of mystical monadism. In the Jain metaphysics, which in historical time originated in the sixth century B.C., the world is divided into the living *(jiva)* and the non-living *(ajiva)*. A living being consists of a soul and its material body. Jivas are infinite in number and in their pure condition are characterised by unlimited bliss *(sukha)*, power *(virya)*, knowledge *(jnana)* and perception *(darsana)*. But most *jivas* are said to be clouded by influxes of 'subtle karmic matter'. Liberation *(moksa)* involves the removal of the karmic weight that binds the *jiva* to cycles of reincarnation, so that it can rise beyond the heavens to the top of the human-shaped cosmos, the macrocosmic person, where the liberated *jivas* exist in omniscience, bliss and isolation. The Samkhya philosophy postulated an infinity of conscious selves or *purusas*, in addition to the transcendental self, *Purusa*. The selves are bound to the woeful cycle of reincarnation by misidentification with the impermanent evolutes of the primal matter, *prakriti*. Individual liberation, resulting in a state of pure intelligence and isolation, is achieved through a loosening of false identifications with the productions of matter.[27]

Leibniz's monadology is an instance of the organic philosophy. The general approach of organicism is to hold that active, living organisms are the constituents of the world, and in Leibniz's philosophy the world consists of a hierarchy of monads. Organicism is often related to idealist positions, which take mind, ideas or consciousness to be the basis of the world, and it is opposed to materialist concepts of lifeless, inert substances. The organic tendency has ancient roots, and is found at the beginning of Western philosophy in the ideas of the Milesian philosophers. An interesting development occurs when animism or panpsychism is combined with the atomic speculations of nature philosophy: the concept of soul-atoms emerges. Attributed to the Greek philosopher Ecphantus is the idea that the universe is composed of a limited number of atoms that "owe their movement not to weight or external impact but to a divine power which he calls mind and soul."[28] W. K. C. Guthrie suggests that Ecphantus combined the Pythagorean idea of mathematical monads with the atomism of Democritus,[29] and notes a suggestion by W. Kranz that Ecphantus' indivisible, self-powered units may have influenced Giordano Bruno's theory of atoms or monads.[30] Bruno's atoms are spherical, equal in size, animated by the soul of the universe, and are similar to Leibniz's monads in that they are centres of activity, of internal force. Besides its activity in the atoms, the world soul acts as a principle of growth and organisation in the mineral, vegetable and animal realms. In the higher levels of existence—animals, human beings and celestial bodies—the individual soul of the organism also contributes to the activity of the body.[31]

The role played by Leibniz's predecessors and contemporaries in the development of his monadological thought is not clear. Several thinkers have been linked with the monadology, including Nicholas of Cusa, Giordano Bruno, the Helmonts and Anne Conway. The links with Cusa and Bruno are perhaps tenuous, although the theology and philosophy of Nicholas of Cusa contain some suggestive ideas. Cusa supposed that there is no privileged, fixed centre in the universe, for each thing is a centre. There is a coincidence of opposites between the smallest and the greatest, the minimum and the maximum, the centre and the circumference. Whereas God is the absolute maximum, the universe is a limited or restricted maximum, an infinity contracted to a relative infinity. The universe in turn exists in a restricted fashion in each thing. Each creature is a microcosm that contracts the universe, mirroring the universe and God, and human nature has the capacity to be the perfect image, reaching above and below through its mid-position in the chain of being. In Christ, the capacity reaches its fulfilment.[32]

Perhaps of greater significance is the link with the Helmonts, Jean Baptiste (1577–1644) and his son, the colourful "Scholar Gypsy", Francis Mercury (1614–98), and with the English countess, Lady Anne Conway (1631–79), a friend of both Henry More and the younger Helmont.[33] It seems that Leibniz had worked out the basic philosophy of plural substances by the mid-1680s, before coming into contact with the vitalistic and monadic ideas of the younger Helmont and Conway, but it is likely that their ideas helped him to develop and clarify the details of his own position.

The elder Helmont, an important figure in the history of chemistry, adapted the vitalism of Paracelsus (1490–1541). He supposed that the world is composed of a plurality of autonomous beings, arranged into organic hierarchies. The *archei* (a term borrowed from Paracelsus) are characterised by self-consciousness of varying degrees of clarity, and are self-developing and self-determined according to their internal nature, like Leibniz's monads, whose changes derive from within. A significant feature of this stream of vitalistic thought was the idea that matter and activity are united, in contrast to views that took matter or the material body to be passive.[34] The vitalistic, body-spirit monism was taken up by the younger Helmont: the spiritual and the corporeal are transformable into one another, since matter, wrote van Helmont in his *Cabbalistical Dialogue,* "is made by a coalition or clinging together of spiritual degenerate dull monades or single beings, and this coalition is called creation."[35] The monads have fallen from a state of knowing into a stuporous condition, in which they cling together to form matter, although in time they will return to a free state. The material state is likened to a sleep or a death of the living, spiritual monads.

Van Helmont contributed his *Cabbalistical Dialogue* to Baron Knorr von Rosenroth's *Kabbalah denudata* (1677), which was known to Leibniz before his meeting with van Helmont in 1696. Sections of the *Kabbalah denudata* presented a form of sixteenth-century Kabbalism that had a decidedly vitalistic outlook.[36] This was the Kabbalistic thought of the mystic and visionary, Isaac Luria (1534–72), who saw souls and interrelations everywhere, and maintained a theory of the metempsychosis *(Gilgul)* of souls as a process leading towards universal restoration *(Tikkun)*.[37] In Luria's account of the creation, the original divine light—the Adam Kadmon filling the primal space created by the withdrawal *(Tsimtsum)* of God—is dispersed into a world of punctiform lights,[38] *Olam Ha-Nekudoth,* an idea that can be compared with Gnostic and Manichaean cosmogonies of divine soul-sparks that fall into the depths. However, in comparing such ideas—monadic, vitalistic, alchemical, gnostic, Kabbalistic—it is important to distinguish between monisms and dualisms: the idea of soul-sparks trapped in a world of darkness and matter sets up a dualistic opposition between the spiritual and the material, unlike monistic views in which matter consists of soul-aggregates. In the former view, the way to restoration lies in the release of the soul-spark from its imprisonment in the alien world of matter, whilst in the latter view, the monadic soul-spark comes to a clear knowing in which the material world is found to be a spiritual world of monads. In the terms of our experiential monism, the spirit-matter dualism is discarded along with mind-body dualism, because structure, feeling, and knowing, including those aspects likely to attract the label 'spiritual', come together as experiential constituents in an experiential substratum that supports and includes transient experiences. This experiential approach is a monism with regard to mind-body and spirit-matter distinctions, but it is a pluralism in the sense that a multiplicity of total experiences has been posited.

In a full investigation of the historical background of monadological ideas, we would have to consider in detail a number of interrelated ideas that we have touched on here and in other chapters, such as microcosm-macrocosm comparisons, the 'whole in each part' doctrine, the idea of the *imago Dei,* and various mirror metaphors and analogies. Leibniz, we have seen, described the monads as living mirrors that reflect the universe, and he added that the advanced monads, the rational souls or minds, mirror not only the created universe, but also an image of the Deity.[39] The rational soul has an activity of its own, reproducing on a small scale the works of God. To illustrate this point, Leibniz mentions the creative activity of dreaming, and the scientific discovery of God's order in the great world that enables man to create order in his own little world.

In his study of the mirror-metaphor applied to the soul and God, Hans Leisegang[40] connects Leibniz's living mirrors with the scholastic notion of the soul as a simple living substance, and points out a distinction made by Witelo between the imaging power of the soul, represented by the eye, and the manner in which mirror-images are formed. Unlike the mirror, which produces its image mechanically and passively, the 'soul as eye' plays an active role in the creation of images. To appreciate this distinction, it is necessary to consider Plato's theory of sense-perception, and its later developments, especially Augustine's understanding of perception, in which the *active* nature of the soul's perception is brought across. In Plato's theory, visual perception occurs through a meeting of light from the object with an inner light of the eye.[41] His theory lends itself to an interpretation in which the inner light or fire of the eye is a metaphor for the activity of the soul, or in modern terms, the *constructive* nature of the perceptual and cognitive processes, an interaction between the perceiving mind and the environment.[42] Unlike the glass or metallic mirror, the soul-mirror or mind-mirror is *living,* for it recognises, understands, interprets, responds, creates, feels.

THE UBIQUITY OF THE WORLD-CENTRE

In Chapter Eight, we followed the changing notions of the absolute rest-state in Western astronomy. In the Aristotelian cosmology, based on the homocentric spheres of Eudoxus, the universe was possessed of an absolute, single centre, the fixed cosmic centre to which the earth-element gravitated. The earth was located in a state of rest at the centre, and around the cosmic centre revolved the spheres of celestial bodies. The astronomies of Hipparchus and Ptolemy blurred the picture by introducing extra centres through the use of eccentrics and epicycles, but the closed Aristotelian universe and its unique cosmic centre continued to hold the imagination outside the discipline of pure mathematical astronomy. For a brief period in the sixteenth and seventeenth centuries, the sun was elevated by some to the role of cosmic centre, but soon the idea of an infinite universe pushed aside the idea of a physical cosmic centre, and the state of absolute fixity was transferred to space itself, an absolute frame without a centre. It is true that there were still centres in the new universe, the centres of the plural solar systems, but none of these had the status of fixed cosmic centre. In the modern relativistic cosmology, the idea of a universal centre continues to be absent, and it is said that the expansion of the universe is not centred on a particular origin. There is no special point or frame in the relativistic universe. Absolute, fixed, three-dimensional space has disappeared too.

In the system of Totalities, the importance of the centre is recognised, for each Totality is a spacetime experience organised about a centre-of-experience, yet it is also true that all points have the same status because each worldpoint corresponds to the centre of one Totality. Each point is a centre-of-experience in one Totality, and is off-centre in other Totalities, where it constitutes a represented centre-of-experience. Given the importance of the role of plural centres in the system of experiential Totalities, it may be of interest to consider briefly the idea of the centre in religious contexts. It has been noted elsewhere[43] that religious world-views entertain a single world-centre, in contrast to modern relativistic cosmologies. In fact, religious and philosophical views have not been tied exclusively to the notion of a single world centre.

An important example of the symbolism of the single centre is the *axis mundi,* the axis about which the universe revolves. We have noted before that from the perspective of the earth, the heavens rotate once a day about an axis that passes through the poles of the Earth and extends above the northern hemisphere to the Pole Star in the northern half of the celestial sphere. The world-axis is a widespread theme, and is intimately connected with the mythology of transience and permanence, of change and stability. The circumference spins, but the centre is stationary. The stillness of the axis is Being to the moving wheel of Becoming, the cycle of the seasons, the circle of the Zodiac. In Christian imagery, Christ is at the centre, the Four Apostles at the periphery, or in Buddhist iconography, the primordial Buddha *Vairocana* is located at the centre of the mandala of meditation buddhas. The centre as *axis mundi* is frequently represented as a central mountain, such as Mt Meru of the elaborate Indian cosmologies, or the cosmic centre may take other forms, such as a tree, pillar, temple, sacred city, or a stone, like the *omphalos,* the navel-stone of the world located at Delphi.[44] As well as being the 'still point of the turning world', the eternal in the transitory, the centre represents the point at which all diversities and levels of existence meet.

The centre as *creative point* is another expression of divinity associated with the centre, and leads us from the singular to the plural. For the Pythagoreans, the point was the first step towards the construction of the three dimensions of space, through one-dimensional lines, to two-dimensional planes, to three-dimensional solids. In the *Zohar* of the Kabbalah, it is the primordial point that builds the cosmos, like the *bindu* of Indian thought, the simple dot with which the complete, manifest universe can be constructed. The centre has figured in alchemical ideas, with the usual implications of divinity and eternity, and appears as the *lapis* and the creative point.[45] Jung saw in these images an expression of the structure and dynamics of the mind, in which the "total personality", the Self, acts as a unifying centre for the peripheral components of the psyche, including the ego.

The creative point that builds up a three-dimensional universe implies a plurality of divine centres. Are there more explicit references to plural centres? In Leibniz's monadology there are, of course, the *points-of-view* from which each state of a monad constitutes a unique perspective on the world, and further instances of plural universal centres are to be found in some of the authors implicated in the history of monadological thought. Nicholas of Cusa criticised the earth-centred and star-bounded cosmology popularised by Aristotle, and denied that the universe has a specific centre or a definite boundary. Every point can be regarded as the centre of the universe, and God, through omnipresence at all the centres, can be called the centre of the universe. God is in the universe, contracted in every thing, and the universe is in God. This notion is not intended pantheistically, with God and the universe identified: God contains all things in the sense that He is the cause of all things. The relationship is one of image to original. The universe is an image of God, and each thing, including man, is also an image of God.

Cusa described the universe as *a sphere whose centre is everywhere and circumference nowhere,* an image employed by mediaeval scholastics and very popular among Renaissance thinkers.[46] For Bruno, the innumerable, animated worlds constituted the many centres, and the mathematician and religious thinker Blaise Pascal was later to recall the image in his *Pensées* (1669).[47] In the later writers, following Cusa, it is the *universe* or *nature* that is called a sphere whose centre is everywhere, whereas in the earlier versions, beginning with the second definition of God presented in a twelfth-century, pseudo-Hermetic text, the *Liber XXIV philosophorum,* it is *God* who is the infinite sphere with centre everywhere and circumference nowhere.[48] The *infinite* sphere in the Hermetic original became an *intelligible* sphere amongst the early users of the phrase, such as Alain de Lille (*c.*1116–1202),[49] but Thomas Bradwardine (*c.*1290–1349) re-employed the description 'infinite', using the infinite sphere as a metaphor for the unbounded immensity of God. Bradwardine employed two other definitions of God from the *Liber XXIV philosophorum,* one of which equated God with a sphere having "as many circumferences as points."[50] In the thought of Nicholas of Cusa, the shift from God to the universe may have followed because he regarded the universe as an image of God.

The spherical God identified in some way with the cosmos goes back to ancient Greek thought, but was *finite,* in accordance with the ancient Greek preference for the finite or bounded over the infinite. The God of the philosopher Xenophanes (*c.*570–*c.*470 B.C.) was sometimes attributed with sphericity, perhaps through associations with the "well-rounded" Being of Parmenides,[51] and the divine cosmos in Plato's *Timaeus* was spherical. The novel departure in Cusa and later writers is the view that the divine sphere constitutes a universe with a *multiplicity* of centres throughout space. As a religious statement, the view may imply that God or the divine is to be found within each being, within every person, the indwelling divinity or image of God in each member of the plurality. The mystically rich image of plural centres had been expressed by Plotinus, who likened the centres of souls joined at a common centre, the One, to the great circles of a sphere,[52] and he used the analogy of a choral dance to depict the relationship between the souls and the supreme god, the One, the centre of centres. The idea of the soul's centre was employed widely in later Western mystical thought.

Buddhist cosmology also provides a notable instance of the multiplication of centres. The earliest Buddhist cosmologies followed the general pattern of the old Indian cosmological model—the world is like a disc, with a single world-centre, the *axis mundi* Mt Meru, and another mountain encircling the disk. In between are various continents and rings of mountains. In the Buddhist scheme, the circumferential mountain is made of iron and is called the *cakravala*, which is also the name given to the world system as a whole. Above the disc is located a series of heavenly realms and meditation realms. Of interest to us here is the development of the single world-system of the *cakravala* into much grander cosmological schemes, having a multiplicity of centres. Randy Kloetzli[53] describes various stages in this development. The first step beyond the single world-system is described as the *cosmology of thousands* or the *Sahasra*-cosmology, because of the frequent occurrence in this type of system of the number *one thousand* and its mathematical multiples and powers. The single *cakravala* world becomes a unit in a much larger world-system, which consists of thousands-upon-thousands of *cakravalas,* and therefore contains thousands-upon-thousands of Mt Merus and surrounding continents. A well-known version is the *trisahasramahasahasralokadhatu,* sometimes translated as the "threethousandth great thousandth universe" or the "triple chilicosm". This vast universe of world-systems is the realm of a single Buddha, a *buddhaksetra,* or Buddha-field. The Buddha-field is a region of the world-system, a cosmos in itself over which a single Buddha exerts spiritual power, guiding beings to liberation. A Buddha's knowledge is unlimited, reaching all the Buddha-fields. The *Sahasra* cosmologies are in turn dwarfed by a cosmology of the Mahayana, termed by Kloetzli the *Asankhyeya*-cosmology or *cosmology of innumerables.* Here the trichilicosm Buddha-field is itself a unit, for there are now an incalculable number of Buddhas and Buddha-fields located throughout space, "as numerous as the sands of the Ganges". The single Buddha-field, which in some respects is a single field of knowing, is replaced by the innumerable Buddha-fields of innumerable Buddhas, implying a multiplicity of fields of knowing. In Mahayana Buddhism, distinctions were made between Buddha-fields, according to their purity, with three categories described: pure, mixed and impure fields. Suffering and ignorance are rife in impure fields, while the pure fields, or Pure lands, are paradise-like, bejewelled, luminous and golden. In the *Vimalakirtinirdesa Sutra* the distinction no longer applies to different Buddha-fields, but refers to different ways in which the same Buddha-field is regarded, depending on the purity of the mind of the beholder. The world of suffering is a Pure Land to one with clear-sight. The notion is perhaps related to the "all is well" insight into the Eternal Now, found in accounts of mystical experience.

The cosmology of innumerables is not the end of the story, however, for the *interpenetrating* universes of the Mahayana elaborate the picture even further, as we shall see in Chapter Fourteen. Finally, we may note that in the Tantric development of Buddhism, the idea of a plurality of cosmic centres shows in the ascription of a mandala to each practitioner, which in meditational practice is centred in the body. The mandala is a cosmic symbol, representing the universe and its deities or forces, and the association of the mandala with each practitioner expresses the idea of the individual as microcosm.

A personal vision of the world-centre and its plurality was described by the Oglala Sioux holy man Black Elk (1863–1950) to the writer John G. Neihardt. Black Elk recounted that he fell ill at the age of nine, and while close to death had a vision in which he saw the "shapes of all things in the spirit" from a mountain top.[54] In his account of the vision, Black Elk described the mountain as Harney Peak in the Black Hills, adding, "But anywhere is the centre of the world."[55] It has been debated whether Neihardt's transliteration provides a fair expression of Black Elk's story,[56] but whatever the case may be, the remark conveys an important idea: *the ubiquity of the world-centre.* Commenting on the vision, Joseph Campbell took it to be "a key statement to the understanding of myth and symbols".[57]

12. FLUX AND THE SUBSTRATUM

We shall now consider whether the change from one absolute spacetime to a plurality of relative spacetimes enables us to develop some of the issues covered in earlier chapters. Two areas will be considered: the relationship between Being and Becoming, and the notion of the substratum.

THE INTERDEPENDENCE OF BEING AND BECOMING

In Chapter Six, the idea of spatializing time into a static spacetime raised a significant problem: how was transient experience to be derived from a substratum having a tenselessly static nature? We looked at one common response to the problem, which is to imagine that consciousness crawls along worldlines. But the idea of a crawling consciousness was unattractive because it implied a separation between the experiencer (the crawling consciousness) and the experiential content distributed through spacetime (sense-representations, feelings, thoughts). If we take the whole of spacetime to be experiential, then the idea of a *temporary* localisation of experience at small regions of spacetime is not appealing. The whole of spacetime is experience, not just the experiences associated with the brain-states of organisms. Having rejected the idea of crawling consciousnesses, we conjectured that all transient experiences are permanently set in experiential spacetime. The traveller is at every step of the journey, and transient experience shares in the tenseless permanence of the experiential substratum.

We went on to consider the possibility that astructural and psychological facets of experience, such as meaning and feeling, give our ordinary experience its transient quality and its direction of transience, the experiential 'arrow of time'. The transformation of the daffodil seed into the flower, for instance, defines a meaningful developmental direction. Understanding of the growth of the plant distinguishes between the two time-directions of the process. Furthermore, I suggested that transience might be a quality of each individual moment, and derive from a complex composition that contains structural, cognitive and feeling contents from a span of temporal states with varying degrees of intensity or clarity. An experiential world was presented in which the static, overall spacetime experience (the Eternal Now) contains numerous sub-experiences characterised by transience (the Transient Nows). The spacetime *as a whole* is fluxless, but some of its regions have the characteristic of transience, and these regions are the moments of our ordinary experience.

In Chapter Eleven, we abandoned the idea of a single, absolute spacetime in favour of a plurality of relative spacetimes, each of which is organised around a centre, the centre-of-experience. Thus, instead of one experiential spacetime containing the transient moments, there are many experiential spacetimes, each containing the transient moments.

Now, we might conjecture that at the centre of each Totality there is one such transient experience, and that these *central* moments may be the moments of ordinary experience. Off-centre moments may not be fully transient experiences if their location off-centre means that they are experienced together with the overall static spacetime. Each Totality, then, would contain all moments distributed throughout itself, but only the moment at the centre would have the full transient quality of our familiar experiences. Each moment of experience would be a little island of experience at the centre of one distinct Totality. The Totalities provide the elements of ordinary experience, the central experiential moments of partial perception, cognition and feeling.

I am suggesting, then, that the transient moment may need to be central for it to be a moment of our familiar experience, a moment experientially distinct from the overall static experience, unlike off-centre moments. But the central moment is still an intrinsic part of the Totality, and the two are causally linked.

The association of each Totality with one transient moment might serve to reinforce the intimate connection between Being and Becoming. It is conceivable that a Totality exists only in conjunction with its central moment of transience. If a stream of flux were to end, there might be no further Totalities, the support disappearing with the supported. There would be no bedrock without flux, no flux without bedrock, no Time without Eternity, no Eternity without Time.

We have supposed that transience is a quality of each moment and that no special linking of moments is required to generate transient experience. Each central moment is a 'psychological present', a drop containing the flow in itself. If this supposition proves unsatisfactory, and the single moment is insufficient to account for transient experience, we might have to introduce a linking of central moments across Totalities. Becoming would be a linking across a sequence of Totalities, whereas Being would be the experience of a Totality in its entirety.

How would we explain the linking of central moments from different Totalities? Would we have to introduce flux as something external to the Totalities, an extrinsic time in which a 'consciousness' leaps from Totality-centre to Totality-centre? This approach would be analogous to the 'crawling of consciousness in the single spacetime' theory, and, from the experiential perspective, suffers from the same drawback: experience is already experience, and does not need 'consciousness' to come along and turn it into experience.

It is interesting to consider the maximum number of transient moments that would correspond to one second of physical time. The quantum theory supplies us with estimates of the minimum time unit, and the smallest of these is in the order of 10^{-44} seconds, the Planck time. With this figure, the upper limit for the number of moments per second of clock time is in the order of 10^{43}. Hence, a maximum of 10^{43} Totalities would supply moments for one second of clock time (compare with twenty-four frames per second for a standard ciné film). One transient moment, then, could span a vast number of temporal states, although the number may be severely reduced by the rate at which the perceptual processes construct new representations.

A matter that we have touched on before is the nature of the divide between our ordinary experience and the experiential substratum. This is now a divide between the transient moment at the centre-of-experience and the rest of the Totality. Why is our normal scope of experience restricted to the transient moment and its limited span of temporal content? The moment cannot be said to hide the rest of the Totality in the usual perceptual sense, as a wall might be said to hide a secret garden. The wall blocks out the light from the garden, and we see the wall and not the garden. But the Totality, unlike the garden in the analogy, is an *experience* independent of sensory processes. It seems that the transient moment, through its cognitive/feeling content and complex temporal span, is able to constitute a separate experience from the rest of the Totality. As self-systems we span the divide, but the experiential self is not directly aware of its roots in the substratum. In Neoplatonic terms, the higher level of the soul is always in touch with the intelligible realm of things, but the lower part of the soul is excluded from a direct apprehension.

Is the separation fixed or are there experiences in which substratal experience and transient experience are blended? Some accounts of universal mystical experience suggest that a blending may be possible. Everyday thoughts, feelings and the world of nature are interfused with a background of fluxless presence, an experiential immanence of the divine in the mundane, a 'marriage of heaven and earth', a twilight meeting of the stable and transient lights.[1] Perhaps Traherne expressed this blending in the account of his infant vision of the eternal manifesting in the familiar:

> And young men glittering and sparkling Angels, and maids strange seraphic pieces of life and beauty! Boys and girls tumbling in the street, and playing, were moving jewels. I knew not that they were born or should die; But all things abided eternally as they were in their proper places. Eternity was manifest in the Light of the Day, and something infinite behind everything appeared.[2]

The composition of the transient moment, the 'psychological present', seems to be modified in such a way that the substratal experience is admitted alongside the transient experience.

A related matter is the problem of how memories of universal mystical experiences are formed. It seems that in the experiences, only some parts of the experiential substratum are actively discriminated and remembered. This is suggested by the lack of detailed knowledge that mystics are able to supply, even though they may claim that all is understood during the experience. The total understanding is not retained beyond the experience, but specifics may have been singled out during the experience and are later recallable. This is not very different from our usual visual experience, in which we might be presented with a large landscape, but select only a few features, influenced by our previous experience and knowledge, and our current mental set. In the case of familiar experience, the discriminating and memorising processes can be viewed as *local,* working on the sensory information presented to the brain. The processes of focusing attention upon, and forming memories of, a distant hill in our visual experience take place within us, for in a representative theory we imagine that the cognitive processes are taking place in the brain, working on visual information provided by the senses.

But in a universal mystical experience, an object billions of miles away or billions of years in the past or future, can be discriminated (since the experience is *complete* in its spatio-temporal content), yet there is no transmission of information via the senses to the brain for discriminative and memory process to work upon. How, then, is the knowledge of the distant object discriminated and remembered, when there is no information propagated to the brain for local processing? This is a difficult question to answer, and is not helped by our current lack of understanding of ordinary brain processes, including those involved in perception and memory. Perhaps the answer may lie in a *local availability* of 'distant information', an idea that will become clearer in the following chapters.

Being and Becoming are interdependent in the scheme we have outlined here. The moments of transient experience are special parts of the total experiences. Becoming depends on Being because its moments are parts of Being, structurally and causally, and contain representations of other parts of Being. Being provides the complete causal structure that underlies the transient moments of Becoming. However, Becoming is more than a partial representation of Being, a moving image of eternity. Transient moments are parts of the Totalities and share in their structure and causal relations. As such, they can be causal centres, and the experiential self can be a causal centre, actively playing a role in the contents of the substratum. It also seems to be the case that transient experience has characteristics that are not found in *quite* the same form in the substratal experience. These characteristics—the thoughts, feelings and perceptions peculiar to the transient moment—direct a whole range of activities that make up the developmental contents of experiential spacetime. As beings in time, we build eternity with the development of our lives, tenselessly creating a stationary image of our activities. In the scheme presented here, Being and Becoming are inseparable: they cannot exist without each other, and neither is more fundamental than the other.

THE SCOPE OF THE MOMENT

Each transient moment is part of a Totality, so we can say that each opens out to a complete spacetime substratum. Loosely speaking, we can say that each moment of time embraces the whole of time. We have already encountered this sort of idea in Chapter Four, in Traherne's description of eternity ("an inward infinity to this Moment"), and it is not uncommon in mystical thought. It is embodied in the idea that eternity is to be found in time. In the scheme we have come to here, time and eternity are not the opposites they are sometimes made out to be: in the instant of flux, the *nunc fluens,* is to be found the 'timeless moment' or 'eternal Now', the *nunc stans.*

The idea has had currency in some Buddhist schools. For instance, in the *Saravastivada* school of early Buddhism (school of "the teaching that everything *is*"), it was maintained that past, present and future exist simultaneously in each of a plurality of permanent indivisible elements of existence, the *dharmas.* The presence of all time periods in an instant is a familiar idea in Mahayana Buddhism. *Nirvana* is to be found only in *Samsara,* the world of birth and death. In the Hua-yen and T'ien-t'ai schools, the idea is incorporated in the broader notion of the presence of the whole in the part, an idea that we shall examine in the following chapters. In the *Treatise on the Golden Lion* by Fa-tsang (eighth century A.D.), regarded as the third patriarch of the Hua-yen school, the 'ninth mystery' recognises temporal arising and decay from instant to instant, yet admits in each instant the presence of past, present and future. In T'ien-t'ai thought, there is the principle of the immanence of "3,000 worlds in a thought moment". For example, in the *Ta-ch'eng chih-kuan fa-men,* said to be written by Hui-ssu (514–77), an instant of thought is equated with the full span of time because all things are one mind.[3]

The Hua-yen and T'ien-t'ai doctrines exerted a considerable influence on the Ch'an (Japanese: *Zen*) schools. Dogen (1200–1253), who introduced the Soto tradition of Zen Buddhism to Japan, wrote on *uji,* or 'Being-Time'. Each dharma-moment is a total exertion *(gujin)* of reality and contains the three periods of past, present and future.

THE SUBSTRATUM REVISITED

The shift from a single absolute spacetime to a plurality of relative spacetimes calls us to reconsider the idea of the substratum. The concept of relative spacetimes introduces a new feature into the picture of the substratum, namely *plural wholes.* There are many relative spacetimes in place of one absolute spacetime. The original stimulus for positing an underlying world was the desire to have a single, complete basis, structural and causal, for all our partial and relative experiences. However, instead of a single, complete basis, we have arrived at a plurality of complete bases, total experiences that are equivalent to one another, containing the same events and causal relationships, but different perspectives and worldpoint separations. The Totalities are distinct experiences, which do not constitute portions of one, single, spatio-temporal structure.

How is it that there are all these distinct, whole experiences in the first place, all equivalent to one another and organised from a centre? The question may incline us to retie the knot that was severed in the previous chapter. In seeking unification at a deeper ontological level, we would be following the personal idealists who bring together the members of their pluralities into a single system by introducing a unifying basis. As James Ward noted,

> A plurality of beings primarily independent as regards their existence and yet always mutually acting and reacting upon each other, an ontological plurality that is yet somehow a cosmological unity, seems clearly to suggest some ground beyond itself. The idea of God presents itself to meet this lack. The Many depend upon God for their existence though still dependent on each other as regards their experience.[4]

Thus, if a theistic world-view holds, the unifying basis of a plural creation is likely to be viewed as God. This is the case in Leibniz's monadology. On the other hand, it has not always been thought necessary to postulate a divine basis: in McTaggart's version of personal idealism there is no God underlying the community of selves. Leibniz's monadology is more traditional, with the independent monads linked through their dependence on God, who has created the monads as self-evolving wholes and enables them to continue once created. Thus God is the ultimate underlying basis in Leibniz's system, creating and continuing the monads, and pre-establishing the future correlation of monadic states at the creation. Unlike Leibniz's monads, the spacetime Totalities described here are not in flux, and it would not be appropriate to ascribe them a common basis that created them and continues to maintain them in time. The basis underlies the Totalities out-of-flux, giving them a tenseless existence. The alternatives of *creation-in-time* versus *timeless derivation* have figured in the long-running debate over Plato's account of the creation in the *Timaeus.* Is the progressive creation of the cosmos by the demiurge to be interpreted literally as a creation in time, or is Plato's temporal language a metaphorical way of expressing timeless derivation?[5]

The introduction of a unifying basis or source gives rise to what is basically a three-level metaphysical system. Firstly, there are the plural streams of *transient experience,* experiences characterised by Becoming and incomplete scope. In our experience, the transient moments of these streams probably contain a span of temporal content. Underlying the streams of experience is a substratum that can be divided into two metaphysical levels. The experiential *intermediate substratum* consists of a plurality of whole experiences, the

Totalities characterised by Being, each a complete spatio-temporal version of the world. The substratum at this level is plural and underlies the plural, partial transient experiences. Then there is an ultimate level of the substratum, the *ultimate substratum* that provides a unifying source for the plural Totalities, a single, common origin that unites all the Totalities and transient experiences.

What might be the nature of this ultimate substratum? As the origin of the experiential intermediate substratum, it is a source of complex, plural, luminous, spatio-temporal structures, all-encompassing knowings and loving. Would it be experiential itself, like the Totality-experiences and transient experiences it supports? In the discussion of the mind-body problem, we connected transient experience with the substratum by adopting the monist solution of making the substratum experiential. It would therefore be a pity to reintroduce a divide in the deepest level of the ontological scheme by making the ultimate basis non-experiential. This would shift the divide to a deeper level, between the ultimate level of the substratum and the experiential level of the Totalities. If the ultimate basis is experiential, what sort of experience might it be? In Chapter Four we looked for clues in mystical experiences having a completeness suggestive of universal experiences, but noted that a range of mystical experiences have been reported, and that *stages* of mystical and meditational experience are sometimes distinguished. Some of these experiences might belong to a stage ontologically prior to the universal experience, and might therefore provide us with some indications about the nature of the ultimate basis. I am not sufficiently familiar with the literature of mysticism to explore the subject with any assurance, and will confine my attention to an idea that has been highly influential in Western mystical thought, namely the Plotinian One.

Plotinus, we have noted before, posits a level of *Nous,* which is not the summit of his metaphysical system. This Intellect-Being level may be similar to our intermediate substratum, for it is eternal and contains a multiplicity of intellectual objects. Intellect is identical with its objects: the knower and known are found to be identical, constituting a self-knowing. Thought at this level is 'timeless', not spread over a succession of transient experiences, unlike our discursive, conscious thinking. The identification of intellectual object and subject has a precedent in Aristotle's conception of the Prime Mover, which is "thought thinking itself". Unlike Aristotle, Plotinus does not give this 'self-thinking thought' the first position in his metaphysical system. Plotinus places *the One* above the intelligible universe of *Nous.* The idea of a higher level was not the innovation of Plotinus, although he elaborated the concept in a new and systematic manner. The idea can be traced to Plato's *Form of the Good,* or to the *One* posited by Speusippus (*c.*407–339 B.C.),[6] Plato's successor at the Academy, and later thinkers from a variety of philosophical currents (Platonic, Neopythagorean, Hermetic, Gnostic) elaborated schemes in which a supreme God (sometimes called the 'grandfather') is distinguished from a secondary

God, *Logos*, *Nous*, or divine creator (demiurge), or 'father'. In the *Republic,* Plato used the analogy of the Sun to illustrate the relationship between the Good and the world of Forms. The Good is to the Forms as the sun is to our perceptual world. Plato's Good is "the cause of knowledge and truth, and you will be right to think of it as being itself known, and yet as being something other than, and even more splendid than, knowledge and truth, splendid as they are."[7]

The problem of ineffableness that we noted in the earlier discussion of mystical experience faces us again, but to an even greater extent. Plotinus says that the One is only a provisional name, not to be taken literally as a numerical designation.

> We are in agony for a true expression; we are talking of the untellable; we name, only to indicate for our own use as best we may. And this name, The One, contains really no more than the negation of plurality.... If we are led to think positively of The One, name and thing, there would be more truth in silence: the designation, a mere aid to inquiry, was never intended for more than a preliminary affirmation of absolute simplicity to be followed by the rejection of even that statement: it was the best that offered, but remains inadequate to express the nature indicated. For this is a principle not to be conveyed by any sound; it cannot be known on any hearing but, if at all, by vision; and to hope in that vision to see a form is to fail of even that.[8]

The ineffableness of experience at this level is likely to hinder a discussion of the subject. Like Plato's Form of the Good, the Plotinian One is beyond Being: it cannot be said *to be,* at least not in the way that the intelligible universe is said *to be,* which exists as an eternal object of contemplation. The Plotinian One is without shape, is beyond Being, Intellect, Life, yet is the source of everything and the centre of centres. Because it is *other than being,* the One has frequently been given names that distinguish it from Being, such as *not-Being,* or Scotus Erigena's (1266–1308) *Nothing (nihil).* The description of this level has always proved difficult, and it is often said that it cannot be described. The negative theology details what the ultimate is *not*, the *neti neti* of the Indian *Upanishads,* the "not this, not this", arguing that our everyday concepts and experiences give us little or no help in understanding it. In Christian thought this ineffable summit of the metaphysical scheme has sometimes been called the Godhead, and in Vedanta, the *Nirguna Brahman* (Brahman without qualities).

In the Plotinian scheme, the One is not simply an intellectual device, a level introduced on purely logical grounds to bring unity to multiplicity. The One can be approached, and union with it is attainable, but whether it is valid to regard the One as experiential is not clear to me. The issue is complicated by a problem we encountered in earlier discussions of mystical experience: experiences may be transitional, involving features from various levels. Thus, descriptions of union with the One may involve experiential features belonging to derivative levels. It may not be possible to remember the experience without these additional features.

The One is said to be always present with us, but we are not often present with it.[9] To become present with it is to make the mystical ascent to the apex of the soul. Plotinus' description of the methods of ascent derives from Plato's treatment.[10] Besides the prerequisite of moral purification, the ascent is made through the appreciation of beauty or through intellectual activity. According to Plotinus, the ascent to the intelligible order is the first stage. The level of Intellect, the universal intelligence inseparable from its content, is in turn the launching-point for the next stage, the ascent to the One. Intellect is described as having two powers: the first is cognition of its own content, the cognition of the intellectual object by the Intellect, the union of the seeing and the seen, whilst the second is a going beyond Intellect to the One, the source of Intellect. This step is described as an intoxication:

> the first seeing is that of Intellect knowing, the second that of Intellect loving; stripped of its wisdom in the intoxication of the nectar, it comes to love....[11]

Is it appropriate to attribute to the One any familiar experiential features, such as the feeling of love, or is this transitional between Intellect and the One, accompanying the reversion of the Intellect to the One? Plotinus frequently states that there is no cognition at the ultimate level, no knowing or thinking, the One knowing "neither itself nor anything else".[12] The lack of cognition is also expressed as the One's lack of self-awareness or self-intellection.[13] There is no trace of duality at this level, no duality of knower and known, not even the united knower and known of the *Nous* level.

What of luminosity, found in transient experience and the eternal level of Being? In his description of the ascent from Being to the One, Plotinus continues to use the language of light:

> ... by these methods one becomes, to self and to all else, at once seen and seer; identical with Being and Intellectual-Principle and the entire living all, we no longer see the Supreme as external; we are near now, the next is That and it is close at hand, radiant above the Intellectual.
>
> Here, we put aside all the learning; disciplined to this pitch, established in beauty, the quester holds knowledge still of the ground he rests on, but, suddenly, swept beyond it all by the very crest of the wave of Intellect surging beneath, he is lifted and sees, never knowing how; the vision floods the eyes with light, but it is not a light showing some other object, the light is itself the vision. No longer is there thing seen and light to show it, no longer Intellect and object of Intellection; this is the very radiance that brought both Intellect and Intellectual object into being for the later use and allowed them to occupy the quester's mind. With This he himself becomes identical, with that radiance whose Act is to engender Intellectual-Principle, not losing in that engendering but for ever

> unchanged, the engendered coming to be simply because that Supreme exists. If there were no such principle above change, no derivative could rise.[14]

The passage seems to suggest that in union with the One, a formless radiance is taken on, but the description might be metaphorical, drawing on Plato's Sun and light analogy. Plotinus also uses the vocabulary of touch and contact to convey the experience of union. But again it is unwise to draw any conclusions from such descriptions, without further evidence.

In Christian mystical philosophy, the ineffability of God became a prominent theme. The negative *(apophatic)* theology, rooted in the thought of Philo Judaeus, Clement of Alexandria (*c.*150–215) and Gregory of Nyssa (*c.*335–*c.*398), found an influential expositor in the pseudo-Dionysius (or 'Dionysius the Areopagite', late fifth or early sixth century A.D.), a Christian with strong Neoplatonic leanings. These writers drew on the story of Moses' ascent to the "thick darkness"[15] at the summit of Mount Sinai. The mysticism of Dionysius exerted a considerable influence on later Christian mystical thought, and the idea of divine darkness recurs frequently in later mystics. In the *Mystical Theology,* the idea of darkness is prominent, and is used to express the unknowableness of God in the mystical union. God dwells in a Divine Darkness hidden by the light of manifestation.

The extreme expression of negative theology denies us any knowledge of the nature of the ultimate basis. We can say it is the Source or Cause of derivative levels, but that is about all we can say. The lower orders are then made the subject of a positive theology, for the attributes of the manifestations of the Hidden God, the *deus absconditus* (or the Unknown God, the *deus ignotus)* are describable to some extent. Through the reflections in the mirror-like realms of Intellect and Sense we may catch a glimpse of the One. The footprints may be traced across the pastures of eternity and the shifting sands of the temporal world.

In earlier chapters we came across the association of space, light and the divine. Henry More, we have seen, regarded space as "a certain rather confused and vague representation of the divine essence or essential presence" and pointed out that the attributes ascribed to God and space are the same. It was suggested that space, light, fixity and divinity were likely to be associated with one another if a philosophy drew upon universal mystical experiences, which are characterised by a fluxless, luminous spatiality. In the present chapter we have met another level of mystical experience, and this level has also attracted space symbolism. The nothingness of space may be viewed as an apt symbol for representing the ultimate basis, which as the One or Godhead of mystical experience, is difficult to characterise in any positive way. Space as a negation of attributes symbolises the unmanifest source or God, whereas space as a luminous dimensionality represents the manifest God or the manifest intelligible creation.

Comparable usages are to be found in Buddhist thought. *Nirvana,* the goal of the Buddhist path, was closely linked with space *(akasa),* and the two were sometimes ascribed similar attributes: not subject to change, infinite, unobstructed, and so forth.[16] *Akasa* was also linked with luminosity, and its etymology was seen in the root *kas*, 'to shine'.[17] Another Buddhist concept, employed extensively in the Mahayana, is that of *sunyata,* 'void' or 'emptiness', which is sometimes explained as a generalisation to all things of the earlier Buddhist denial of the independent self-essence or inherent existence of the person. The interpretation of *sunyata* varies from school to school. Sometimes the usage seems to be akin to the negative theology of Western mystical thought, an assertion of ineffableness. Emptiness is beyond all concepts and affirmations. The equivalence of emptiness and form *(rupa)* is expressed in the Wisdom sutras (the *Prajnaparamita* literature), and emptiness is identified with mind *(citta)* in the *Yogacara,* an idealist school of Buddhism. Sometimes emptiness is equated with the absolute, *tathata* or 'suchness', the permanent and uncreated, distinguished from the phenomenal, yet also united with it. The realisation of *sunyata* is said to be an experience of awakening *(bodhi)* and is rather more than the negative terminology may suggest. Emptiness, viewed positively, is seen as an actuality underlying phenomena, the *dharmakaya*, which is characterised by permanence and luminosity. In this positive sense, Emptiness may be akin to the Western space metaphor for the level of manifest God (Being, the Intelligible Realm, Eternity).

13. DEEP STRUCTURE

In Chapter Eleven, the idea of relative spacetimes was advanced, substratal experiences of universal spatio-temporal scope, having the same content but differing perspectives. It was not merely the centres-of-experience and their corresponding perspectives that varied from Totality to Totality—the magnitudes of space separations and time intervals between identical worldpoints varied from Totality to Totality, in accordance with relativistic theory.

In this scheme, the term *worldpoint* has acquired a significance beyond its meaning in relativistic physics, in which it signifies a point-event, an event at a place and time. In the scheme of Totalities, it has become an elementary structural feature of the spacetime: the structural framework of spacetime is composed of worldpoints set in spacetime. In Chapter Eleven, the worldpoints in a Totality were interpreted as representing the centres-of-experience of the other Totalities. We can develop this interpretation of the worldpoint, and explore in greater detail the structure of the intermediate substratum, the level of plural, total experiences.

THE POINTWORLD

We can speculate that each worldpoint represents not only a centre-of-experience of another Totality, but represents the *whole* of the other Totality, including its entire cosmic structure. Each Totality, then, contains within itself (at its worldpoints) detailed representations of all the other Totalities. In other words, one relative spacetime perspective contains within itself all the other relative spacetime perspectives. One substratal experience contains representations of all other substratal experiences, making a Totality a true whole and a community of experiences.

Let us clarify the terminology. The basic four-dimensional pattern of worldpoints,[1] which comes in a variety of unique but equivalent versions, could be called the *cosmic pattern.* This pattern is repeated at every worldpoint, but with differences to suit the perspective from the particular location. The cosmic pattern is, in its multiple versions, the basic pattern of the universe throughout its entire spatio-temporal extent. The term *Totality* refers to a whole spacetime perspective, and has the cosmic pattern as its overall, structural pattern, but also has versions of the cosmic pattern repeated at each worldpoint. The cosmic pattern is found at each worldpoint, modified according to the perspective from the worldpoint. The design of each great tapestry is repeated at every point in the design, with variations that reflect the position in the design. A worldpoint is not only a point in the world, but also the world in a point, a *pointworld.*

THE LARGE AND THE SMALL

The idea of the whole spacetime cosmos represented in its microstructure takes us to a puzzle that is receiving widespread attention in current physical work: what is the relationship between the cosmos, described by the general theory of relativity, and particle physics, described by quantum theories? Can general relativity and quantum theory be combined into a theory that treats satisfactorily both the cosmic and the microphysical? In Chapter Fifteen we shall take a look at the basics of quantum theory, but in the meantime let us explore the roots of the modern scientific concern with the large and the small.

We have seen that in the seventeenth and eighteenth centuries, the closed universe gave way to the infinity of space, and the instrument that opened up the heavens was the telescope. Human vision leapt into the cosmic immensities through the doorway of the 'optic glass', and the human imagination followed in its wake, dreaming of other worlds and their exotic inhabitants. In the same period, the compound microscope opened up the world of the very small, revealing unsuspected domains of highly-detailed microstructure and vast populations of tiny, curiously-fashioned organisms. It was natural to speculate that structure and life continued to ever smaller levels, making the infinity of the world into a double infinity. To the centrality of human beings in the great chain of being was now added the human centrality in the scale of things, humankind positioned between the telescopically large and the microscopically small. For the scientist, the magnification of experience by optical accessories enlarged the field of scientific investigation enormously, and the exploration of the great and the small has continued unabated, with the invention of instruments of ever greater power. Paradoxically, the advances in cosmology and atomic theory have brought the two areas of study closer together. Scientific work in one area leads back to the other, especially if a unified picture of the world is sought, combining the physics of the large and the small.

Outside the discipline of pure scientific investigation, the telescopic and microscopic enlargement of the experiential scope was a source of fascination for the writers, poets and philosophers of the age, and also for the general public. For some, the new science was a subject of amusement or scorn. The activities of the early investigators, with their observations of fleas or the mountains of the moon, were an easy target for parody and satire.[2] In 1726, Jonathan Swift (1667–1745) captured the satirical mood in his account of Gulliver's travels to the diminutive people of Lilliput and the giants of Brobdingnag, and Swift's lines on the flea are worth quoting:

> So, naturalists observe, a flea
> Has smaller fleas that on him prey;
> And these have smaller still to bite 'em,
> And so proceed *ad infinitum.*[3]

Popular expositions spread the new discoveries to a wide audience. Notable was Fontenelle's *Entretiens sur la pluralité des mondes (Conversations on a Plurality Worlds)* of 1686, in which a philosopher explains to his lady pupil that a leaf is a great world of mountains and abysses, and that a grain of sand supports millions of living creatures. For many, the wonders of the microscopic world and the immensities of the heavens had an uplifting effect, and were a testament to the wonders wrought in nature by the divine creator. But the double infinity could also be a source of existential fear, especially the vast, lonely spaces of the infinite void. In an effort to depict the godless man's anxiety in the new universe, the mathematician and theologian Blaise Pascal gave a fine description of a worlds-within-worlds universe. In the *Pensées* (1669), he describes man at the midpoint of the "two abysses of the infinite and the nought",[4] between the infinitely large and infinitely small. From the body of the tiny mite and its small component structures—legs, veins, blood droplets—we are led downwards to the smallest thing in nature, the atom. Even within this minute atom, the immensities of nature are to be found:

> Let him see there an infinity of universes, each with its firmament, its planets, its earth, in the same proportion as the visible world, on this earth animals, aye and mites, in which he will find again the seed of the former mites—and still without end or rest, finding the same thing in the other things, let him lose himself in these marvels as astonishing in their littleness as the others in their extent, for who would not marvel that our body, which but a moment ago was imperceptible in the universe, imperceptible in the bosom of the whole, should now be a colossus, a world, or rather a whole in respect to the nothingness which we cannot reach.[5]

The revelations of the microscope appeared to support the principle of plenitude and the organic conception of nature. Matter, on close inspection, yielded a world replete with tiny organisms. Leibniz could find support for his monadic organicism in the discoveries of microscopic organisms, and in the associated preformationist theory of animal development, the idea that an organism pre-exists in a miniature form within its seed. Leibniz gave a picturesque description of his infinitely divisible world of organic matter:

> Each portion of matter may be conceived as a garden full of plants, and as a pond full of fish. But every branch of each plant, every member of each animal, and every drop of their liquid parts is itself likewise a similar garden or pond.[6]

The observation that matter can be divided into smaller and smaller parts has often raised the difficult question: how far can the division of matter proceed? The modern atom yielded a nucleus with orbiting electrons, and inspired a worlds-within-worlds analogy: in the early twentieth-century atomic model, associated with Hantaro Nagaoka (1865–1950) and Ernest Rutherford

(1871–1937), a massive, positively charged nucleus was orbited by negatively charged electrons, and the atomic system could be likened to the solar system, with its central sun and orbiting planets. But the divisibility of matter was not to stop here. The nucleus was found to contain protons and neutrons, and these in turn have been resolved into groups of quarks. Is there a limit to physical division, a truly fundamental particle that defies further analysis into physical components? The issue has yet to be settled.

As far as the pointworld idea is concerned, the ultimate units of matter are *physically* indivisible: as whole spacetime representations they cannot be split into separate parts, but as representations they contain a great deal of internal microstructure and have dimensions. It is interesting to note that the idea of microscopic spacetime universes within large-scale spacetime was studied by Soviet physicists, in connection with the physics of charged particles and black holes. The closed Friedman universe—the closed, positively-curved spacetime discussed in Chapter Ten—can be treated as a physical particle that has no net charge, for the charges in the closed universe balance one another. It is then imagined that an additional charge is introduced to the neutral, closed universe-particle in order to create a charged particle, a semi-closed universe connected to the external spacetime by a spacetime neck. These semi-closed, charged particle-universes have been called *friedmons.*[7] The idea was a response to a problem encountered in classical and relativistic theories of charged particles: if a charged particle has a small but finite size, like the old corpuscles, why does it not fly apart under the mutual repulsion of its charged parts? Alternatively, if the particle is taken to be a point, the zero size leads to an infinitely large field-energy at the particle. Physicists use a mathematical technique, called *renormalization,* to transform the infinities into finite values. The friedmon theory was essentially a means of constructing an extended, charged particle that is prevented from flying apart by gravitation, by its spacetime micro-curvature. According to V. L. Ginzburg, the friedmon appears to the "faraway outside observer" as a particle, and this "unconventional but far from trivial approach" to the question of primary matter is interesting because it links the macrocosm with elementary particles and bears on the relationship between the general theory of relativity and quantum mechanics.[8]

The idea of the friedmon differs from the pointworld in an important respect: there is no suggestion that the friedmon is a microcosmic representation of the macrocosm from the perspective of its spacetime location. The friedmons seem to be tiny, semi-closed particle-universes that are not tied to one another or to the universe as a whole in any profound sense. Pointworlds, on the other hand, are tiny, perspectual representations of our spacetime cosmos, with properties that would relate directly to the overall universe they represent. Pascal's atoms, the atomic solar system, and the friedmons are independent particles, and could contain widely differing structures and contents. In contrast, pointworlds—like the units in Leibniz's metaphysics—are essentially the same, equivalent to one another. Each state of a monadic atom is a perspective on the current state of the universe, and so every piece of matter expresses the universe. Similarly, the pointworld interpretation supposes that the spacetime universes at the worldpoints are all the same, yet unique. Their structures display the spacetime pattern from their specific point-locations. The units are not physically divisible, for they are complete spacetimes containing the entire course of transformations, all creations, dissolutions, fragmentations and unions.

POINTWORLD DIMENSIONS

How might a Totality be represented at a worldpoint within another Totality? How is the pointworld, with its own set of spacetime dimensions, to be represented in the spacetime dimensions of its host Totality? Two possibilities suggest themselves to me:

1. A *common* embedding-dimension scheme

Suppose that the Totality structure consists of a *closed* four-dimensional spacetime surface, like the closed Friedman universe, embedded in a five-dimensional space. The pointworld might then be a tiny representation of the Totality embedded in the *same* five-dimensional space as the Totality. Attached to each worldpoint on the surface of the large 5-D hypersphere is a tiny 5-D hypersphere, which is a representation of the large sphere from the perspective of the worldpoint. Imagine a three-dimensional analogue in which the spacetime has one spatial dimension and one time dimension, plus the embedding dimension, (1+1+1)D. This constitutes a closed 2-D spacetime, and the universe consists of a 2-sphere, the surface of the familiar 3-D sphere. The surface of the sphere is dotted with worldpoints, and at each worldpoint is a small spherical 3-D representation of the large 3-D sphere. As each little sphere is a representation of the large sphere from the *perspective* of the worldpoint, it might be valid to suppose that the small sphere is attached to the inside surface of the large sphere. Thus, the surface of the large sphere acquires a 'thickness' on its inner surface, consisting of small, spherical representations.

For clarity, the diagram of the Totality (Figure 13.1.) contains only three worldlines, each consisting of a sequence of three worldpoints. The diagram shows a view from the outside, although the actual experience would be from the centre-of-experience, which is indicated by the star on the surface of the large sphere. The small spheres are the pointworlds, and the eight circled dots are the worldpoints, the centres-of-experience of the pointworld representations. The star indicates the central or *primary* centre-of-experience of the Totality, whilst the dots indicate the *secondary* centres-of-experience, the experiential

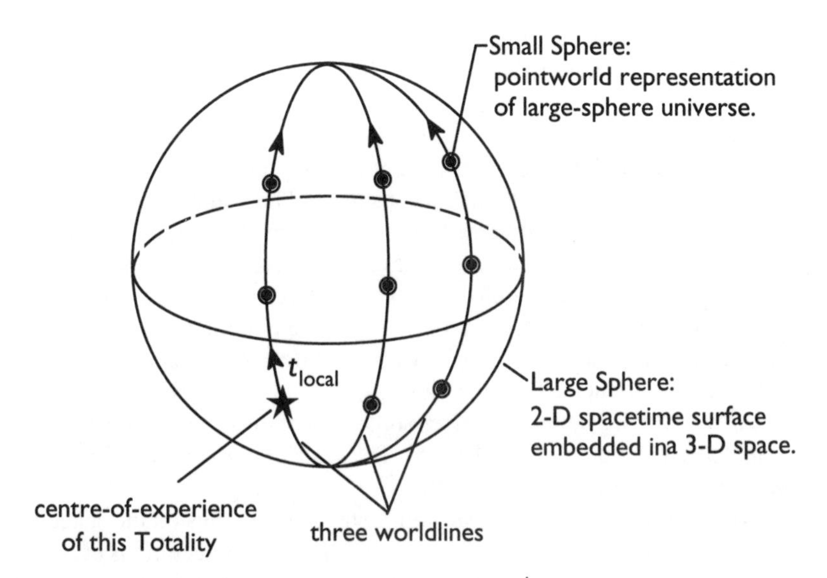

Figure 13.1. 2-D spacetime analogue: pointworlds embedded in the same embedding space as the overall spacetime.

centres of the pointworlds. The whole world-system consists of nine Totalities, so eight further diagrams would be required for a complete picture of the intermediate substratum. It has been assumed that there is no pointworld representation located at the primary centre-of-experience (in the diagram there is no little sphere at the star), for the Totality as a whole (the large sphere) constitutes the perspective from the primary centre.

An interesting feature of this model is the natural way in which a minimum length emerges. Pointworlds cannot overlap one another, for each is a distinct, closed spacetime representation of the overall closed spacetime. They have the characteristic of *impenetrability,* or *antitypia,* to use the ancient term employed by Leibniz. In consequence, the worldpoints on the large spherical surface must have an absolute minimum separation between their centres in embedding space that is in the order of one pointworld diameter. This is illustrated in Figure 13.2.

The value of the minimum separation of worldpoints, spatially and temporally, is therefore dependent on the size-ratio between the Totality and its pointworld representation. In the case of the sphere, this is the ratio between the diameter D of the Totality and diameter d of the pointworld. The minimum separation between worldpoints implies that nature proceeds in leaps: there is a minimum spacetime separation between each temporal state of an object. This is an interesting feature of the model because it has a bearing on the questions of finite divisibility and discontinuous motion raised by Zeno's paradox and quantum theory.

The sizes of the pointworld and the large spacetime can be compared if we assume that there is indeed a connection with quantum theory. In this case, the diameter of a pointworld can be estimated to have the same order of magnitude as the Planck length, which is a theoretical minimum length obtained by combining three fundamental constants of nature, the velocity of light *c*, the gravitational constant *G* and Planck's constant *h*. The Planck length, given by $\sqrt{(Gh/c^3)}$, is about 10^{-33} centimetres. To obtain an estimate of the diameter of the spacetime cosmos, we assume that the closed Friedman model is applicable. Using an estimate for the Hubble constant, deduced from galactic redshifts, a radius of curvature in the order of 10^{28} cm may be obtained. As a very rough estimate, the diameter d of the pointworld would then be about 10^{60} times smaller than the diameter D of the closed spacetime in which it is embedded (that is, $D/d = 10^{60}$). Figure 13.3. gives some idea of these very large and small sizes in relation to more familiar lengths. The scale of human life is fairly close to the midpoint of the great and small.

This first explanation of pointworld dimensionality relies on the spacetime pattern being spatially closed and temporally limited. Spacetime is curled-up into a finite, hollow geometry, enabling the finite, scaled-down pointworld representations to be located in the embedding space, perhaps on the inside surface. If space is not closed, then the Totality spacetime pattern would be infinite, and there would be an undesirable overlapping of the spatially-infinite embedded worlds. They would no longer be *point*worlds. If time is unlimited, as in the Einstein 'cylinder' universe or in an infinitely oscillating universe, there would again be problems, with the embedded representations extending infinitely through the embedding spacetime.

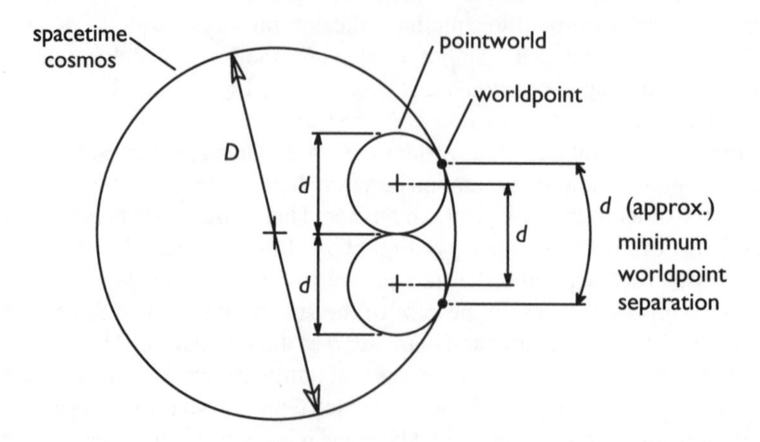

Figure 13.2. The minimum separation of worldpoints, owing to the impossibility of experiential pointworlds overlapping one another. (The magnitude of d relative to D is greatly exaggerated in the diagram.)

Scale (cm)	Object	Unit
	'Radius' of closed universe?	
	Limit of observable universe	
10^{28}	Furthest observed objects	
	Most distant galactic clusters	
	Diameter of local supercluster	
10^{24}	Distance to the Andromeda galaxy	
	Diameter of our galaxy	
10^{20}		
	Distance to Sirius	
	Distance covered by light in one year	ly
10^{16}		
	Diameter of solar system	
	Earth-Sun distance (astronomical unit)	AU
10^{12}		
	Diameter of Sun	
	Diameter of Saturn	
	Diameter of Earth	
10^{8}		
	Mount Everest	
	Mount Snowdon	km
10^{4}		
	Tree	
	Child	m
	Apple	
10^{0} = 1 cm	Hazelnut	cm
	Poppy seed; grain of sand	mm
	Micro-organism	
	Cell	
10^{-4}		µm
	Wavelengths of visible light	
	Molecules	nm
10^{-8}	Atoms; wavelength of X-rays	Å
	Wavelength of gamma rays	pm
10^{-12}	Atomic nuclei	
	Protons; neutrons	fm
10^{-16}	W and Z bosons (transmit weak force)	
10^{-18} – 10^{-32}	? nothing known for certain at these scales	
10^{-33}	Planck length (scale of embedded dimensions?)	

Figure 13.3. The scale of lengths, calibrated in powers of ten (centimetre units).[9]

2. A *separate* embedding-dimension scheme.

The second approach to pointworld dimensionality avoids the overlap or intertwining of spatially- or temporally-open representations, by placing the spacetime representations in their *own* embedding dimensions. The pointworld, then, has no extension at all in the five dimensions of the large-scale Totality pattern. Its extension is completely internal. In the first approach, a pointworld has no extension in the 4-D spacetime surface (in which it appears as an extensionless point, the worldpoint), but has extension in the 5-D embedding space. In the second approach, the pointworld has no extension in the 4-D surface *or* the 5-D embedding space, for its extension is contained in a further set of five dimensions. In the 5-D space of the Totality, the pointworld is an extensionless point with its own internal dimensions, and there is no pointworld overlap because the pointworld is not extended in the large 5-D spacetime of the Totality. This means that any spacetime pattern, spatially closed or open, temporally finite or infinite, can be accommodated, but there is no longer a simple explanation for a minimum separation between worldpoints.

To illustrate the idea of the unextended pointworld, we have to consider a universe that has a manageable number of dimensions. Consider a zero-dimensional space, consisting of a dot or point. Let us suppose that the dot-universe is of limited duration, the dot having five temporal states from creation to extinction. The spacetime consists of one worldline along which

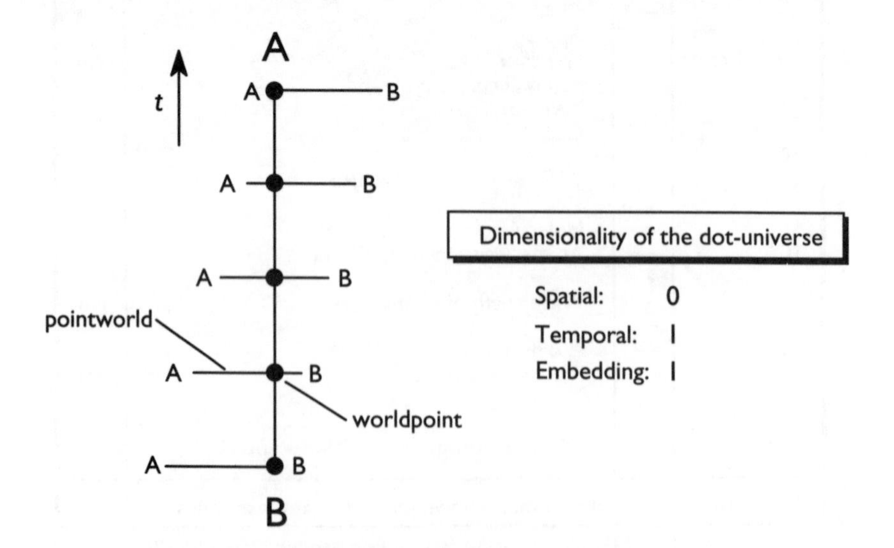

Figure 13.4. The dot-universe: the linear spacetime is represented at each point-state. Note that there is no overlapping of the linear pointworlds because they are not extended in the dimension in which they are separated from one another.

are spaced the five worldpoint states of the dot. Now let us suppose that each state of the dot is a pointworld. This means that at each worldpoint in the linear spacetime, there is a representation of the whole spacetime from the spacetime perspective of the worldpoint. Each representation is one-dimensional, like the large original, and lies in an extra dimension. This makes the whole spacetime universe into a two-dimensional plane, (0+1+1)D.

If the planar universe were an experiential universe analogous to a Totality, the whole system would consist of five planar universes, each with the primary centre-of-experience at one of the dot-states. If we take our spacetime universe to be, say, a closed five-dimensional sphere or a string of such spheres (oscillating universe), then the full dimensionality of the Totality rises from five to ten when we include the pointworlds. The pointworlds are unextended points in the large-scale spacetime, but in the full, ten-dimensional view are five-dimensional spheres.

KALUZA-KLEIN THEORIES

The idea of dimensions-within-dimensions has had some currency this century, and in recent years has come to the fore in the supergravity and superstring theories of theoretical physics. A brief look at these recent speculations will be of interest, owing to their use of extra spatial dimensions and the curved spacetime concept of General Relativity to explain the basic forces of nature. Of course, there is much more to the modern physical theories than the idea of extra dimensions, and the theories differ in some significant ways from the pointworld picture presented here. For instance, the extra dimensions of the current scientific theories are *purely spatial*—the spatialized time dimension occurs only as one of the four familiar spacetime dimensions. Extra time dimensions would not make much sense in the current physical worldview. In the pointworld picture, the extra time dimensions are merely the time dimension of the large spacetime represented at the worldpoints—they are not mysterious, extra time dimensions, additional and unrelated to the familiar time dimension. It is also worth bearing in mind that the extra spatial dimensions of current speculations may one day be abandoned for more promising concepts, as so often happens in the development of physical theory. Yet the appearance of embedded dimensions in physics is of sufficient relevance to warrant a brief look.

The use of extra dimensions in physics is part of the long-running attempt to unify the physical picture of the world. In the discussion of the aether in Chapter Eight, we noted that electrical and magnetic forces were unified in the nineteenth century, by the theory of electromagnetism. This unification left two distinct forces in nature, the electromagnetic and gravitational, which are quite different from each other and are difficult to bring together in one physical description. An early attempt this century, put forward by G. Nordström in 1914, brought gravity and electromagnetism together by deriving them both from a five-dimensional version of electromagnetism. Although this attempt was not satisfactory, the idea of a fifth dimension re-emerged in the context of Einstein's General Relativity, when Theodor Kaluza (1885–1954) reformulated the gravitational field equations of General Relativity in five dimensions, instead of the usual four, and found that the result is equivalent to the gravitational field equations *plus* the electromagnetic field equations in four dimensions. In this way, electromagnetism can be interpreted as an expression of a five-dimensional, curved spacetime, with four space dimensions and one time dimension. But we experience a world of three spatial dimensions, not four, so it may be wondered what has become of the extra spatial dimension if it is taken to be a real structural facet of the underlying world and not just a mathematical expedient to bring about unification. If it is supposed that the fifth dimension is curled up into extremely small circles at points in 4-D spacetime, then it can be argued that the existence of an extra dimension has not been discovered in the past because the dimension is so small. The usual four dimensions of spacetime are referred to as *expanded,* to distinguish them from a *curled-up* or *compact* dimension. This circular dimension gives a particle an extra freedom of movement—we can imagine a particle that is stationary in 3-D space but has some movement round the curled-up, circular dimension. In 1926, Oskar Klein (1894–1977) investigated Kaluza's five-dimensional spacetime theory in the light of quantum mechanics, and estimated the radius of the compact circular dimension to be about 10^{-30} cm.

There is an analogy that helps to bring across the idea of a compact dimension. Consider a long cylinder, such as a pipe or a drinking straw. From a distance, the cylinder appears to be one dimensional, a line, but on closer inspection a two-dimensional surface is revealed (Figure 13.5.).

The Kaluza-Klein type of theory was resurrected towards the end of the 1970s in the hope that it would provide a way of unifying the forces of nature. In the meantime, two extra forces had been discovered, the *strong force* that acts between quarks, the component particles of protons and neutrons, and the *weak force* that shows itself in the beta decay of atomic nuclei. The weak force and electromagnetism were successfully united in *electroweak theory,* and attempts were made to include the strong force, described by *quantum chromodynamics,* in a more general theory, a *grand unified theory* (GUT). This left the gravitational force on its own, distinct from the other three forces. The next unification, the marriage of the quantum theories of electroweak and strong forces to the classical gravitational theory of General Relativity, has proved to be a great challenge. The Kaluza-Klein type of theory has appealed to physicists who have sought to bring gravity into the unified fold: the four known forces of nature would be derived from the curvature of a spacetime having a number

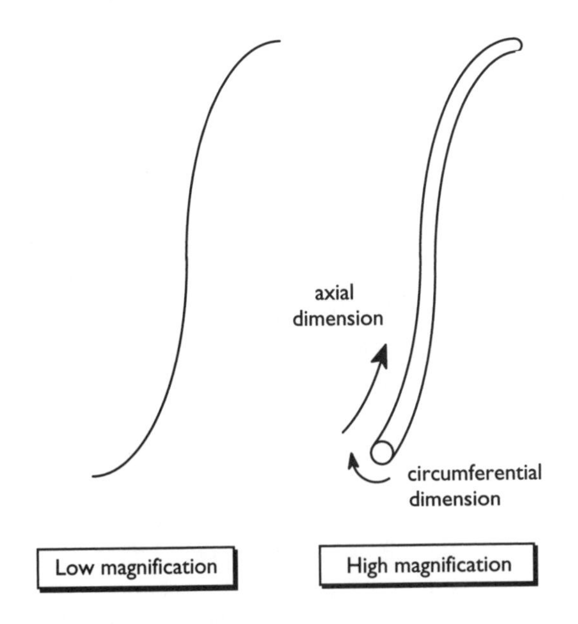

Figure 13.5. Cylinder, showing expanded and compact dimensions. The axial dimension of the cylinder corresponds to a familiar expanded dimension of spacetime, whereas the circumferential dimension, round the surface of the tube, corresponds to a curled-up dimension of spacetime.

of compact dimensions. In the *supergravity* theories, a total of eleven dimensions (seven compact space dimensions plus the four familiar spacetime dimensions) came to have a special appeal, but eleven dimensions proved to be unsatisfactory, because the number does not give nature the handedness that is found in the weak force interactions, first observed in the beta-decay of a radioactive isotope of cobalt.

In the meantime, another approach was undergoing development, namely *superstring* theory, which utilises the concept of a *string* to explain gravitational force, and again brings in extra dimensions. The string, which has a small extension in one dimension, replaces the conventional, zero-dimensional point-particle of physics in an effort to get round the problematic infinities of the sort we noted in the discussion of friedmons. The infinities become worse when attempts are made to give the force fields a quantum treatment, and are intractable in the quantum account of gravitational fields at point-particles. The strength of the superstring theory is that the problematic infinities, and related mathematical difficulties, can be lessened or removed all together when particles are interpreted as vibrational states of extended strings. In spacetime, the string consists of a *worldsheet,* in contrast to the worldline traced by the dimensionless point of earlier physical theories. Superstring theory was initially based on a total of ten dimensions, consisting of the usual four spacetime dimensions with six additional compact space dimensions, and there have been speculations that the ten-dimensional spacetime may be an approximation to a spacetime of infinite dimensions.[10] Since 1984 there has been a great deal of interest in superstring theories, and some physicists hope that superstrings will eventually provide a *Theory of Everything* (TOE), describing the four forces in one theory, with gravitation successfully incorporated in a quantum theory. Superstring theories are promising, but require further development, and confirmation by experiment. They may yet require significant changes if they are to provide an accurate mathematical model of the physical/structural aspects of the world.

DIMENSIONAL LEVELS

The structure of the spacetime Totalities can be elaborated by pursuing the worlds-within-worlds idea and its extrapolation to infinity that we have seen in the seventeenth- and eighteenth-century flights of imagination. Each pointworld is an embedded cosmic pattern, and therefore its inner spacetime structure is also a pattern of pointworlds—there are pointworlds within pointworlds. In each pointworld, all the other pointworlds are represented, and a pointworld representation corresponding to the large-scale spacetime, the Totality, is one of these. The original large-scale spacetime could be called the *ground-level* spacetime to distinguish it from its exact pointworld representations. Now the pointworlds within the pointworlds are also spacetime patterns, and therefore contain further pointworlds, and this progression continues endlessly to give an infinite chain of pointworlds-within-pointworlds.

In the first scheme of pointworld dimensionality discussed above, each pointworld on the inner surface of the ground-level sphere has pointworlds on its own inner surface, and so on *ad infinitum*. Each level of embedded pointworlds introduces four extra curled-up dimensions. This is illustrated in Figure 13.6. 'A(0)' marks the primary centre-of-experience and 'B(-1)' is a diametrically-opposite worldpoint, at the antipodes of the spherical universe.

In the second model of pointworld dimensionality, the levels of pointworlds do not share the same embedding space. The embedding occurs in level-upon-level of embedding space, continuing downwards indefinitely ('downwards', of course, is used metaphorically, referring to dimensional levels, not directions in three-dimensional space). So each Totality consists of a ground-level spacetime, throughout which are nested cosmic patterns in ever-descending dimensional levels. If we subscribe to the basic, five-dimensional cosmic pattern of closed spacetime, then each successive level contributes five dimensions to the full dimensionality of the Totality, which is therefore an infinite multiple of five. Whatever the method of pointworld inclusion in a Totality, a pointworld

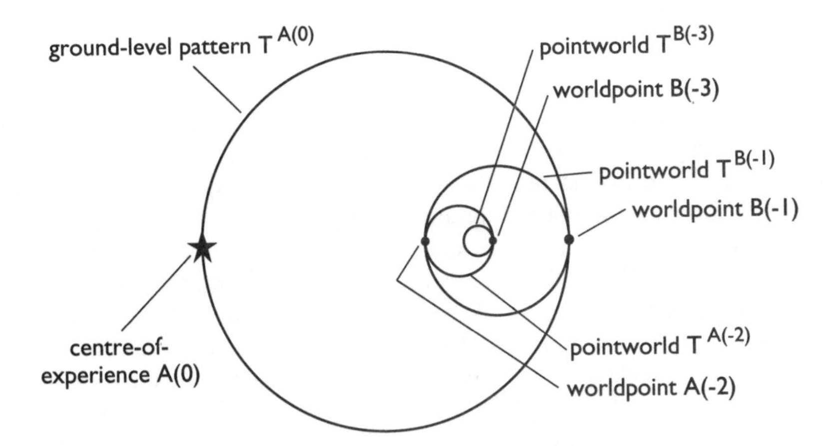

Figure 13.6. Closed, spacetime pointworlds-within-pointworlds in a single Totality with centre-of-experience at A(0) (pointworld sizes greatly exaggerated). The number in brackets indicates the level of representation, the ground-level labelled zero, and each subsequent level by a negative integer.

Pattern $T^{A(0)} = T^{A(-2)} = T^{A(-4)} = \ldots$

Pattern $T^{B(-1)} = T^{B(-3)} = T^{B(-5)} = \ldots = T^{B(0)}$, the ground-level pattern of the Totality which has B as its primary centre-of-experience.

OXO

XOO OOX

OXO OOX XOO OXO

primary centre-of-experience

Ground Level

a secondary centre-of-experience

First Descending Level

Second Descending Level

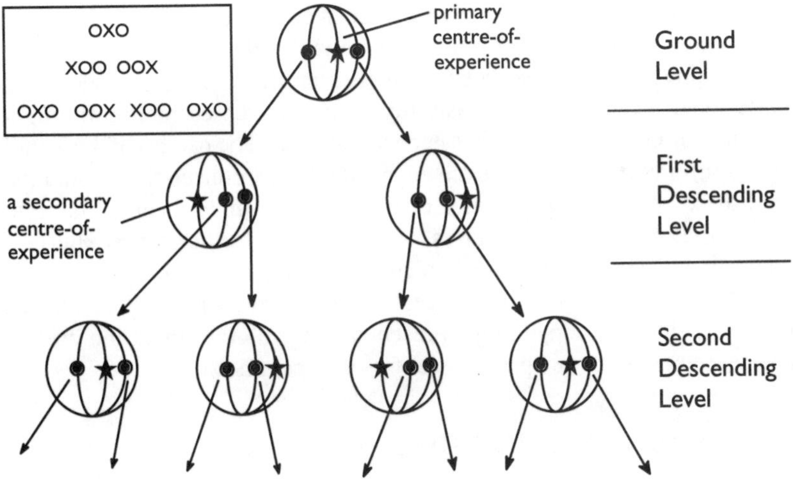

Figure 13.7. Schematic representations of descending dimensional levels, for a universe containing three worldpoints. Note that the ground-level pattern (oxo) is absent in the first descending level but reappears in the second.

at any dimensional level is a complete representation of a Totality. Figure 13.7. provides two schematic representations of a Totality, showing the ground-level spacetime with descending levels of spacetimes. The universe is the same one illustrated in Figure 13.1., but with three worldpoints instead of nine, for the sake of clarity. Again, this Totality is just one of the Totalities that constitute the complete world-system at the intermediate level. The inset diagram is a simplification of the main diagram, using the letter 'X' for primary and secondary centres-of-experience and the letter 'O' for off-centre pointworlds.

The dimensionality of the Totality has been extended infinitely at the microscopic level. A question arises: is it reasonable to extend the dimensionality of a Totality 'upwards' as well as 'downwards'? This would mean that the ground-level pattern is itself set in a higher-level spacetime along with representations of the ground-level spacetimes of all the other Totalities. The higher-level spacetime—in which the cosmic pattern is about 10^{60} times larger than our own, according to the earlier estimate—would be just the first of an infinite series of ascending levels.

The *expanded* dimensions of everyday experience, our four 'familiar' spacetime dimensions, would then be *compact* dimensions in the higher levels. It may be that the idea of ascending dimensions is only compatible with the second scheme of pointworld dimensionality, for this model can accept infinitely large dimensions at a point, unlike the 'common embedding space' scheme. In the latter, Totalities with ascending levels could not be represented as distinct pointworlds in the ground-level space, for there would be overlap between the greater dimensions.

In summary, the original Totality can be deepened and extended into a vast spacetime architecture of infinite dimensional levels. The basic pattern in its various equivalent forms has been infinitely reproduced throughout descending dimensional levels, and the possibility of further representation throughout ascending dimensional levels has been touched on. The pattern of the Totality, with its infinite dimensional levels, is infinitely reproduced throughout itself. What these bewildering infinities of dimensions simply mean is that a total experiential perspective contains within itself all other total experiential perspectives. This leads to an infinite multiplication of perspectives within one perspective, the Totality. Furthermore, there are many such Totalities, all unique yet equivalent, each containing representations of all the others and itself, and each associated with one primary centre-of-experience.

COSMOS AS ATOM: THE KOSMON

By making each worldpoint into a pointworld-representation of a Totality, cosmology and microphysics are brought together. A connection between the cosmos and the world of microphysics has long been suspected by physicists impressed with the numerical coincidences between physical values and their combinations. From the early 1920s, Eddington was fascinated by intriguing similarities between various dimensionless numbers formed from the physical constants of cosmology and microphysics. He suggested that the total number of particles in the universe may govern the values of the fundamental constants, including the masses of the electron and proton, thus forming a bridge between the cosmic and microphysical worlds. He deduced the total number of particles in the universe to be in the order of 10^{79}:

$$N = 2 \times 136 \times 2^{256} = \text{approx. } 10^{79}$$

The derivation used no observational data, but was based on a line of reasoning that considered the number of wavefunctions in a relativistic, finite, positively-curved space, each wavefunction being associated with four measurements. Eddington had first produced a quantitative estimate by dividing the estimated mass of the universe by the mass of a hydrogen atom, a calculation that gave a figure in the order of 10^{79}. The number N, which is necessarily a whole number, assumed great importance in Eddington's theorising, and he connected it with two other large dimensionless numbers with magnitudes in the order of 10^{39}, which is approximately the square root of N. One of these numbers is the ratio between the electrostatic and gravitational forces acting between an electron and proton, the so-called *force-constant.*

The 'big numbers' question has been approached in another way, first suggested by Paul Dirac (1902–84) in 1937. If the ratio of unity between the large dimensionless numbers reflects some underlying law of nature that is preserved throughout the evolution of the universe, then some of the so-called constants of nature incorporated in these numbers, such as the gravitational constant G, Planck's constant h, and the electric charge e, may have to vary with time to keep the ratio at unity. This will be the case if the Hubble constant is used to derive the large numbers, for in most cosmological models the value of the constant varies with the age of the universe. Some of the other constants may then have to change to counter-balance the change in the Hubble constant. The large size of the dimensionless numbers is then attributed to the advanced age of the universe. This time-dependency can be avoided if a true time-constant is used in the derivation of the large numbers, in place of the Hubble constant. The duration of the closed Friedman universe expansion-contraction cycle could be used instead, as this would be a true constant for the universe. Related to these matters is a question concerning the compact dimensions of Kaluza-Klein theories and the expansion of the universe.[11] Why is the expansion of our familiar three-dimensional space not accompanied by an expansion of the compact space dimensions of the Kaluza-Klein theories, which apparently would be detectable as changes of fundamental constants such as G? In the pointworld picture of the spatially-closed universe, the cosmic space expansion is included in the compact dimensions, for the curled-up, compact dimensions contain the complete time-evolution of the universe. The compact dimensions are simply pointworld micro-representations of the large expanding-contracting universe, and as such have the same size wherever they may be located in the spacetime universe.

The ultimate objects of study in cosmology and microphysics, the cosmos and the fundamental particle, turn out to be the same in the pointworld scheme. The fundamental particle consists of a worldline of pointworlds, a worldline-group of Totality micro-representations. Since each state of the particle is one perspective on the cosmos (Greek *kosmos,* the mathematically-ordered universe), the particle might appropriately be named a *kosmon.* Information concerning the overall spacetime cosmos would provide information about the fundamental particle, and vice versa, for the cosmic pattern is found in the large and the small, the ground-level spacetime and the pointworld particle-state. For instance, the 'shape' or geometry of the cosmic pattern would recur at the cosmic and microphysical levels. In the chapter on General Relativity, we considered the overall geometry of spacetime, which is the geometry of the cosmic pattern. If the universe is not expanding, the cosmic pattern is not curved temporally. The 'cylindrical' spacetime of Einstein's solution is an example of such a cosmic pattern, and would form the cosmic pattern and fundamental particle. If we accept the expanding universe theories, we have a number of options. Firstly, there is the closed model, expanding and contracting. If the embedding dimension of curved spacetime is interpreted in a realist fashion, the cosmic pattern is spread over the four-dimensional surface of a 5-D sphere. This gives the 5-D spherical cosmic pattern. But if the universe is temporally infinite and continues to expand forever, then the cosmic pattern has no boundaries, and space is hyperbolic or flat. If these are the pointworlds, then not all of the embedded dimensions are circular, and there is no limiting radius for the spatial diameter of the expanding universe. Finally, if the universe is oscillating then the pattern would be in the form of a sequence of 5-D spheres, unending if the universe undergoes an infinite number of oscillations. If we embed a sequence of 5-D spheres in the surface of a 5-D sphere, then one of the internal dimensions at a worldpoint, the cosmic time dimension, is extended beyond one oscillation. If the universe oscillates forever, then the extension in its five-dimensional space is infinite. If it oscillates a finite number of times, then the extension is the length of a number of spacetime hyperspheres linked together. At each worldpoint of the pointworld string of spacetimes, there would be another such pointworld string, and so on, *ad infinitum.*

The fundamental particle or 'atom' of the scheme, the kosmon, has some special features that are worth emphasising. Clearly, the form of atomism that has emerged here is very different from the ancient Democritean and Epicurean atomisms, the atomism of the corpuscular philosophy, the chemical atomism of the nineteenth century, and the atomism of the early twentieth century. It is also different from current particle theories, but here there are some potential areas of contact.

1. *Internal Structure:* The kosmons are not simple entities devoid of internal structure. Each pointworld state of a kosmon is extended in its inner dimensions, having an infinitely detailed internal structure. This internal structure is a representation of the spacetime cosmos, and contains further inner dimensions. Thus each state of the kosmon 'atom' contains representations of its own states and the states of all the other kosmons. Democritean atoms had no inner structure, and the fundamental particles of modern physics, such as the electron, have generally been viewed as unextended and structureless.

2. *Distinguishability:* Kosmons are equivalent to one another but are not identical. Each temporal state of a kosmon represents a unique perspective of the cosmos, for the pointworld states are embedded representations of Totalities, which have equivalent but unique spacetime structures. In the chemical atomism of the nineteenth century and early twentieth century, the atoms of each element were viewed as identical. The kosmons, on the other hand, fall into a different tradition, in which each particle is viewed as different from every other, because the spatio-temporal attributes of location vary from particle to particle. The Stoics[12] held such a view, and Leibniz provided a famous expression of the idea in his *Principle of the Identity of Indiscernibles:* no two things can be exactly alike. Leibniz's monads, of course, illustrate the principle.

3. *Wholeness:* each state of a kosmon is a representation of the whole cosmic spacetime. It is an atom which has whole states, each containing its past, present and future states and the states of all other kosmons. This is in contrast to most other concepts of atoms, which present atoms as fragmentary parts of a whole, lacking completeness in themselves. The usual reductionistic implications of atomism are avoided here, because the fundamental particles are whole structures. Pointworld particles build up the patterns of objects and the patterns of objects build up the particles—neither is more basic than the other.

4. *Experience:* In the current discussion, the emphasis has been on the spacetime structure of the kosmon-states, on the physical aspects of the Totality and its micro-representations, but it is important to stress that the kosmons are not simply structural, for their pointworld states are substratal

experiences, experiential perspectives of the entire, spatio-temporal cosmos, and are therefore characterised by whatever astructural facets belong to substratal experience. The materialist reduction of psychological experience to physical particles is rejected because atoms and their structures are whole experiences. The discussion in Chapter Four suggested that structure in the underlying basis might involve some kind of transparent colour quality, and that the experience has pronounced noetic (knowing, understanding, meaning) and feeling (love, benevolence, compassion, beauty) characteristics. The pointworld states of kosmons are therefore not to be regarded as lifeless things , as purely material or physical particles, but as experiences characterised by universal intelligence and the universal loving attitude, each unique but equivalent, and multiplied infinitely throughout dimensional levels of the cosmos. Each is a living continent of knowing and feeling, and in the universal experience would be discerned as an intelligible, living 'Other', rather than an inert 'It'. The physical terminology of 'pointworlds' and 'kosmon' particles is a way of focusing the discussion on the structural facets, but could be misleading if the other experiential features were overlooked.

5. *Multiple Location:* Unlike classical atoms, which have single, discrete spatial locations, each state of a kosmon is infinitely multiplied throughout the spacetime universe, within the inner structure of its past and future states and in the states of other kosmons. This multiplication also applies to patterns of pointworlds, to composite objects, as we shall see in the next section.

6. *Transformation:* In the older theories, the material atoms of nature were often regarded as unchanging and everlasting, and unaffected by any impact. In alternative views, the corpuscles could be broken up into smaller chunks of matter, and could coalesce into larger pieces. The particles of modern physics can undergo transformations into one another during particle interactions, and can be very short-lived, decaying into other particles. The mutual annihilation of the electron and the anti-matter positron into gamma radiation is a well-known example. Now, the kosmon cannot be broken into parts, being a whole spacetime cosmos, but it undergoes internal transformation as it changes its location from state to state. There is a continual transformation of inner structure from temporal state to temporal state. The changes consist of a shift of centre with an accompanying change of perspective on the total spacetime pattern and alterations of worldpoint separations that this entails. The inner structure of the particle undergoes geometrical transformations that correspond to shifts of points-of-view between successive states.

In modern thought, the atomism of the kosmons is closest to the monadic atomism of Leibniz, whilst in the ancient world, its kinship may be with an idea of Anaxagoras of Clazomenae (*c.*500–*c.*428 B.C.), if only to a limited extent. The feature of Anaxagoras' philosophy that interests us here is his understanding of parts, an understanding that avoids reductionistic elementarism or atomism. According to Anaxagoras, everything contains something of everything else, and therefore things cannot exist separately.[13] Infinite divisibility implies the relativity of size-descriptions—something is small or large in relation to other things.

It seems that Anaxagoras hoped to overcome the deficiencies of theories that entertain constituents having nothing in common with the things they constitute: Anaxagoras asked how hair could originate from something that is not hair or flesh from something that is not flesh.[14] The units of the system, the 'seeds' or 'portions', were termed *homoeomeries* by Aristotle, 'things with like parts'. Each of these portions is infinitely divisible into smaller portions, and each contains all of the diverse ingredients that make up the world. Each tiny portion of matter therefore contains something of hair, something of flesh, and so forth. In this way, Anaxagoras avoided the reductionism of theories that postulate one or a few basic elements or a bare world of atoms in motion. However, it is not very clear exactly what he intended, and various interpretations have been suggested. One problem is the ambiguous statement that a portion of everything is in everything. What is meant by 'everything'—material ingredients, qualities, opposites, or complete things such as trees and people? Another problem stems from Anaxagoras' view that something derives its characteristic features from its most abundant constituents. Thus, a strand of hair would be made up of constituents that are themselves predominantly constituted of hair, although they contain something of everything else as well. The characteristic features of the strand of hair would therefore be traced to a predominance of hair-ingredients in ever smaller constituents, *ad infinitum,* and it has been argued that this 'infinite regress' fails to explain what distinguishes one substance from another.[15]

Anaxagoras is also noted for his introduction of Mind as the chief principle, a mind that knows everything, is distinctly corporeal, but is not present in every portion. Sense-perception, unlike Mind, finds only the predominant portions constituting a thing, not the entirety of portions. Mind arranged all things in the past, present and future, and initiated a rotating universe. Although Anaxagoras' philosophy of nature is obscure, it presented a number of suggestive ideas on which later thinkers could draw, such as an all-knowing, creative Mind, and the idea of parts that are microcosmic in the sense of containing something of everything. Two thousand years later, Nicholas of Cusa recalled the philosophy of Anaxagoras while discussing his own microcosmic ideas, arguing that each thing 'contracts' or reflects the universe within itself: *Quodlibet esse in quodlibet,* every thing is in every thing.[16]

MULTIPLE LOCATION

The system of Totalities and pointworlds invites us to revise our ideas about the spatial location of an object: we tend to think that an object is located in a single place, but the idea of pointworlds suggests that objects have multiple locations.[17] This is because the cosmic pattern of objects is reproduced, in its various equivalent forms, in each distinct Totality and throughout the inner, dimensional levels of the pointworlds. An object is infinitely represented in the spacetime perspectives contained in one spacetime perspective.

It follows that in the underlying world, a particular substratal object is not only located in the place we would normally ascribe to it (namely, in the ground-level cosmic pattern), but is also to be found throughout the cosmos, in the descending dimensional levels of every kosmon-state, and maybe in ascending dimensional levels, if these also exist. Tables, chairs, gardens, birds and trees are multiplied throughout the entirety of every Totality, as indeed are we all. The patterns of our bodies would be found in every particle within our bodies, and in every particle outside our bodies. If we had access to universal experiences, we might observe our bodily forms distributed throughout the universe at an infinite number of dimensional levels, in every chair, table, garden, bird and tree. Similarly, all these forms and every other form would be found infinitely reproduced in each one of us. The chair, the table, the garden, bird and tree, would be found in the inner dimensions of each particle in our bodies, as would the whole planet Earth, sun, solar system, galaxy, supercluster of galaxies, and the entire universe in its full spatio-temporal extent.

The distribution of an object throughout a Totality is such that the instances of the object become more and more numerous, and the objects smaller and smaller, the further down the hierarchy of dimensional levels we go. With an infinite number of Totalities, or a hierarchy of infinitely ascending and descending levels, there would be infinite numbers of each object in each level, but the infinities would become greater and greater further down the dimensional tiers. As far as the mathematical treatment of the system is concerned, we might hope that the increasing infinities at decreasing scales yield finitudes, like the terms of infinite series yielding finite sums.

In summary, an object, regarded as singular and ascribed just one location in the classical picture of the world, would have representations distributed throughout a spacetime Totality in infinite dimensional levels, and in all the Totalities. This feature of the substratal experience I have termed *multiple location.* The location of the object in the central, ground-level spacetime cosmos of a Totality, which is usually viewed as the only location of the object, could be called the *primary location* of the object in the substratum, to distinguish it from its representations in other dimensional levels. There would also be a perceptual form of multiple location—the sensory objects in moments of transient experience would be distributed endlessly throughout the cosmos, as parts of the pointworlds.

TRANSFORMATION AND SYMMETRY

We shall consider the transformation of kosmons in a little more detail. Consider the motion of a kosmon. In the spacetime view, the kosmon in motion consists of a static line of pointworld states, but from the flux-perspective we can imagine that the kosmon changes its pointworld states as it moves from place to place. To consider a translatory motion, I could imagine that a kosmon moves towards me. If I were able to examine the internal changes of the kosmon that accompany its motion, I would find that my body of kosmons has moved towards its centre. Our views of the universe are different: my view is from my centre-of-experience; the kosmon's view is from its perspective. Our views are different, but are transformable into each other. The closer the particle has moved towards my body, the closer my body-kosmons have moved towards the particle-centre in the kosmon. If I examined the inner dimensions of the kosmon more widely and deeply about its centre, gazing downwards in the dimensional sense (and perhaps 'sideways' and 'upwards'), then I would find the movement displayed from all perspectives, including my own current perspective represented within the kosmon. There is an infinite number of representations of the motion, from all perspectives. The inner state of the kosmon, being a representation of a Totality, contains all perspectives on the motion within itself. Furthermore, the motion is not only represented in the kosmon and in my body-kosmons, but in all the kosmons in the spacetime universe. The motion is a public affair, accompanied by transformations in all kosmon states.

Rotational motions with respect to the rest of the universe would also be depicted within the inner states of a body of kosmons. In fact, the individual kosmons comprising a spinning body would largely retain their spatial orientations relative to the rest of the universe. This is because the kosmon states are experiential spacetime perspectives, and the rotation hardly alters the spatial perspective (Figure 13.8.). In this respect, the kosmon can be likened to a gyroscope or spinning-wheel, which resists alterations to the spatial orientation of its axis.

We may wonder how the structure and transformations of kosmons tie in with inertial motion and inertial mass. There is clearly some kind of connection with the Machian-type of argument that relates the inertial behaviour of matter to the physical universe at large. In the kosmon model, the universal structure

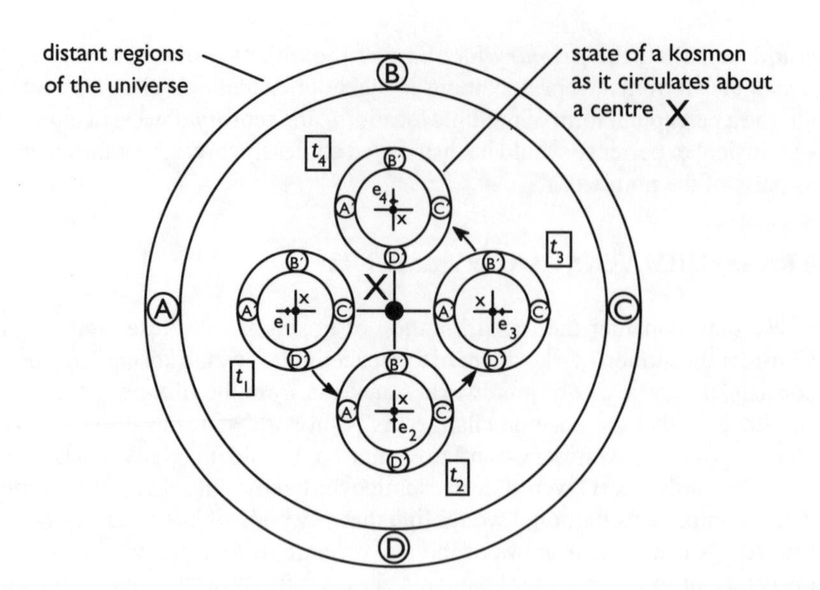

Figure 13.8. Maintenance of the spatial orientation of a kosmon as it revolves round a centre X. The centres-of-experience of the successive kosmon states are marked e_1, e_2, e_3 and e_4. A, B, C and D are distant parts of the spatial universe, and are represented in the pointworld states of the kosmon as A′, B′, C′ and D′.

is contained in the particle, and this internal spacetime structure undergoes transformation as the particle changes its perspective or state of relative motion. Acceleration would involve internal changes, in the curvature of worldlines and spacetime curvature, in accordance with general relativity. All this is rather vague, and requires detailed elaboration.

The idea of transforming the inner structure of the kosmon is related to the notion of *symmetry,* a concept of immense importance in recent physical work. Objects exhibit symmetry when transformations leave them unaffected. For instance, the square is a geometric shape that is left unchanged by rotations about its centre, through multiples of the angle 90° (90°, 180°, 270°, ...). The square is also left unchanged by mirror reflections in the four axes that divide it equally. The circle has greater symmetry: rotations through any angle about its centre and reflections about any axis through its centre leave the circle unchanged.

The study of symmetries in physical transformations has become an important tool in particle physics, and has figured in all the theories that attempt to unify the forces of nature, including the recent superstring theories.[18] Various kinds of symmetry are considered in particle physics, including the familiar space symmetries of translation, rotation and reflection *(parity),* as well as symmetries that apply to abstract or 'internal' spaces. In addition to providing a means of classifying particle properties and transformations, symmetry considerations have been used to derive the conservation laws of physics. Mathematically, this involves a demonstration *(Noether's theorem)* that a conserved quantity is associated with the invariance of a dynamical description (the *Lagrangian)* under a transformation.

The connection between symmetry and conservation laws can be interpreted in causal terms, in a way reminiscent of Leibniz's Principle of Sufficient Reason: there is a reason why something is the way it is, or happens in the way it happens, rather than otherwise. Symmetry is a lack of sufficient reason. A totally symmetrical, spatial environment provides no reason for a spontaneous change to occur in a particular direction. A particle has no reason to change its motion, whether translatory or rotational, unless the situation is made asymmetrical in some way, say, by the presence of a force. Conservation of linear momentum is connected with translational symmetry, conservation of angular momentum with rotational symmetry, and conservation of energy with the symmetry of 'translations in time' (that is, processes proceed in a manner that is independent of the time at which they occur). An important development in the use of symmetry in physics was the idea of the *gauge field,* conceived by Chen Ning Yang and Robert L. Mills in 1954. The gauge field has the role of restoring lost symmetry at each point in space and time. The gauge theories introduce the notion of special particles that carry forces between other particles—the photon is the gauge particle for electromagnetism, and the graviton is the hypothetical carrier of gravitational force.

If the pointworld concept has any validity, we may wonder what relationship pointworlds and kosmons have with the particles currently described in modern physics, including the force-carriers. Symmetry considerations may provide a link, with symmetries and asymmetries described in modern physics having some connection with the structural transformations between pointworld states at various dimensional levels. The motions of a kosmon or a group of kosmons from one location to another in the flux-perspective correspond to a sequence of pointworld states. The changes in internal structure from state to state will depend on the nature of the motion, and may be associated with the various forces of nature described in the flux-view. In other words, the particles, fields, forces, charge and spin of quantum particle physics may be ways of describing the symmetry transformations that relate the curved spacetime structures throughout the various dimensional levels of the kosmons.

The idea of symmetry seems to be peculiarly apt for particles having internal spacetime structures which are mathematically transformable into one another, whereas it is not so obvious why symmetry is applicable to the particles of current physics, which have usually been viewed as structureless points. Besides considering the overall transformations of pointworld structure, we would also have to look at the curvatures of the spacetime in which the pointworlds are located. In the experiential spacetime, the pointworlds might be embedded in luminous curved spacetime, architectures of spatial *lux* connecting the point-world atoms. This curved spacetime, carrying the pointworlds, might have the form of shafts, columns, sheets or ripples of luminosity. It is possible that the surfaces currently being examined in superstring theories might be relevant: spatial cross-sections of the luminous drapery, in which the pointworlds are embedded, the 'worldsheets' of luminosity, might correspond to the particles described in current particle physics. In other words, the spacetime structure consists of pointworlds *and* the curved regions of spacetime through which the pointworld states are arranged, and it might be the latter feature of spacetime, the spacetime surfaces of luminosity, that the particle theories of modern physics have usually described.

14. MINUTE PARTICULARS

A study of relative motion and relativistic theory has led us from the idea of a single spacetime experience to a plurality of spacetime experiences, a system of total experiences, or *Totalities*. In Chapter Eleven we noted the idea of a plurality of minds in Leibniz's metaphysics, and came across related ideas in earlier philosophies. In Chapter Thirteen, conjectures on the detailed structure of spacetime were presented, leading to a universe that is structured through infinite dimensions: the whole spacetime structure is represented at each structural point, and this pointworld representation constitutes the fundamental particle-state of the system.

The route we have followed to the system of Totalities and pointworlds has been somewhat indirect: after a consideration of experience and the mind-body problem, we made an excursion into the study of mystical experiences to gather clues, and then concentrated on relative motion and spacetime. We might wonder whether any ideas comparable to the notion of pointworlds have been reached through *direct* experience. This may be a possibility if the experiential approach to the mind-body problem has some validity, but again the problematic use of mystical accounts as sources of information is likely to complicate the matter.

For example, the prior understanding of the experiencer may influence the features of the universal experience that are discriminated and remembered. Thus, in the case of the atomic structure of the world, an individual lacking some conception of atoms as structural units of matter would not be able to interpret the relevant features in terms of the atomic theories of philosophy or science.[1] Furthermore, the models presented to experiencers by contemporary atomic theories may bear little resemblance to the experiential actualities. For instance, in Chapter Thirteen we entertained the highly tentative notion that some particles considered in modern physics may correspond to luminous sheets of space in the experiential spacetime substratum—now, such sheets or strands would not be recognised as particles unless, perhaps, one were familiar with the recent superstring theories and therefore able to interpret the luminous sheets as higher-dimensional structures that correspond to the particles discussed by physicists in their descriptions of a three-dimensional world in flux. The pointworlds located in the luminous sheets *might* be recognisable as particles or atomic structural units, but an individual who encountered pointworlds in a universal experience would have difficulty relating them to the pictures of atoms and sub-atomic particles in current physical theory.

Experiential insights that may have relevance to the pointworld concept are found in the works of Plotinus, Traherne and Blake, and comparable ideas exist in Mahayana Buddhist descriptions of interpenetration. It is, of course, open to debate whether the ideas are experiential in origin or are the product of gradual philosophical development. We should therefore consider the possibility that the ideas we shall encounter are not drawn from direct experiential insights, but have arisen as interpretations, misinterpretations or novel combinations of earlier ideas. In the case of Traherne, I shall attempt to bring out the main traditional ideas in which he clothed his insights. However, it seems to me that the contribution of the past was not to furnish Traherne with his ideas, but to provide him with a language in which he could understand and express his experiential insights. We should be wary of reducing the accounts to mere combinations of earlier ideas, just as we should avoid literal interpretations of the accounts that overlook the contribution made by traditional ideas to their formulation.

THE SMALL IS GREAT

In the discussion of time and eternity in *Enneads* III.7.3., Plotinus describes eternity in a way that could have suggested the idea of an *eternity in a point* to later thinkers.

> We know it is as a Life changelessly motionless and ever holding the Universal content in actual presence; not this now and now that other, but always all; not existing now in one mode and now in another, but a consummation without part or interval. All its content is in immediate concentration as at one point...[2]

Of greater interest, however, is the appearance of the *whole in the part* idea in Plotinus' account of beauty at the level of the cosmic intelligence *(Enneads* V.8.). The passages allude to the *Phaedrus* of Plato, in which Socrates tells of the chariot-ascent to the vision of absolute reality, the colourless, shapeless realm of Forms beyond the summit of the heavens.[3] Plotinus' description of the intelligible world is no mere reworking of Plato's account: the Plotinian intelligible realm is a living, transparent, luminous world in which all things are found in each thing, the parts being wholes.

> ... all that is not of process but of authentic being they see, and themselves in all: for all is transparent, nothing dark, nothing resistant; every being is lucid to every other, in breadth and depth; light runs through light. And each of them contains all within itself, and at the same time sees all in every other, so that everywhere there is all, and all is all and each all, and infinite the glory. Each of them is great; the small is great; the sun, There, is all the Stars; and every star, again, is all the stars and sun. While some one manner of being is dominant in each, all are mirrored in every other. ... In our realm all is part rising from part and nothing can be more than partial; but There each being is an eternal product of a whole

> and is at once a whole and an individual manifesting as part but, to the keen vision There, known for the whole it is.[4]

A. H. Armstrong has suggested that "the whole of this amazing description of the intelligible world ... seems to express some kind of direct visionary experience of Plotinus himself."[5]

Later in the same work, Plotinus invites us to imagine the visible cosmos as a step towards envisioning the intelligible cosmos. When the vision comes, the distinctness and infinity of each whole part are revealed.

> Nor is each of those divine wholes a power in fragment, a power totalling to the sum of the measurable segments: the divine is one all-power, reaching out to infinity, powerful to infinity: and so great is God that his very members are infinities.[6]

In Chapter Seven we noted that the medieval 'whole in the part' idea goes back at least as far as the Plotinian discussion of the soul, and in the last chapter we considered the earlier and somewhat different 'whole in the part' notion of Anaxagoras. In the current chapter we have seen that Plotinus applied the 'whole in the part' idea to the level of *Nous,* as well as to the soul. Beneath the One, Plotinus places this eternal *Nous* and its multiplicity of intelligible objects, followed by the mutable Soul and individual souls, which in turn are reflected in the sensory world of Nature and matter. The metaphysical systems of the later Neoplatonists became more elaborate, with further levels introduced, such as the *henads* of Syrianus and Proclus, intermediate between the One and *Nous,* and in some sense parts that are wholes.[7]

AN INFINITE SPHERE IN A POINT

Thomas Traherne provides some remarkable descriptions of the deep structure of the world. It is true that his works demonstrate a knowledge of Plotinian mysticism, the Hermetica, the Christian Platonism of Florence and Cambridge, Christian mysticism and theology, as well as a familiarity with contemporary thought on ethical, philosophical and scientific matters. But his inspired descriptions of the world encountered in inward vision, and the autobiographical passages in his writings, suggest direct, experiential insights. Indeed, Traherne relates that "*it was the actual knowledge of true* Felicity *that taught him to speak of* Vertue."[8] The infinite, eternal Mind described in the ancient texts attributed to Hermes Trismegistus,[9] the infinite space and plenitude of contemporary cosmological thought, the microscopical revelations of minute structure, the traditional theologies and mystical philosophies—these provide Traherne with a language for interpreting and communicating the content of his mystical experiences. The differences between Traherne's earlier and later work may suggest that a few years were to elapse before he attained the fluency of idea and expression that we encounter in the *Centuries*.[10]

Traherne found within himself an infinity and eternity of objects. To explain his experiential discovery, and its finer details, Traherne weaved together several traditional ideas and metaphors, including the *imago Dei* in the soul, the total presence of God and the soul in the part, the principle of plenitude, the soul as a mirror of the eternal and divine, and God and the cosmos as an infinite sphere. For example, he combines a plenitude argument with an appreciation of the need for limits: infinite love requires infinite space and time for its expression, yet these infinities are not enough—infinite love must also be expressed within the limitations of *finite* space. In this manner our souls are made infinitely deep, "for God is there, and more near to us than we are to ourselves."[11] The plenitude is a consequence of God's omnipresence wholly in every centre, for He communicates "Himself wholly in every centre" (C.II.82).

> THE Omnipresence and Eternity of GOD are so far from filling the Soul, that they fit it only to be filled with infinite Objects. For by the Indwelling of GOD all Objects are infused, and contained within. The Spiritual Room of the Mind is Transcendent to Time and Place, because all Time and Place are contained therein: There is a Room in the Knowledge for all Intelligible Objects: A Room in our Esteem for all that is worthy of our Care and Desire. I confess this Room is strange and Mysterious. It is the Greatest Miracle perhaps in Nature. For it is an Infinite Sphere in a Point, an Immensity in a Centre, an Eternity in a Moment. We feel it, tho we cannot understand it.[12]

Infinite love is expressed in the smallest space and the smallest moment of time.

> my Soul is an infinite sphere in a centre. By this may you know that you are infinitely beloved: God hath made your spirit a centre in eternity comprehending all, and filled all about you in an endless manner with infinite riches. (C.II.80.)

Other seventeenth-century writers found inspiration in the idea of an infinite universe, or prized the small and microcosmic things of the world, but few, if any, esteemed both the infinite and the finite in quite the same manner as Traherne. Henry More, for instance, exulted over the infinite spaciousness and plenitude of the universe, as Marjorie Nicolson describes in her account of scientific influences on seventeenth-century poetry, *The Breaking of the Circle*. The ancient ideals of circular motion and sphericity were disappearing, challenged by the infinite void and the rectilinear motion of the new science, and More the Platonist could see a re-emergence of ancient wisdom in the collapse of the bounded universe before the infinite.[13] Yet in important details, Traherne's understanding of the infinite is different from More's. Traherne accepted that there was an immovable spiritual space distinct from matter, but he opposed any tendency towards identifying extended God and extended spirit with infinite space. Traherne felt that such identifications with empty space failed to recognise the positive attributes of God, His life, knowledge, choice, freedom, will, power, joy, glory.[14] However, Traherne could accept More's weaker view that space is a shadow of the Divine essence.[15]

Traherne's understanding of God's relation with infinite space differs from More's in a fundamental respect. Traherne supposes that the indwelling of God fills each soul-centre with infinite objects, and his position therefore has similarities with the traditional idea that we noted in Chapter Eight: the divine omnipresence occurs through God's whole presence in every part, the 'whole in the part' idea traceable through Christian writers to Plotinus.[16] Traherne gave expression to the idea in the *Meditations on the Six Days of the Creation,* a work that was first published in 1717 and attributed until recently to Susanna Hopton. In the final section, the sixth day of Creation is described, and much is made of the creation of man in the image and likeness of God, a common idea in Traherne's understanding of the soul. After some traditional microcosm-macrocosm analogies—the parts of the human body are likened to parts of the Temple of God, and the head of man to the spherical universe—Traherne explains the indivisible presence of God and the soul:

> I bless thy Name for the Indivisibility of my Nature, my Soul being like a noble Centre of thy divine Omnipresence, because it's filled with it; and indivisible, because wholly in the whole, and wholly in every part, as thou art.[17]

Now it was this kind of understanding—God and spirit "wholly in the whole, and wholly in every part"—that More opposed, along with the Cartesian dualism of unextended spirit and extended body, the 'Nullibist' position.[18] To clarify his idea that spiritual substances are incorporeal and extended, More thought it a valuable exercise to remove "two vast Mounds of Darkness",[19] the Cartesian Nullibism and the traditional 'whole in every part' account of the omnipresence of God in the universe (and the presence of a spirit or soul in a body).[20] More gave the name *Holenmerism* to the idea, and explained that Holenmerians invoke the notion to avoid making the soul divisible or corporeal, and to explain how the soul is affected simultaneously and perceives simultaneously in every part of the body, when just one part of the body is affected. More thought it ridiculous that a whole be divisible into wholes, rather than into parts, and he raised a series of objections. These objections reflect the difficulty faced by More in reconciling his notion of spirit with the traditional idea. According to More, an extended spiritual substance expands or contracts to fill a body, a property he calls "essential spissitude".[21] More is therefore unable to understand how a spirit can be fully in the whole body and yet fully in a part or point of the same body, requiring the spirit to be many thousand times greater than itself at the *same* time. If it is argued that the spirit is solely at the points of the body, then More wonders how a spirit can be fully at one point and also at all the other points, for its full presence at one point would leave nothing over for the other points. More finds unconvincing the explanation of an instantaneous motion of the spirit from point to point.[22] He dismisses the idea of a spirit wholly contained in a point, a "physical monad", as "very ridiculous", and the idea of the divine majesty and amplitude contained in a point is even worse, being "intolerable" and "plainly reproachful and blasphemous".[23] According to More, an extensionless point is a "pure Negation, or Nonentity".[24] Matter, space, spirit and God have to be extended in order to exist.

Traherne's position is no simple re-statement of the 'whole in every part' doctrine, and, as we shall see, his microscopic points are not bare mathematical points. Nor is his position a typical expression of the microcosm-macrocosm idea that was common among seventeenth-century poets. It would seem that Traherne's understanding is directly mystical, drawing on the 'interior illumination' of his mystical experience, in which the soul, as an image of God, was found to be an infinite sphere in a centre, an "Inward *Sphere of Light*".[25] Through a meditative withdrawal 'inward' from sensory experience, an infinite room of treasures and joys can be found within.[26] Because a creature is made in the Image of God, it is

> able to see all eternity with all its objects, and as a mirror to contain all it seeth: able to love all it contains, and as a Sun to shine upon its loves: able by shining to communicate itself in beams of affection and to illustrate all it illuminates with beauty and glory. (C.III.61.)

Through his inward vision, Traherne finds that

> Every man is alone the centre and circumference of it. It is all his own, and so glorious, that it is the eternal and incomprehensible essence of the Deity. (C.V.3).[27]

Thus, Traherne transfers the popular *infinite sphere* metaphor for God and the universe onto the soul. God and the divine universe indwell in the soul, investing it with the divine immensity and making it an infinite sphere *in* a centre. The infinite universe is contained in the soul, for "the dimensions of innumerable worlds are shut up in a centre" (C.IV.81.).

> Where it should lodge such innumerable objects, as it doth by knowing, whence it should derive such infinite streams as flow from it by Loving, how it should be a mirror of all Eternity, being made of nothing, how it should be a fountain or a sun of Eternity out of which such abundant rivers of affection flow, it is impossible to declare. (C.IV.81.)

With his notion of the infinite sphere in the soul-centre, Traherne might simply have meant that each person, each 'centre', is capable of mystical experience of the eternal world, that inward illumination reveals the divine world of intelligible objects. The passages we have considered so far do not necessarily imply that the eternal world is represented structurally at each of its *point*-centres, although one of the descriptions quoted before is suggestive, the "Spiritual Room of the Mind" described as an "Infinite Sphere in a Point". Now, Traherne's detailed descriptions of the soul, including his account of the soul's experience of other souls, and his references to the infinite in the smallest of things, may indicate that deep structure is indeed to be found in Traherne's universe. In the eternal view, one soul finds that other souls contain the eternal world within, and that a grain of sand is infinite.[28]

Souls are infinite in depth. Each is a "miraculous abyss of infinite abysses, an undrainable ocean, an inexhausted fountain of endless oceans" (C.II.83.). There is not "a sand nor mote in the air that is not more excellent than if it were infinite" for "the smallest is greater than an infinite treasure" (C.III.20.).

> "O what a treasure is every sand when truly understood!" (C.II.67.)

God's infinite power has to be 'moderated' by expression in the finite, in order to make the plenitude truly infinite. Mere infinite extension of objects would not yield an infinite plenitude: an infinitely-extended material body would exclude variety because it would prevent the existence of other extended bodies. Instead, "all Corporeals must be limited and bounded for each others sake".[29] The infinity of things is contained within the finitely-extended body, making it infinite in depth and interrelated with all others:

> In all Things, all Things service do to all:
> And thus a sand is Endless, though most small.
> And every Thing is truly Infinite,
> In its Relation deep and exquisite.[30]

Although souls are infinite, they are not lost in one another, and one soul "can examine and search all the chambers and endless operations of another: being prepared to see innumerable millions" (C.II.71.). It is a wonder that is "infinitely infinite" (C.II.72.),[31] each soul seeing all souls in every other soul:

> one soul which is the object of mine, can see all souls, and all the secret chambers, and endless perfections, in every soul: yea, and all souls with all their objects in every soul. Yet mine can accompany all these in one soul: and without deficiency exceed that soul and accompany all these in every other soul. (C.II.72.)

One soul can "measure all souls, wholly and fully", each of which is itself "fathomless and infinite" in its powers (C.II.71.). There are "innumerable infinities" in the soul of man:

> One soul in the immensity of its intelligence, is greater and more excellent than the whole world. The Ocean is but the drop of a bucket to it, the Heavens but a centre, the Sun obscurity, and all ages but as one day. It being by its understanding a Temple of Eternity, and God's omnipresence, between which and the whole world there is no proportion. ... And as in many mirrors we are so many other selves, so are we spiritually multiplied when we meet ourselves more sweetly, and live again in other persons. (C.II.70.)[32]

Love is the greatest of principles, and by finding God's universal love in oneself, one comes to sit on the throne of God, which is to "inhabit Eternity" (C.IV.72.). Traherne relates that he found himself on this "throne of repose and perfect rest", and thereby attained a pure vision in which: "All things were well in their proper places, I alone was out of frame and had need to be mended" (C.III.60.).

TO POSSESS ALL THINGS IN ONE POINT

It may be wondered whether Traherne's remarkable ideas were shared by any of his contemporaries. We cannot look into this matter in any depth, except to note that there are similarities between Traherne's expressions and those of Peter Sterry (1613–72), an early Cambridge Platonist and a chaplain of Cromwell. Caroline Marks mentions similarities in her paper on Traherne and the Cambridge Platonists,[33] and two of her quotations from Sterry suggest that the similarities extend to the idea of the whole in a point. Many other passages in Sterry's works confirm the observation. According to Sterry, "thou knowest what the Spirit means" if you can answer the following in the affirmative:

> Canst thou tell a way to possess all Things in one point, in a *Unity* of Life? Hast thou lookt on all Things *at once,* and seen them in a *Harmony* of Beauty? Hast thou taken in the Times and Motions of all Things Created and Uncreated in a *Concent* of Pleasures? Didst thou ever yet descry a glorious *Eternity* in each winged *Moment* of Time; a Bright *Infiniteness* in the narrow *points* of every dark Object?[34]

Man is an Image of the whole Creation, formed by God from the dust of the ground (*Genesis* 2.7), and thus:

> Man is as a living Crystal, in which the entire Form of all the world visible, and invisible is seen transparently in the whole Glass, and in every point of the Glass, by a ravishing concurrence of all parts in each, the minutest part, with a most

> beautiful, and divine Harmony arising from the accurate mixture of that Precious Dust.[35]

Christ is a mirror in which the smallest is found to contain immensities:

> *All Things, as they are known in Christ, are a Treasure.* ... This is the true multiplying, magnifying, and glorifying Glass. Each Dust is here known in the bright Form of a Beautiful Star; each Star is discovered here to be an Heaven of Stars, a new world of Glories. ... The least Point, that a Spiritual Eye can touch upon in the *Person of Christ,* is a fresh spring, a full Sea, a great and bottomless deep of all Beauties, Excellencies, and Joys that may render any thing perfectly, universally desirable.[36]

Sterry makes considerable use of the 'Image and Similitude of God' text in *Genesis* to explain his understanding of Man, world and God, and he also mentions the traditional explanation of the soul's presence in the body.[37] Sterry finds precedents for the idea:

> 'Tis true, as *Euthydemus* the Heathen taught of old; *All things are in each thing:* Or as St. *Paul* since him hath Preacht upon clearer grounds: God is *a Fulness filling all in All, Eph.* 1. 23.[38]

Vivian de Sola Pinto describes Sterry's reading as "oceanic", covering religious, philosophical, literary and scientific areas, including biblical, rabbinical, Platonic, Plotinian, Christian mystical thought, the Church Fathers, Nicholas of Cusa, Leo Hebraeus,[39] Ficino, Campanella, and Jacob Boehme.[40] But whatever ideas and images Sterry was able to borrow to frame the 'whole in the point' idea, he clearly presents it as an experiential reality, a feature of the world that is visible to those who have the "Spiritual Eye". We may wonder whether Sterry himself was inspired by the "Marvellous Light"[41] he describes, or whether he met individuals who had direct experiential insights. Some cross-fertilisation of ideas between Sterry and Traherne cannot be ruled out (it seems that Traherne could be exceedingly talkative when conversing on subjects that interested him),[42] but as Marks points out, most of the similarities between their writings could not have been transferred through their published works.[43] Similarities may be attributable to the common pool of ideas and metaphors, including Neoplatonic, on which both drew.

If a comprehensive history of our current topic is ever written, it will have to take into account the strands of thought that we noted in the discussion of pluralistic idealisms in Chapter Eleven, and also provide a broader treatment of the veneration of the small, including the moral and religious aspects. Here we have concentrated on the structural and causal/relational aspects, and have come across Pascal's atomic worlds, Traherne's infinite soul-sphere in a point, the living crystal of Sterry, and the living mirrors of Leibniz. There was clearly something in the air in the second half of the seventeenth century, and we should not underestimate the contribution of the microscope, with its revelations of intricately detailed structure and organisation in minute things. But the appreciation of the small as a mirror of the universal is not peculiar to the age. We have come across it in the fifteenth century in Nicholas of Cusa's contracted universe, and in the fourteenth century in Jan van Ruusbroec's sparkling stone, the tiny pebble that is Christ, the eternal light and "a flawless mirror in which all things live."[44] And it would be remiss to pass over a significant instance in the thirteenth century. In Robert Grosseteste's (*c.*1175–1253) philosophy, theology was blended with a scientific interest in the particulars of nature. Here we find some familiar ideas: the presence of the whole in the part, a metaphysics of light, the creative point,[45] the image of God linked with microcosmism, and the mirror-metaphor applied to parts reflecting the whole. In *De Intelligentiis,* Grosseteste considers the presence of spiritual beings in matter, and, following Augustine, decides that an angel or intelligence is wholly present in the body it occupies, like the soul in the body, and God in the universe.[46] Grosseteste links microcosmic thought with the *imago Dei,*[47] and describes the greatness of the very small: all creatures are mirrors of the Creator, even the most minute and insignificant of things in the universe, the indivisible *atomus*.[48] The *atomus* exhibits the nature of God: "If we had nothing else to contemplate but a speck of dust, it would display in its essence the nature of God."[49]

TO SEE A WORLD IN A GRAIN OF SAND

Over a hundred years after Traherne and Sterry found the eternal in the point, the mystical apprehension of the whole in the part recurred in Blake's visionary Imagination. Blake applies the term *Minute Particulars* to the plurality of members of the divine community, and provides various images for these "little ones",[50] the most famous being the grain of sand in *Auguries of Innocence,* the small and finite grain that contains infinite space and eternal time:

> To see a World in a Grain of Sand
> And Heaven in a Wild Flower,
> Hold Infinity in the palm of your hand
> And Eternity in an hour.[51]

The grain of sand appears again in the poem *Jerusalem:*

> There is a Grain of Sand in Lambeth that Satan cannot find,
> Nor can his Watch Fiends find it: 'tis translucent & has many Angles,
> But he who finds it will find Oothoon's palace; for within
> Opening into Beulah, every angle is a lovely heaven.[52]

'Satan' or the 'satanic' refers to the opacity that obscures the heaven within. The image of the grain unites the material and the spiritual, for the material grain holds the divine eternity within itself. It is also called the "Gate of Los", a gate of "precious stones and gold" through which the prophet sees the eternal world, unhindered by the 'vegetative' senses.[53] It is also the diamond covered in the mine, and the "centre" that "holds the heavens of bright eternity".[54] Eternity is obscured by sense-perception—the Minute Particulars become grains of sand, and the microscope and the telescope of the scientist cannot penetrate into the hidden vistas of the vast and small, for the instruments simply magnify the sensory image, alter its "ratio".[55] They do not take experience beyond the sensory image. When Blake sees a world in a grain of sand, it is not the tiny world spied by a seventeenth- or eighteenth-century microscopist, a world of matter swarming with creatures. Rather, it is an eternity. The sensory space of each man's perceptions, the "Globule of Mans blood", deceptively interpreted as a universe of infinite void and material atoms by the mechanical/Newtonian philosophy, is bounded by larger and smaller spaces, the great and small eternities of the imaginative vision. Blake associates the rationality of the mechanical philosophy with the limited world of sense-perception, and contrasts the two with the expanded vision of Imagination. In the most contracted state of vision ("May God us keep From Single vision & Newton's sleep!"[56]), the Minute Particulars appear as dead, inert pieces of matter, "degraded & murder'd" in the "caves of solitude & dark despair",[57] or "harden'd into grains of sand",[58] "like the black pebble on the enraged beach",[59] lashed by the sea of space and time. Satanic opacity fuses the fine details of the Particulars into a slumberous mass. In the expanded vision of Imagination, the apparently dead grains of corporeality are seen to be luminous particles that hold eternity within.[60] The visionary sees the detailed structure of the world:

> A Spirit and a Vision are not, as the modern philosophy supposes, a cloudy vapour, or a nothing: they are organized and minutely articulated beyond all that the mortal and perishing nature can produce. He who does not imagine in stronger and better lineaments, and in stronger and better light than his perishing and mortal eye can see, does not imagine at all.[61]

In alchemical terms, the dark *prima materia* turns out to be the *lapis*, familiar to all as inert matter but recognised by few for what it is.[62] In the vitalism of Francis Mercury van Helmont, noted in Chapter Eleven, matter is an aggregate of stuporous monads, and in Leibniz's monadology matter is composed of monads with highly confused apperceptions. Similarly, Peter Sterry explains that "materiality and corporeity" are "spiritual and Divine forms"[63] to God, and:

> *He, to whom all things are naked and bare, seeth all things* in every one, and *every one* in all forms at once. The night of materiality and corporeity, before him shineth with a determinate Beauty, with a bright Transparency, as the day

> of spiritual substances. The contracted shades and darknesses of Individuals and particulars, are as the ample and full light of Universals.[64]

It is likely that Blake drew some of his inspiration from a stay at Felpham in the early 1800s.[65] There, in a cottage by the sea, Blake felt close to the eternal in nature, and found life idyllic during the early part of the stay. In a letter to a friend, Blake described a vision on the yellow sands:

> In particles bright
> The jewels of Light
> I each particle gazed,
> Astonish'd, Amazed;
> For each was a Man
> Human form'd.[66]

Each grain of sand, every stone, rock, fountain, tree, cloud, meteor, star are "Men Seen Afar", and as the vision expands further, the jewels of light, the beaming particulate "men", appear as "One Man". This is the Divine Humanity or "Jesus", the community of beings in Eternity seen from a distance as one person: "every Particular is a Man, a Divine Member of the Divine Jesus",[67] "reflecting each in each".[68] To gaze upon a Particular is to recognise a fellow Being, an intelligible, loving whole and a member of the Divine Humanity, the company of Eternals. Blake also makes use of the 'Minute Particular' idea to express his views on morality, knowledge, science and art. The empty espousal of morality, global creeds of good and evil, harsh impositions of right and wrong, the "barren mountains of Moral Virtue",[69] are worthless—it is in the details, the particulars of life, the loving acts, that virtue is to be found.

> He who would do good to another must do it in Minute Particulars:
> General Good is the plea of the scoundrel, hypocrite & flatterer,
> For Art & Science cannot exist but in minutely organized Particulars
> And not in generalizing Demonstrations of the Rational Power.
> The Infinite alone resides in Definite & Determinate Identity;[70]

Wisdom and happiness are to be found in the Particulars, and

> As Poetry admits not a Letter that is Insignificant, so Painting admits not a Grain of Sand or a Blade of Grass Insignificant—much less an Insignificant Blur or Mark.[71]

THE JEWELLED NET OF INDRA

The visions of Traherne and Blake have affinities with the cosmic visions presented in some forms of Mahayana Buddhism and its later developments.

In these, the idea of "everything in everything" (sometimes referred to as *interpenetration)* is common, and receives philosophical elaboration.[72] The collection of texts called the *Avatamsaka Sutra,* or *The Flower Ornament Scripture,* composed in India in the first two or three centuries A.D., contains grand visions of a cosmos characterised by luminosity and complete interpenetration. A striking example is to be found in the thirty-sixth book of the collection: in 'The Practices of Samantabhadra' there is a summary of the kinds of knowledge that are attained through the practices of the *bodhisattva.* These include a knowledge of the "ten kinds of universal entry", of things entering one another:

> all worlds enter one point, one point enters all worlds; all beings' bodies enter one body, one body enters all beings' bodies; untold eons enter one instant, one instant enters untold eons; all Buddhist principles enter one principle, one principle enters all Buddhist principles; untold places enter one place, one place enters all places; untold faculties enter one faculty, one faculty enters untold faculties; all faculties enter nonfaculty, nonfaculty enters all faculties; all perceptions enter one perception, one perception enters all perceptions; one utterance enters all utterances, all utterances enter one-utterance; all pasts, presents and futures enter one time frame, one time frame enters all pasts, presents and futures.[73]

Other notable examples adorn the *Sutra.* In passages of visionary cosmology, a universe of many world-systems is described.[74] Here the atoms contain infinite oceans of worlds, yet retain their distinctness.[75] Webs of light, containing all lands, extend through each world-system, and in each world system the whole universe is to be found.[76] A noteworthy description occurs in the section of the *Avatamsaka Sutra* entitled 'The Incalculable'. An exercise in the generation of huge numbers by repeatedly taking squares (and some fourth powers), starting with 10^{10} (ten thousand million, or 10,000,000,000) yields a magnitude translated as the *unspeakable.* The square of 10^{10} is taken about one-hundred-and-twenty times, and the result, the unspeakable, forms a basic numerical unit of the comos.[77] In each of the numerous atoms of this vast universe are equally numerous lands.[78] The Sutra elaborates on the unspeakable number of universal time-periods, or *kalpas*, enumerated by equating one atom to ten myriad unspeakable aeons.[79] Numberless lands exist in a point the size of a hairtip and in every point in space,[80] yet these lands exist together without impinging on one another or causing the hairtip to expand.[81] The lands in an atom are themselves constituted of atoms, but "the atoms in these lands are even harder to tell of."[82]

The Sutra was influential in China, Korea and Japan, where its ideas were elaborated in the doctrines of the Hua-yen school (*Hwoam* in Korea, *Kegon* in Japan), and was popular among Ch'an and Zen Buddhists, and similar doctrines are to be found in the T'ien-t'ai school (*Tendai* in Japan), which took the

Saddharmapundarika Sutra (Lotus Sutra) as its chief work. A number of metaphors or analogies were used to express the idea of interpenetration. One is the *Jewelled Net of Indra.* Each gem of this net is found to contain within itself reflections of all the other gems in the net, and all the reflections in all the gems. To the same end, mirror-metaphors are invoked, reminiscent of the mirror-metaphors of Traherne and Sterry noted earlier. Multiple mirrors arranged in a circle or sphere create infinite inter-reflections that serve to illustrate the workings of interpenetration.[83]

There is also the metaphor of the *Tower of Vairocana* in the *Gandavyuha Sutra,* the final text of the *Avatamsaka Sutra.*[84] The pilgrim Sudhana is shown a tower by the *bodhisattva* Maitreya. This tower symbolises the *dharmadhatu,* the realm of dharmas.[85] It is the unchanging world that is experienced in the unobstructed vision of a Buddha. Here each thing is discovered to contain every thing, without compromising its distinctness or the distinctness of other things. Sudhana's entry into the tower represents the opening of the mind to a full, unobstructed knowing and blissful experience of the *dharmadhatu.* The tower, adorned with jewels, is as vast as space and contains within itself other similar towers, infinitely vast. Each tower is reflected in the objects in every other tower, yet the towers maintain their discreteness—individuality is not lost in the collective, and Sudhana sees himself in all the towers. A western architectural parallel to Vaïrocana's Tower of Light and Space is the Gothic cathedral of the medieval Christian world, the earthly representation of the heavenly city of Jerusalem. The cathedral hints at the luminous heaven to come through its sacred architecture of towering spaces, transparent stained-glass windows, shafts of light, resplendent treasures of gold and jewels, and a solid frame of stone that nevertheless suggests a weightlessness, a freedom from the pulls of the world. The cathedral stood for the incorruptible spiritual temple mentioned in 1 *Peter* 2.5, into which believers are to be incorporated as living stones.[86]

In the Hua-yen philosophy, each particular thing or 'particle of dust' *(anuraja)* contains the whole *dharmadhatu.* This is the idea of things being *rolled-up* or *contracted,* all things appearing in a single particle. It also follows that each thing is *spread-out* or *expanded,* the single particle permeating or being included in everything else.[87]

The causal interdependence of things, a basic idea in Buddhist philosophy, takes on a new form in the interpenetrative philosophy of Hua-yen. Because all things are implicated in each thing, and each thing in all things, there is no independent self-existence—in this way, everything can be said to be 'empty' of individual self-nature. The interdependence expressed in Hua-yen was one of the aspects of the philosophy that led to comparisons with the process metaphysics of Whitehead. Yet it has also been appreciated that there are significant differences between the two understandings of interpenetration. Hua-yen and process philosophers agree in their recognition of a world in flux, but Hua-yen philosophy also has an overtly eternalistic side to its metaphysics. The unchanging *dharmadhatu* seems to be comparable to some Western notions of Eternity or Being, for it contains all times, future as well as past and present. Furthermore, in the *dharmadhatu,* all ages interpenetrate one another—the past, present and future are found in the past, in the present and in the future.

Some advocates of process philosophy have been unhappy with the idea of a future that exists as much as the present, and which penetrates into the present and the past. There is the objection that, in such a scheme, free will is compromised and determinism implied. We have noted before, in the discussion of time and eternity in Chapter Five, that William James opposed the 'block universe' for similar reasons, and that Whitehead considered the future to be open, unformed.

Interpenetration in process philosophy is partial, consisting of the expression of the past in the present, an accumulation of the past in the advancing present. Steve Odin[88] has termed this mild form of interpenetration *cumulative penetration,* to distinguish it from the thoroughgoing form of interpenetration expressed in Hua-yen thought. Whereas the temporal interpenetration decribed in Hua-yen Buddhism implies causal contributions at an event from *all* places and times (*symmetrical causation,* in Odin's discussion), the causation of process metaphysics consists of the efficient causation of relativistic physics. This is a cumulative penetration into the Here-Now of the events associated with the past light-cone of the Here-Now (*asymmetrical* causal relations). Events contemporary with the Here-Now (those in the cross-section of relative simultaneity) are only weakly immanent in the Here-Now, through their indirect connections by way of the common causal background of the past.[89] Two widely separated events have indirect causal connections through the common events in their causal histories. In contrast, both contemporary and future events are *directly* implicated in symmetrical causation.

Odin is an advocate of the process approach, arguing that it is supported by our experience of flux, of "a past surging into the present and a present surging into the future."[90] He also objects to the exclusion of free will and creative emergence that he associates with symmetrical causation. Francis H. Cook[91] has suggested that the point of contention over causality in the Hua-yen/process dialogue may not be that significant, for he points out that efficient causation is not denied by Hua-yen metaphysics, and suggests that the idea of causation from the future may not be an essential feature of the Hua-yen philosophy, having been introduced to account for a passage in the *Avatamsaka Sutra* in which past and future events are described as present.

However, we should not be too hasty to exclude the possibility that events in the 'future' and the 'elsewhere' regions of spatio-temporal relation have causal implications for the Here-Now. In Chapter Six, I supposed that notions of causality may be required that are broader than the efficient physical causation, leading from past cause to present effect, and from present cause to future effect. A broader understanding of causal relations, including the meaning of and reasons behind events, is particularly needed if the substratum is not purely structural or physical, but is organised inseparably from cognition and feeling. It was also pointed out in Chapter Six that it is a subject of dispute whether determinism implies a lack of freedom of choice, or whether determinism is actually required for personal freedom and responsible action. I would not advocate the term *symmetrical causation* as a general label for the causal structuring of a world having complete temporal interpenetration, for the term may obscure the different kinds of relation existing between events, the different degrees of significance of various relations, and the meaningful distinctions to be made between past and future relations.

THE MIRROR AND THE HOLOGRAM

The mirror and the mirror image have long provided a rich source of analogy and metaphor in both western and eastern thought.[92] In philosophical, theological and mystical contexts, the mirror-metaphor could stand for God, Christ, angels, the world, the mind, the microcosm, man, the soul, knowing and self-knowing, and was linked with a wealth of related ideas and metaphors through the Platonic and Neoplatonic philosophies of image, and through the biblical references to images and mirrors, notably the *imago Dei* of *Genesis* and St Paul's "For now we see through a glass, darkly; but then face to face" (1 *Corinthians* 13.12–13). Of particular interest to us in the present chapter have been the mirror-analogies of multiple reflection for 'whole in each part' ideas. The multiplication of images may be expressed as an inter-reflection between a multiplicity of mirrors, or as the fragmentation of one mirror into many reflecting parts. A mirror has the property that each of its parts reflects an entire image, a fact that is shown clearly when a mirror is broken into pieces,

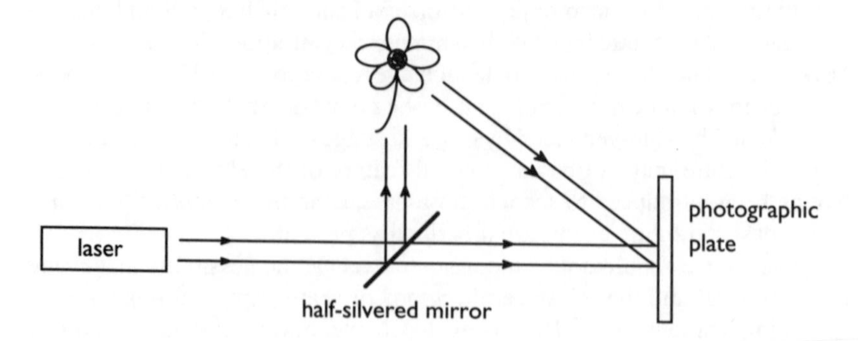

Figure 14.1. Recording a hologram.

into many little mirrors.[93] Herbert Grabes[94] notes that this characteristic of the mirror was often used to illustrate the whole presence of Christ in each piece of bread during the Eucharistic transubstantiation of bread and wine into Christ's body.

Another optical analogy or metaphor has become available since the end of the 1940s, when Denis Gabor developed a new photographic technique called holography. The invention of the laser—a source of coherent light—in the early 1960s, made holography a practical proposition, and the new technology inspired holographic analogies and models for things that show holistic characteristics. A hologram is a special kind of photographic record, produced by the interference of two beams of coherent light from a common source. One beam passes directly to the holographic plate, whilst the other is reflected from the object. The two beams rejoin at the plate, which records the interference pattern of the two beams. In this manner, a record of the light reflected from the object is obtained that includes information on the *phase* of the reflected light waves, unlike traditional photographs which contain no phase information. The extra information in the hologram enables a three-dimensional image to be reconstructed.

Various features of the hologram and the holographic image provide material for analogies:

1. The *holistic* distribution of information on the hologram: the entire holographic image of an object can be reproduced from any part of the hologram, for the whole image is recorded locally in each region of the holographic plate. If the hologram is broken into a number of pieces, a complete image can be recreated from each individual fragment, although the image is poorer in quality.

2. The *encoded* nature of the holographic record: the hologram does not itself contain a recognisable image of the photographed object. The record on the hologram consists of an interference pattern, an unrecognisable pattern of dots. When the hologram is illuminated, the pattern creates interference in the light, resulting in the construction of an image of the photographed object. Whereas the traditional photograph is a representation that *resembles* the original, the hologram record is a representation that is *not* a resemblance. Only the reconstructed image resembles the original.

3. The different *dimensionality* of the record and image: the image created by illuminating the two-dimensional pattern of the hologram appears as a three-dimensional image. Furthermore, different facets of the image become visible when the viewing angle is changed.

In these features of holography, a number of thinkers have found analogies, metaphors, and even explanatory models, that could be applied to neuroscience, physics and questions of ontology. The name *holographic paradigm* has been given to the various ideas, diverse in range, which have drawn on holographic analogies.[95] Such analogies are helpful, but they can also lead to the reductive kind of thinking that takes an analogy, scientific or otherwise, and turns it into an all-encompassing statement about the nature of reality. This results in absurdly over-stated claims, in which the universe is said to *be* something, rather than to *be like something in a particular respect.* Thus, one sometimes comes across claims that the universe is a machine, a hologram, a computer, and so forth. Obviously the wide scope of our experience cannot be squeezed into such limited conceptual frameworks without much being lost in the process. Similarly, the mirror can be useful for bringing across a number of ideas: 'whole in the part' interpenetration; the formation of resemblances; sensory, cognitive and linguistic representations; multiple representations and perspectives; self-perceptions, self-image and self-consciousness; self-revelations in mystical states; the role of others in the formation of the self-concept; clear and distorted self-understandings; the unconscious, including cognitive schemas and unconscious processes; psychotherapeutic processes; ontological theories, and so forth. However, the mirror provides only metaphors and analogies, and these are necessarily limited. For the multiple, experiential perspectives of the pointworlds, the mirror can serve only as a loose analogy, even for the structural content. Pointworlds, for instance, would not show the mirror-inversion of structure that we encounter in our familiar reflecting mirrors. Much more significantly, however, mirror-metaphors fail to bring across the full breadth and depth of experience: they are drawn from the mirrors of our visual sense-experiences, which present us with images of structure and colour. The glass mirror reflects shape, size, arrangement, motion and colour, but is empty of feeling and meaning, and thus fails to mirror experience in its fullness (unless, that is, experience has become empty of feeling and meaning, in which case the mirror may become a symbol for the objectification of the person into a thing viewed externally or divested of value).

A holistic model of the substratum will not be a great step forward from the mechanical philosophies if it remains purely physical or structural. The universe would be like Jorge Luis Borges's labyrinths of inter-reflections, in which meaning is promised but stays out of reach. It is true that holistic models, including holographic models, avoid an analysis into discrete parts through their advocacy of a 'whole in the part' notion, and that in comparison the Newtonian mechanics was holistic in only a very limited sense, through the gravitational attraction interconnecting each piece of matter with every other. Yet it should be stressed that an interpenetrative structuring of the world does not in itself overcome the essential feature of the mechanical philosophy that we have challenged here, namely the parsimonious conception of substratal qualities as purely structural, mechanical or physical. A holistic physical world would contain physical parts or processes that 'reflect' or 'contain' one another, but would still be devoid of colour qualities, feeling, meaning, and so forth. From philosophical and psychological points-of-view, such a holistic physical substratum would not be a great advance on the physical substratum of mechanical philosophy, for it would lead again to the mind-body problem, and might encourage a devaluation of some aspects of experience through a narrow focus on structure and physical attributes. I would suggest that a 'whole in the part' model, whether couched in holographic or specular analogies, will prove satisfactory only if it forms part of a broader understanding that takes into account the full range of experience and does not limit itself to the structural/ physical.

Among the holographic analogies, those of the neuroscientist Karl H. Pribram and the physicist David Bohm have been especially significant. The holistic aspect of holography was used by Pribram in the mid-1960s to suggest the manner in which memories are stored in the brain, for the work of Karl Lashley in the 1940s had suggested that memories are not confined to particular areas of the cerebral cortex. Then, in the early 1970s Pribram extended his theory into a holographic model of brain functioning, including an account of the role of the brain in constructing perceptions from frequency inputs. In this later development, all three of the holographic analogies noted above seem to be used. I am not sufficiently familiar with Pribram's ideas to provide a reliable explanation of his theory of perception and his ontology, but it seems to me[96] that Pribram takes the 'external world', or a world mediating between objects and perceptions, to be a 'hologram' in the sense that its contents have the holistic 'whole in the part' property, and, like the holographic record, have a very different organisation from the perceptual images. In other words, our sense-experiences represent, but do not resemble, the external world. The brain acts as an intermediary, constructing experiences from the hologram-universe, a 'frequency domain' that does not have the temporal and 3-D spatial characteristics of our constructed sense-experience. Clearly, this view is rather different from the position we have developed here, in which the relationship between objects in sense-experience and the experiential, substratal objects is one of approximate resemblance. Both Pribram's 'frequency domain' and our experiential pointworld substratum are holistic, but the 'whole in the part' feature of the pointworld substratum does not derive from the type of encoding of information that we find in the hologram.

A holographic analogy has also been employed by David Bohm in his approach to physics, and to the relationship between matter and consciousness. Bohm[97] posits an *enfolded* or *implicate* order in the physical world, having some kind of 'whole in the part' characteristic, and this implicate order underlies the *explicate* behaviour of physical bodies, including the quantum behaviour of matter. Bohm supposes that the mental realm of thoughts and feelings is similar to the physical realm, in that it is an explication of an implicate order. The encoding of the holographic pattern serves as an analogy for the implicate order. The holistic pattern, an implicate order, acts as a substrate for the holographic image, which is the *unfolded* or *explicate order*. For instance, the unfolded 3-D holographic image of a rose is contained implicitly in the hologram—we do not see the image of the rose on the hologram plate, but a pattern of dots. When the pattern is illuminated, the familiar image of the rose appears, drawing from each part of the hologram. Bohm's ontology, like Pribram's, seems to posit a relationship of 'representation without resemblance' between the deep substratal order and the sensory order.

In the next chapter we shall take a look at the surprising aspects of quantum physics that have invited holistic interpretations.

15. THE PHYSICS OF THE SMALL

In Part III, a highly speculative picture of the microstructure of the world has taken shape: worldpoints came to be viewed as pointworlds, each a complete experiential perspective on the whole spacetime cosmos, containing within itself all the other cosmic perspectives. In this way, cosmology found its way into microphysics, with the cosmic pattern repeated endlessly in the microstructure of spacetime. The fundamental particles consisted of successions of pointworlds: each temporal state of the particles, the unique but equivalent kosmons, consisted of a full representation of the spacetime cosmos, and therefore had an internal structure reflecting the positions and motions of all particles in all spatial and temporal locations throughout the spacetime universe. The fundamental particles are therefore intimately connected with one another through their inner structure, and the form of atomism can be called holistic.

We have arrived at a holistic model of substratal microstructure through a consideration of relative motion and relativistic spacetime. The description of the very large—General Relativity and its curved spacetime—has come to have a place in the description of the very small. Now, it is interesting that the physics of the small in the twentieth century, quantum physics, which has yet to be linked successfully with the physics of the large, displays characteristics that could be considered holistic: it seems that particles show interconnections that were totally unsuspected in classical physics.

The aim of the current chapter is to provide a glimpse into quantum physics, so that we can begin to assess whether the holism of quantum theory may bear any resemblance to the holism of the pointworld model. We shall take a look at the distinctive features of quantum theory that set it apart from classical mechanics and note several interpretations that have arisen to account for these peculiarities.

THE PROBLEM OF INTERPRETATION

As a tool for describing and predicting experimental results, quantum theory has been immensely successful, but the quantum effects observed in the laboratory and predicted accurately by the mathematical theory are very strange when considered from the classical standpoint. There has been much debate in recent times over the meaning of quantum theory, and a number of interpretations have emerged. For a long time positivist-inspired views were standard: quantum theory was interpreted as a means of describing and predicting the phenomena observed by the physicist, not as an understanding of the processes in a substratum underlying the experimental observations. The approach tended to be anti-realist, influenced by the positivism of the late nineteenth and early twentieth century: scientists were not to ask questions about the nature of an underlying physical world, and about what might be happening in unobserved quantum processes. The probability of an experimental outcome was sought, not an understanding of processes taking place behind the scenes. What was so curious about quantum physics that made the positivist withdrawal from the realism of classical science such an attractive move? The striking features of quantum behaviour can be summarised under four inter-related headings: discontinuity, wave-particle duality, indeterminacy and non-locality.

DISCONTINUITY

The first inklings of the strange new physics appeared at the beginning of the twentieth century. In 1900 Max Planck (1858–1947) applied himself to a problem in the physics of heat radiation emitted by a *black body,* a body that is a perfect absorber of radiation and a perfect emitter when heated. Planck's approach was to argue that the energy of the absorbed and emitted radiation assumes discrete values, or *quanta.* The energy E of a quantum is proportional to the frequency of the radiation, and is given by the equation

$$E = h\nu,$$

where

ν is the frequency of the radiation, and
h is a constant of proportionality, the Planck constant.
$h = 6.62 \times 10^{-34}$ Js (joule seconds, the units of energy and time multiplied together).

This new constant of nature, h, is very small, but has profound implications for physics. Firstly, the introduction of quanta implies *discontinuity* in nature at the microphysical scale. The magnitudes of the quantities used to describe physical processes do not change continuously—there are leaps from one magnitude to another, with intermediate magnitudes missed out.

The discontinuity implied by quantization takes on a profound form in the model of the atom proposed by Niels Bohr (1885–1962). In Rutherford's earlier model of the atom, electrons orbited a heavy central nucleus, like planets orbiting the sun. Classical physics, however, predicted that the electrically charged orbiting electrons would emit radiation and very quickly fall into the nucleus. Bohr's quantization of the electron motion placed the electron in a stable orbit, a discrete *energy level.* Only certain orbits are allowed, and have the energy values deduced from quantization. An electron can shift from one orbit to another: a shift to a lower orbit involves a loss of energy, and a quantum of radiation is emitted, whilst a shift to a higher level is made possible by the absorption of a quantum of radiation. The jumps between the orbits are spatially *discontinuous.* The electron is in one orbit and then in another, without passing through any intermediate spatial locations. Thus, quantum discontinuity is not confined to physical quantities such as energy and angular momentum but applies to something as fundamental as the spatial path of a particle—if the interpretation of the quantized atom is correct, there are spatial gaps between the temporal states of an electron when it jumps between energy levels. In the spacetime view, this would mean that the worldline of a particle across a series of energy levels is not a continuous line, but a sequence of worldpoints separated by gaps of spacetime.

Because space, motion and time are closely related in physical theory, the proposal of spatial discontinuity at the microphysical level has led to speculations that space, time, and even spacetime geometry, might be quantized in some way. Natural minimum lengths and times have been suggested, and the smallest of these have been obtained by combining three constants of nature, the velocity of light *c,* the gravitational constant *G,* and Planck's constant *h.* This gives the Planck length $\sqrt{(Gh/c^3)}$, about 10^{-35} metres (which we used in Chapter Fourteen), and the Planck time $\sqrt{(Gh/c^5)}$, about 10^{-43} seconds (used in Chapter Twelve). In relativistic physics, space and time are not separable, so it may be thought that minimum lengths and time intervals should be treated together as quantizations of spacetime. There have been major uncertainties in these various speculations on the atomicity of space, time and spacetime.[1]

WAVE-PARTICLE DUALITY

Planck's introduction of discrete quanta re-awakened an old question about the nature of light, the transmissive *lumen*—does light consist of continuous waves or discrete particles? We have seen that the wave interpretation had dominated nineteenth-century physics following the work of Young and Fresnel on the interference behaviour of light, but the quantization of physical quantities into packets made it conceivable that light has particle properties. Einstein concluded that Planck's theory implied that radiation is both wave-like and particle-like, with the particles having the quantized energy $h\nu$. In 1905 he found experimental evidence for particle properties in the *photoelectric effect,* the emission of electrons from the surface of a metal exposed to electromagnetic radiation of certain frequencies. The photoelectric effect is difficult to explain using the wave theory of radiation, but can be understood if the radiation is assumed to take the form of discrete packages, with quanta of energy $h\nu$. These packages or particles of radiation were later called *photons.*

By the early 1920s, wave-like and particle-like properties of light and other electromagnetic radiations had been demonstrated in greater depth, and active interest in the wave-particle duality developed. An important step forward was taken in 1923 by Louis de Broglie (1892–1987). He suggested that the wave-particle duality may be applicable to *matter* as well as radiation, and provided a mathematical description of the wave-like aspects of particles. A particle in motion was to be associated with waves, *matter waves* or *de Broglie waves.* In fact, the motion of a single particle was to be treated as the propagation of a wave pulse or *wave packet,* which can be regarded as the combination of a number of waves with slightly different frequencies.

The wave packet moves at the same velocity v as the particle—this is called the *group velocity* of the packet.[2] Whereas a point-particle has an exact position, a wave packet is spread over a volume. Furthermore, the wave packet does not have one specific wavelength, but is a superposition of waves with a variety of wavelengths. The wave description of quantum theory was developed by Erwin Schrödinger (1887–1961), who derived the well-known wave-equation named after him. His approach to quantum theory was called *wave mechanics,* and was soon shown by Schrödinger and others to be equivalent to another approach to quantum theory called *matrix mechanics,* which was developed at about the same time by Werner Heisenberg (1901–76), Bohr and E. P. Jordan (1902–80). Matrix mechanics was based on the mechanics of particles, in contrast to the wave treatment of de Broglie and Schrödinger.

Experimental evidence for the wave-like properties of matter soon appeared. In 1925, C. J. Davisson and L. H. Germer studied the scattering of electrons by nickel crystals and discovered effects that could be explained in terms of the matter waves suggested by de Broglie. The wave-like behaviour of other particles, including neutrons, atoms and even molecules, have also been demonstrated. When objects are rather more massive than these microphysical entities, it is supposed that the wave-like behaviour is too small to detect.

The two-slit interference experiment illustrates some interesting features of particle-wave duality.[3] A beam of photons (or electrons) falls on a screen S_1 containing a single narrow slit, and provides a source of photons for the rest of the apparatus. A second screen S_2 contains two narrow, parallel slits. A detector or photographic plate is used to determine where particles passing through the apparatus meet the plane S_3.

The detector picks up individual photons, so we suppose that when the measurements are taken in the plane S_3, the photons are exhibiting particle behaviour (a *definite* spatial location). But the pattern made up by a very large number of individual measurements of photons in the plane S_3 is found to be a series of fringes, alternating bands of high and low particle detection. The fringe distribution would not be expected from particles, but could be explained if we take the light to consist of waves: interference between light waves from each of the two narrow slits in screen S_2 produces the fringe pattern. Where the waves arrive in step at the detector (say, crest with crest, or trough with trough), reinforcement occurs, and a high detector reading is obtained. Where the waves arrive out of step (say, crest with trough), the displacements cancel out and a low detector reading is obtained. The interference pattern suggests that the light has wave properties, that there are light waves in the apparatus. On the other hand, the individual, localised detection of particle positions in plane S_3 suggests that the light has particle properties, consists of photons. We never observe the light waves directly, but infer their existence from the patterns built up by large numbers of individual particle measurements. In fact, it is possible to use a light source of very low intensity so that only one photon is introduced into the apparatus at a time. Even under these conditions the interference distribution of particle measurements is obtained. The interference pattern cannot, then, be attributed to the interactions of a number of photons that are together in the apparatus at the same time. Furthermore, if one of the slits is blocked, the interference pattern no longer develops. These observations could suggest that each particle introduced into the apparatus is associated with some wave-like influence that responds to the presence or absence of the slots, and is therefore sensitive to the experimental arrangement.

How are we to interpret the wave-particle duality exhibited in this kind of experiment? Are such things as photons, electrons and atoms to be viewed as waves, particles, or something else that can manifest both wave-like and particle-like behaviour? Is there a particle inside the apparatus which follows a spatial path from the source slot, through one of the twin slots, to the detector? If this is indeed the case, how is the wave-like response to the state of the

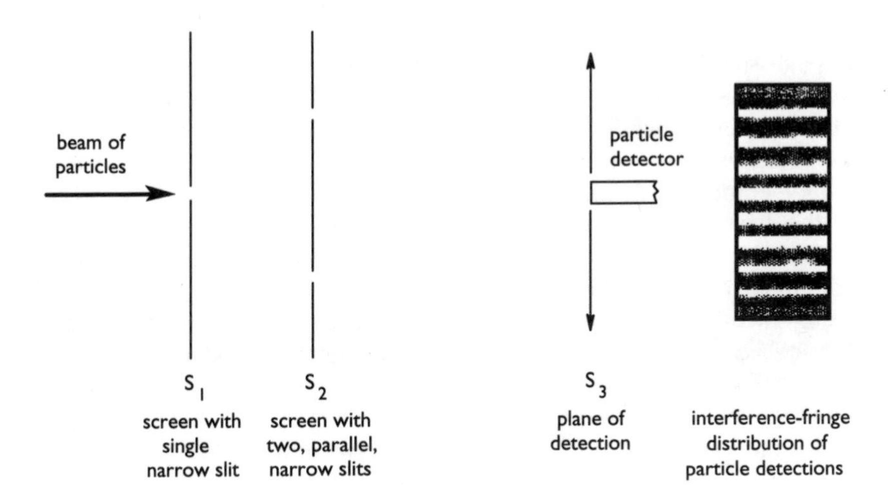

Figure 15.1. Two-slit interference experiment.

apparatus, which we invoke to account for the interference pattern, to be linked with the particle and its path? Could we suppose that there is no particle in the apparatus until the measurement is taken by the detector, and that the photon or electron has the form of a wave until it is detected?

In the early days of quantum theory, a number of interpretations of wave-particle duality were put forward, and de Broglie himself entertained a couple of possibilities.[4] In 1926 he viewed the wave part of the duality as the primary reality: particle-like effects are due to an infinite intensity of the wave at a point, a singularity. This point in the wave has the appearance of a particle, with a definite spatial location and path through space. In the following year De Broglie put forward a related theory in which the waves and particles had equal ontological status: the particle is no longer a wave singularity but an entity in its own right. This is the *pilot-wave theory,* according to which a particle is guided along its path by a wave, the *pilot wave.* In the two-slit experiment, the particle is guided preferentially to regions where constructive interference of the pilot wave occurs. The theory was not well-received, and the idea of pilot waves and unobserved particles with definite positions was forgotten for twenty-five years, until its revival by David Bohm. Theories which stem from de Broglie's interpretation are called *hidden-variable theories,* and we shall consider these shortly.

The difficulties accompanying the ascription of definite positions and spatial paths to particles prompted suggestions in which the idea of a particle localised at a point in space was abandoned. Schrödinger took the wave to be the primary reality and suggested that the electron is an electrically-charged wave-packet of de Broglie waves, extended over a small region of space. The electron is therefore not a *point* particle, but occupies a small region. But the interpretation had a major problem: wave-packets would be expected to spread outwards through space, whereas the particle-like behaviour of an electron does not diminish with time. A position measurement locates an electron in a definite place, however great the dispersion of the wave might become.[5]

The interpretation of wave-particle duality that was to dominate quantum theory for many years utilised Max Born's (1882–1970) probabilistic concept of the wave. In the mid-1920s, Born had suggested that the wave can be interpreted as a *probability wave.* The intensity of the wave (the square of the amplitude) over a small region is proportional to the probability of the particle being situated in that region. It may be wondered what physical existence can be ascribed to a probability wave. Prior to the quantum theory, probability treatments had generally been viewed as a device for coping with a lack of complete information about a subject. With Born, however, the probability description took on some degree of physical reality, for the wave was held to travel through space and change with time in a manner described by the Schrödinger equation.

Born's probability wave idea was incorporated into an interpretation of quantum physics by Bohr and Heisenberg, in which the intensity gives the probability that an *experimental measurement* will yield a particle observation in the region, not the probability of a particle actually occupying a region. The interpretation shifted from a realist or quasi-realist probability wave to an instrumentalist application of probability to the measurements performed by the experimenter. The view that emerged in Bohr's circle in Copenhagen, the so-called *Copenhagen interpretation,* had a strong positivist feel to it. It seems that one factor inclining Heisenberg in this direction was the success of Einstein's operational approach to relativity, which had stressed the use of measurements in the definition of physical concepts such as simultaneity. The Copenhagen interpretation called for the avoidance of ontological questions: physics at the microscopic level was to concern itself with observations and predictions, not with speculation on the nature and processes of unobserved entities. The instrumentalist content of the Copenhagen interpretation equated particles with particle measurements, and waves with the mathematical tools of prediction between measurements, the probability waves.

However, Bohr was willing to accord some value to the use of classical pictures in the conceptualisation of quantum physics, pictures such as the contradictory particle and wave descriptions. His strategy for reconciling them was to argue that contradictory descriptions can be *complementary.* It is acceptable to picture the physical situation when a classical description can be applied to some aspect of the quantum experiment, but the limits of applicability have to be defined, and another kind of description used beyond those limits. The classical particle and wave descriptions are complementary in the sense that each is valid within its own area of applicability to the quantum experiment. In the two-slit experiment, the particle picture applies to the localised particle measurements, whilst the wave picture applies to the system prior to a measurement. In working out his notion of complementarity, Bohr was struggling with the difficulty of applying the realist language of classical physics, with its wave and particle pictures, to quantum phenomena. The complementarity approach seems to hold that a classical notion is valid, but only within its own province of applicability.

I am not sure where this leaves the classical idea of an underlying physical world filled with entities that have particle-like or wave-like properties. There is a pronounced anti-realist slant in the quantum interpretations of Bohr and Heisenberg, but I am not sure how rigorously or consistently anti-realism was expressed. Was the notion of an underlying physical world rejected as a daydream of the old metaphysicians, or was it passed over as something beyond our knowledge? These two attitudes to the idea of an underlying quantum basis could be called *ontological denial* and *epistemological doubt* respectively.

1. *Ontological denial:* there is no world of quantum things-in-themselves underlying quantum effects, and so it is *meaningless* to talk about a particle until a measurement has been taken. The measurement *is* the particle phenomenon: a particle has a real existence only as a position measurement performed by the physicist, and the probability wave treatment is simply a mathematical technique for predicting future measurements from the information provided by earlier measurements. Neither the particles nor the probability waves have any reality beyond the phenomena of measurement and the prediction of measurement.

2. *Epistemological doubt:* there might be an underlying quantum world at work between observations, but we shall not be able to discover the nature of these quantum 'things-in-themselves'. Our scientific concepts of waves and particles are constructs, and should be used instrumentally, with no suggestion that the substratal world of quantum noumena is particle or wave in nature.

Some of Heisenberg's early statements express the former attitude. In a paper of 1925, he describes the idea of a hidden world behind perception as "useless and meaningless"[6] and argues that physics should restrict itself to the description of relations between perceptions.

INDETERMINACY

Heisenberg's thinking was tied up with an important relation that connects the measurement of spatial position, x, with the measurement of momentum p (mass multiplied by velocity). The relation is known as the Indeterminacy Principle or the Uncertainty Principle, and states that if there is a high probability of a position measurement occurring near a location, the probability of the momentum measurement having a certain value will be low. In other words, great observational certainty of a particle's position is accompanied by great observational uncertainty of the momentum, and vice versa. The Uncertainty Principle expresses this relationship mathematically as:

$$\Delta x \times \Delta p \geq \frac{h}{4\pi}$$

The uncertainty in position Δx multiplied by the uncertainty in momentum Δp is greater than or equal to a constant, $h/4\pi$, where h is Planck's constant and π is pi, the ratio of the circumference of a circle to its diameter. A similar uncertainty relationship holds for time and energy measurements.

$$\Delta E \times \Delta t \geq \frac{h}{4\pi}$$

The uncertainty relation means that we cannot know accurately both position and momentum, or both energy and time. How does the uncertainty come about? The answer will depend on the interpretational approach to quantum theory we adopt. One explanation derives uncertainty from the disturbances that the measurement procedure introduces. The act of measuring a particle's position with great precision, using apparatus that interacts with the particle, disturbs the momentum of the particle and introduces the uncertainty. This explanation paints a very concrete picture of the quantum world, suggesting that there is an actual particle with a definite position and definite momentum which can be disturbed by measurement, and is therefore rejected by approaches that assert the ontological primacy of the wave, or which reject ontology all together and argue that it is meaningless to talk about particles and waves, except as particle measurements and as probability descriptions of future measurements.

The uncertainty relation can also be derived from the wave description, interpreted either as the description of a real wave or as the positivist's instrumental probability wave. The uncertainty follows from the mathematics of the wave-packet, which we have noted is regarded as a combination of a large number of waves with different wavelengths. Narrower, more spatially localised wave packets are built up of a larger number of waves of different wavelengths. Now wavelength is related to momentum by a relationship derived by de Broglie when he hypothesised that particles are associated with waves ($\lambda = h/p$, where λ is the wavelength, h is Planck's constant and p is momentum). So the narrower the wave packet (high probability of measuring particle position in a small region), the greater is the range of momenta associated with it (large spread in the probability distribution of momenta).

Thus, a positivist can derive the uncertainty relation from the wave probability distributions of measurements, whilst a realist who supposes that a wave actually exists may interpret the uncertainty relation as an expression of the physics of the wave packet and its superposed waves.

The uncertainty principle provoked much discussion on the subject of causality, for the principle embodied a feature of probabilistic quantum theory that promised to undermine the notion of determinism. The physical determinist view, characteristic of classical science, supposes that one state of a physical system inevitably follows from the preceding state of the system. There is no room for a number of alternative, causal developments leading to the same state or a number of alternative outcomes following the state. Causality is inflexible: a physical system can develop in only one manner. When a physicalist or epiphenomenalist position is taken on the mind-body problem, determinism in the physical world also governs psychological experience. The French mathematician Pierre Laplace (1749–1827), who made major contributions to the mechanics of celestial motion, summed up the determinist view in the famous statement that an intelligence with a complete knowledge of the current state of the material world and its forces would be able to devise a grand equation from which all past and future states would be deducible. In the case of a comparatively simple system like the solar system, a fairly detailed mechanical description of the significant component bodies can be made, enabling accurate predictions of positions and motions.

However, a detailed knowledge of the positions and motions of each component in a mechanical system is generally not possible. For instance, a volume of gas contains such a large number of molecules[7] that a precise knowledge of the positions and motions of every molecule is not obtainable, and the large number would, in any case, present formidable calculational problems if the mechanical information were available. In practice, the scientist employs statistical descriptions, involving average velocities and distributions of velocities, and predictions are made using probability arguments.

In classical mechanics, statistics and probability are simply techniques for coping with a lack of detailed knowledge about a system, the components of which are nevertheless ascribed definite mechanical attributes. Quantum mechanics, as interpreted in the Copenhagen interpretation, with Born's probabilistic wave treated in a positivist fashion, seems to tell us that statistical uncertainty in the mechanical description is not a product of our lack of detailed knowledge of definite, microphysical characteristics. There is no particle with a position or momentum until a measurement is taken. Prior to the measurement, the physicist considers a time-evolving probability wave, which may be viewed as a purely instrumental piece of mathematics for predicting future measurements, or may be ascribed some sort of quasi-reality as a fullness of possibilities from which one actuality manifests when a measurement is performed. The time-development of the probability wave is fully determined, following the Schrödinger equation, but the outcome that will be actualised on measurement from the range of possible outcomes is not determined. The wavefunction description gives probabilities of outcomes, not the prediction of a single, uniquely determined outcome. Thus, it is supposed that determinism breaks down at the transition from the wavefuntion to the actual particle measurement.

The change from the time-evolving wavefunction to the experimental manifestation of a measurement is sometimes called the *collapse* of the wavefunction. It seems that each collapse of a wavefunction introduces an element of chance into the world. This view relies on a particular interpretation of quantum theory. Other interpretations may avoid indeterminism. The hidden variable theories, for instance, suppose that the wavefunction is not a complete description of the quantum system between measurements, and that additional physical factors make the physics fully deterministic.

NON-LOCALITY

According to Einstein's special theory of relativity, no signal can travel faster than light. In consequence, the effects of an event at a certain place and time move out spatially from the event at velocities that cannot exceed the velocity of light. The causal chains that spread out from the event involve *local* causes and effects. A classical causal sequence in physics is like a falling row of dominoes. After an initial push, the individual dominoes topple sequentially and the push is transmitted at a finite speed through the 'local interaction' of one domino falling onto the next domino in the row. There is a time-lag between the causal event in one place and the ultimate effect at a distant location, and the magnitude of the time interval depends on the speed of the propagating signal. In the relativistic spacetime view, this means that the effects of an event are limited to the future light-cone of the event. Now quantum theory seems to allow an instantaneous causal connection, a non-local action between events that are separated by great distances. This implication was made explicit by Einstein in one of his attempts to point out weaknesses in the quantum theory. In 1935, Einstein, with Boris Podolsky and Nathan Rosen, presented a 'thought-experiment' to highlight the non-local implications of quantum theory.

In a simplified version of the Einstein-Podolsky-Rosen (EPR) experiment, we are invited to consider a molecule that flies apart into two atoms, A and B. These fly apart from each other and are eventually separated by a great spatial distance. We might imagine that different observers can obtain an accurate momentum measurement for particle A and an accurate position measurement for particle B, and conservation laws can then be used to work out the momentum of B and the position of A, enabling a complete description of momentum and position to be obtained. But according to the Heisenberg Uncertainty Principle, we cannot obtain precise measurements for the position and momentum of a particle. A probability wave describes the system until a measurement is taken, and this measurement leads to a different probability wave-description for the second measurement. Thus the measurements at A and B are not independent. The widely-separated measurements of particle behaviour are governed by a combined wavefunction, and the measurement at A instantaneously alters the wavefunction description at B, maintaining the uncertainty given by Heisenberg's principle. There seems to be action-at-a-distance—a measurement in one location influences a measurement in another location, and the locations are so widely separated that a signal travelling at the maximum velocity allowed by relativistic theory cannot have traversed the distance. In the domino analogy, the last domino in the row topples long before the transmitted signal of falling dominoes is able to reach it. In 1964 John Bell formulated a theorem that made experimental investigations of non-locality possible, and the experiments that have followed, notably the 1982 experiment of Alain Aspect and his co-workers, have suggested that the quantum theory prediction of non-locality is valid. This is no surprise in itself, for quantum theory is vindicated, but it does emphasise the strangeness of quantum physics when considered from a realist point-of-view. The realist has to entertain either faster-than-light signalling between parts, a pre-established harmony, or a holistic system in which widely-separated parts are intimately connected through the local involvement of the whole in each part.

It is also worth noting briefly a type of quantum experiment in which the state of the apparatus is finalised only after the experiment has begun. These so-called *delayed-choice* experiments raise interesting questions about the nature of causal connections. The final part of an experiment may be chosen long after the experiment has begun, yet the results of the experiment suggest that the final state influences the earlier stages of the experiment: if we hold a realist conception of particles traversing an apparatus, we would have to conclude that the delayed choice near the end of the experiment influences the paths of the particles in the earlier stages of the experiment. This would mean that an action in the future plays some role in the unfolding of prior events. In the 'orthodox' approach, the matter is avoided because there is no consideration of events in the apparatus between measurements: there is no concept of entities traversing the apparatus, no treatment of ontology. Instead, there is a discussion of particle measurements and the probabilistic wave-functions used for predicting measurements.[8]

SOME ALTERNATIVE INTERPRETATIONS

Exactly what constitutes the orthodox or Copenhagen interpretation of quantum physics is not very clear, but it had a pronounced positivist slant.[9] A potential advantage of the positivist approach to quantum theory is its ability to liberate the physicist from perplexing questions about the nature of quantum entities. The realist may be confounded by non-locality and the difficulty of reconciling classical wave properties with classical particle properties in a picture of the underlying world. However, the advantage of the positivist approach may be temporary if there *is* an underlying world containing quantum processes. Furthermore, the vacuum of ontological discussion encouraged by a positivist approach may be filled at the textbook or popular level of exposition by confused interpretations that mix instrumentalism with a simplistic, literal realism or with a woolly-minded idealism that gives the 'consciousness' of the human experimenter a central role in deciding the outcome of the experiment and then concludes that we 'create our own realities'.

In any case, the positivist approach is unlikely to satisfy those who are unwilling to abandon scientific realism completely. Several leading physicists who took part in the development of quantum physics were unhappy about the form it had assumed and regarded it as provisional. Einstein was the most famous dissenter, Schrödinger was another, and in the 1950s de Broglie came to doubt the orthodox interpretation and reverted to the pilot-wave type of approach he had suggested in 1927.

A problematic feature of quantum theory that has stimulated alternative approaches is the change from the wavefunction to the experimental observation when a measurement is taken, the *wavefuntion collapse.* The wavefunction develops with time according to the Schrödinger equation until an experimental operation yields a particle measurement, say, a measurement of position. The outcome of the measurement is not predictable with any certainty, but the probabilities of possible outcomes can be obtained from the wavefunction. After the wavefunction collapses at a measurement, a new wavefunction evolves until the next measurement is taken, and so on. The problem with this account is that it leaves the domain of applicability of quantum theory very uncertain. The problem centres on the role of the experimenter's apparatus in the collapse of the wavefunction. In conventional quantum theory, the intervention of macroscopic, classical apparatus coincides with the wavefunction collapse. The measuring apparatus is classical in the sense that it is not described by quantum theory, and its intervention is only possible because of this. If the measuring instrument were considered in quantum terms, it would become part of a combined wavefunction description, and there would be nothing to bring about the wavefunction collapse into a measurement. Something external to the quantum description has to be introduced to bring about collapse, and in the conventional theory this is the classical apparatus.

This introduces a questionable split between the field of applicability of quantum theory and the domain of classical theory.[10] Where is the dividing line between quantum and classical? What is special about classical measuring instruments that keeps them out of a wavefunction description and enables them to bring about wavefunction collapse? What, in fact, constitutes measurement in quantum theory? Is it the sole preserve of scientists working with sophisticated experimental apparatus, thus implying that quantum physics is confined to a narrow range of events observed in the quantum physicist's laboratory? However, quantum theory is supposed to underlie many of the large-scale phenomena of our experience, such as the solidity and colour of materials. How is it that events in our macroscopic experiences, seemingly based on quantum processes, proceed without the intervention of experimental apparatus to bring about wavefunction collapse?

A fairly recent approach[11] to the problem of collapse and the uncertain role of measurement in quantum theory is to introduce extra terms into the wave equation that allow for the spontaneous collapse of a wavefunction to a particle-like localisation. There is therefore no need to introduce classical macroscopic bodies to bring about collapse. Collapse is intrinsic to the quantum wave. Earlier alternative interpretations have approached the problem of collapse by introducing something additional to the wavefunction and apparatus to bring about collapse, or by denying that collapse actually occurs. One approach, initiated by Eugene Wigner in the early 1960s, reinterprets the positivist stress on experimental observation by suggesting that the experimenter's 'consciousness' actually plays a role in the physics. The wavefunction collapse into a unique measurement is brought about by the consciousness of the experimenter. The physical world does not take on the structural characteristics we ascribe to it until we are actually conscious of it through perception. In other words, localisation into the macroscopic entities of experience takes place only when a conscious mind apprehends the world. The introduction of the concept of consciousness distinct from the phenomena of experience and the underlying world does not recommend the interpretation to me, but others have seen it as a bridge across the mind-body divide, an interactionist dualism giving individual minds a role in the physical world. In another radical approach, often called the *many-worlds interpretation,* it is supposed that the wavefunction collapse into a unique observation does not occur and that measurement has no special role in quantum theory. Instead, the wavefunction, conceived as a wavefunction for the whole universe, contains the superposition of all possibilities as actualities.

The final approach to be noted here is the hidden-variable theory, which originated in one of de Broglie's interpretations of wave-particle duality: the wave associated with a particle can be interpreted as a pilot wave that guides the particle along a trajectory. The hidden-variable picture of quantum physics is realist—an underlying physical world contains particles that have definite spatial positions and momenta. The wavefunction is therefore not a complete description of the quantum system, for it does not take into account other features of the substratum, the *hidden variables,* such as positions and momenta. The idea that the wavefunction contains a number of possible outcomes (which have certain probabilities of being realised when a measurement is taken) is rejected. Instead, there is only one possible outcome, fully determined by the hidden variables and the pilot wave. The problem of wavefunction collapse does not arise, for the particles exist independently of measurement.

In the early 1950s, David Bohm revived interest in hidden-variable theory, and work has continued since. One form of explanation in hidden-variable theories has been to consider a *quantum force,* calculated from the wavefunction. The quantum force, which is additional to the four known forces of nature, is held to be responsible for quantum effects such as the interference behaviour described before. A particle traversing the two-slit apparatus is sensitive to the experimental arrangement through the action of the quantum force, which will be different if both slits are open or one slit is closed. To be responsible for quantum effects, the force must be quite unlike the four familiar forces of nature in some very important respects. Non-locality implies that the quantum force can act instantaneously over vast distances, unlike the influences of the other forces, which cannot travel faster than the maximum velocity *c* of relativistic physics.

The field terminology of physics can be employed, and reference made to the *quantum potential,* analogous to the potentials of electric and gravitational fields. The quantum potential, which depends on the properties of the particle and the experimental arrangement, is added to the wave equation to give a description of the individual particle path. Unlike the potentials of conventional force-fields, the effects of the quantum potential depend on the form, not the magnitude[12] of the potential. This is to comply with the nature of non-local connections, which occur without diminution over vast distances, according to the non-local predictions of quantum theory. Bohm refers to the wave as *active information*—the wave provides information about the whole system at one individual particle, information which in the case of the two-slit experiment includes the state of the slits. The information is active because it enables the particle to respond accordingly, taking into account the rest of the system. The wave, then, is the means by which the whole is expressed in one location, in any one part of the system. How does the individual particle make use of the information provided by the information wave? In one highly speculative suggestion by the physicist Basil Hiley,[13] apparently simple particles such as electrons may contain structure that is presently hidden from us because of its very small scale, and this structure may be responsible for processing the information wave.

QUANTUM THEORY AND THE POINTWORLD MODEL

We shall conclude with a few remarks on the relationship of experientialism, Totalities and pointworlds with quantum physics and its various interpretations. The comparison can be undertaken in only a very general way, since a mathematical treatment of the pointworld concept has yet to be established, and the connection between pointworlds and the fundamental particles of modern physics is uncertain.

In general terms, however, it seems that the physics of the very small described by quantum theory may have some similarities with the experiential pointworld picture of the substratum.

1. *Interpretation*

Of the various interpretations of quantum physics, the pointworld model is closest in its philosophical orientation to the non-local, hidden-variable type of theory. Both are strongly realist, maintaining that there is an underlying world that contains particles with definite positions and qualities of motion, and that the world has this well-defined structure whether or not a macroscopic measuring device, human experimenter or personal 'consciousness' is present to bring about wavefunction collapse. In the experientialist pointworld model, the locations of particles are part of an underlying spacetime experience that covers the full temporal development of the particles. As in the positivist interpretation, the emphasis is on *experience,* but the experientialist conception of experience is much broader, for it incorporates the underlying world behind the description of our familiar experiences. The positivist, we have seen, is not interested in the underlying world, and may doubt whether it is meaningful to talk about one.

2. *Discontinuity*

We have seen that the quantization of certain physical quantities leads to the idea that space and time may be quantized in some way. A particle may be thought to 'jump' from one location to another without occupying intermediate positions, and there has been some speculation that spatial length and time intervals have minimum values, are 'atomic'. In the pointworld view, spacetime is 'quantized' in the sense that each fundamental particle state, each kosmon state or pointworld, is the spacetime unit. This followed from the idea that one spacetime perspective contains all the other spacetime perspectives. The embedded spacetime is the 'atom' of the world, and its spatio-temporal size may provide a basis for the natural atomic space and time magnitudes. In Chapter Thirteen, we noted that the impenetrability of fundamental particles—and a natural minimum spacing of particles—might be related to the impossibility of pointworlds overlapping. A pointworld is an experiential representation of the cosmos, and as such cannot overlap with another representation.

3. *Wave-particle duality, non-locality, causal influence of future states*

It is the peculiar feature of the pointworld model that each fundamental unit is also the whole. The points in a spacetime Totality are embedded representations of the Totality from various perspectives, and have the structures of other Totalities. Thus, everything in the whole of spacetime is represented in the local microstructure. This means that the physical developments in one place are not independent of developments in other places, no matter how greatly separated they may be in space or time. There is no need for any faster-than-light signals to travel between widely separated places, because all information is contained locally in the kosmon itself and in neighbouring kosmons. Suppose that particles, consisting of kosmons, or aggregates of kosmons, pass through the two-slit interference apparatus. The physical details of the experimental set-up, such as the number of open slits and the dimensions of the slits, and even future changes to the apparatus during the experiment, are contained in the kosmons as they enter and traverse the apparatus. The apparatus itself contains representations of the traversing kosmons within its own kosmon microstructure, which means that there is infinite inter-representation of particle in apparatus and apparatus in particle.

Because all is contained locally in the deep structure of spacetime, we do not have to invoke any forces, waves or signals that transmit influences instantaneously over vast distances. In this sense, physics is 'local', and there is no conflict with relativistic physics. The quantum force of hidden variable theory becomes a feature of spacetime curvature, like the four familiar forces of nature in a grand unified theory, and spatial and temporal separations re-emerge as physical realities in the underlying world. On the other hand, physics is 'non-local' in the sense that distant features are represented locally ('the far is in the near'), and it is these local representations of the distant that presumably have an appreciable influence on local developments, as suggested by quantum theory. We may also recall the discussion in Chapter Thirteen on the multiple location of particles and objects. Instead of regarding an object as strictly localised in one place, we can regard it as being distributed throughout the whole spacetime cosmos ('the near in the far'), as representations in the various dimensional levels of embedded pointworlds. Non-locality may turn out to be multiple location.

It is conceivable that kosmons, or aggregates of kosmons, endowed with inner complexity and each a whole in a part, are the type of entity that could give rise to the perplexing wave-particle duality revealed by the early quantum physicists. The underlying physical structure of the world, following the discussion in Chapter Thirteen, might be constituted of interdependent, spacetime particle-states, the pointworlds, embedded in curving spacetime structures that may correspond to the particles described in contemporary particle physics. Exactly how this speculative ontology may relate in detail to quantum theory remains to be seen, but there are at least some suggestive connections in the holistic characteristics of the two systems.

EPILOGUE

The scientific preoccupation with qualities of geometry and motion, and with related mathematical quantities, has proved immensely fruitful. Yet the narrowness of the scientific focus has led to distortions. The mirror of physical theory is severely limited: it reflects only structure and changes of structure, and therefore excludes significant facets of experience or diminishes them with reductive explanations. In the mirror of physical theory, we are liable to find impoverished images of self and world.

However, the physical mirror cannot simply be discarded—over the last four centuries, scientific efforts have yielded an impressive body of theory and observation, and any plausible understanding of the world must find a place for this valuable work. Thus, our design has been to acknowledge the relevance of physical theory, but absorb the theory into a broader approach, transmuting the physical mirror into a living mirror, a theory incorporating physical understanding within an experiential world-view.

The generation of the living mirror has proceeded through ten or so stages. The first called for a recognition of experience in its breadth and integrality. We eschewed the vague notions of *consciousness* and *mind,* and chose instead the deep, broad stream of *experience,* in which sensation, feeling, knowing and extended object are integrated. In experience we find a natural *unity* of contents, including structural content, a unity that provides the key to unlocking the spurious dualisms of the physical-psychological and the material-spiritual. Structure and motion exist as *facets* of experience, and it is a mistake to abstract them into a separate, non-experiential realm called the *physical world.*

Thus, in the second stage, we distilled the essence of the mechanical philosophy, isolating a distinction that took only certain qualities from our unified experience and attributed these to a world supposed to underlie our experiences. These were the qualities of structure and change of structure, of geometry and motion. In this way, we traced the fabrication of the *mechanical mirror* in the early days of modern science, and its subsequent conversion into a subtler, mathematised form, the *physical mirror.*

Next, in the third stage, we recognised that a mirror so fashioned is defective: the substratum reflected in realist physical theory is a poor, dead, skeletal thing that can hardly support our rich, complex experiences. In the fourth stage, we rejected the parsimony of the mechanical philosophy by retaining the idea of a structured substratum but admitting to it additional qualities. It was the crucial stage in the process, for it transformed the substratum into an *experience* in which colour qualities and structure were inseparably united, along with feeling and cognition. Physical theory gave up its claim to be a *complete* description of the substratum—now it was recognised to be a description of the *structural facets* of an underlying, experiential world. According to this viewpoint, physical theory is not simply a tool for making accurate predictions or co-ordinating perceptions, as the instrumentalists and positivists have argued. Nor does it provide a description of an underlying mechanical or physical universe, as many scientific realists have supposed. Rather, physical science describes the structural framework of a global experience that underlies our partial experiences.

The physical mirror had become a *living mirror,* but many details remained uncertain and a fifth stage ensued: hoping to reach a clearer understanding of the experiential substratum, we attempted to ground the theory in experiential evidence by examining a certain type of mystical experience characterised by a sense of completeness. Several promising clues emerged: timelessness, luminosity, love and knowing figured clearly, but beyond these prominent features a description of substratal contents remained highly speculative.

To clarify the living mirror further, we focused on time, space and motion in the substratum, spurred on by the intriguing characteristic of timelessness suggested by the accounts of mystical experience. As a result, the process went through further stages. In the sixth, we addressed the problem of linking our familiar transient experiences with a tenselessly static substratum. Our approach was to find transience in complex, experiential contents that are not purely structural. It was suggested that our familiar experiences are as eternal as the experiential substratum that supports and contains them: "We say goodbye and move on, but the saying-goodbye and the moving-on are permanent." Through special compositions of partial structure, feeling and meaning, moments of experience derive their quality of transience, but are not themselves transient.

Next, we were challenged to reconcile the relativity of motion with the idea of a substratum—this brought about the seventh stage, a stage of division in which the substratum was transformed into a plurality of wholes. Next, eternity and time were brought into a fuller conjunction, their complete interdependence asserted, and our efforts in time esteemed. There followed a stage of unification in which the wholes were brought together at a deeper substratal level, although the details remained obscure. Finally, the idea of plural wholes was extended into a tentative, holistic model of the structure of the substratum, bringing together the large and the small, and revealing the experientiality of matter. This tenth stage involved the multiplication of experience in each whole, including the structural facets, through the inner representation of the other wholes in each whole. Thus, our living mirror came to reflect a living substratum that is itself mirror-like in certain respects. Intimations of a holistic, experiential universe—a world of interpenetrating, experiential perspectives—can be found in mystical accounts, but the holistic extension of the experiential theory must undergo further development, including mathematical, before its value can be assessed. There is the possibility that the model may be open to investigation by experimental means if its structural content proves amenable to mathematical treatment.

Here, then, we must pause, the living mirror generated, yet awaiting refinement, and projecting only faintly the clearer images of self and world that we set out to find. But whatever experiential details and structural models eventually emerge, we have entertained a truly significant possibility—the substratum may prove to be experiential, our living, transient experiences rooted in a world of imperishable life, an experiential bedrock inconceivably vivid and complete. Thus, we may find that meaning and love extend far beyond the personal and subjective, are no mere inconsequential by-products feebly aglow upon a dark, indifferent sea of matter. Rather, meaning and love may prove to be the foundation of all, an ocean of light at the heart of things, glimpsed in the infant's smile, reflected in the eyes of lovers, wrought through the endless struggles of time, yet fully perfected in each moment.

GLOSSARY

anti-realism: in the philosophy of science, the view that scientific theories tell us nothing about an external world, and are simply descriptions of regularities observed in the flow of sensations or between measurements. Contrasted with *realism.*

astructural qualities: the term used here to denote qualities such as colours, tastes, sounds, odours. Sometimes called *sensible qualities* ('of the senses') or, misleadingly, *secondary qualities* (see Chapter Two). Contrasted here with *structural qualities.*

atomism: a theory that posits indivisible parts, the atoms. *Atom:* (a) in modern science, a unit of matter consisting of a central nucleus of protons and neutrons, orbited by electrons. Chemical elements are distinguished from one another by the distinctive number of protons in the nuclei of their atoms; (b) in philosophical and psychological usage, an indivisible unit, whether a unit of matter, sensation, experience, space or time. An atom may be *'unbreakably'* indivisible (cannot be broken into separate fragments) and *structurally* indivisible (a simple unit with no distinguishable parts or structures). Newton's atoms were indivisible in both senses, whilst the chemical atoms of modern science are not atomic in either sense. The atoms postulated in Chapter Eleven cannot be broken into parts, being infrangible 'mirrors' of an indivisible whole, but have internal structures that transform with spatio-temporal location.

constructivism: in epistemology and psychology, the theory that knowledge is produced through the action of innate ideas on the information obtained through the senses. Constructivism can be regarded as a reconciliation between rationalism and empiricism, traceable to Kant's views on the constructed nature of experience. Perceptions are regarded as constructions that go beyond the sensory input, containing organisation and interpretations introduced by the perceiving mind.

dualism: (a) approaches to the mind-body problem that recognise a fundamental distinction between mind and matter, but seek to connect the two in some way, through a one- or two-way action, or through some kind of synchronisation (parallelism)—see Chapter Three; (b) any belief that sets up two irreconcilable substances or things, such as body and mind, matter and spirit, time and eternity. The dualisms of mind-body and spirit-matter are traced in this work to a failure to appreciate the breadth and integrality of experience, and the exaggeration of natural distinctions that exist between the contents of experience.

empiricism: a philosophical position, influential in the history of science, that takes the study of sensory experience as the only source of knowledge. Often contrasted with *rationalism.*

epiphenomenalism: the notion that mind, consciousness or experience plays no role in the course of events—a dualistic response to the mind-body problem that makes material or physical processes fundamental, but does not go to the extreme of materialism by attempting to reduce the mental to the physical. *Epiphenomenon:* 'after-show', an incidental feature of a process, having no causal role.

epistemology: the branch of philosophy concerned with knowledge—what constitutes knowledge, what can be known, what cannot be known, how knowledge can be obtained.

experience: (a) as used by empiricists, *experience* refers merely to sensory contents and the world presented in these, and thus excludes thoughts, feelings, imagination, intuition; (b) as used in this work, *experience* covers the full range of contents, including sensation, thought, emotion, and so forth.

experientialism: a term introduced in Chapter Three to denote the approach to the mind-bodyproblem taken here. This is the view that the substratum underlying our familiar experiences is itself experiential. Experientialism can be regarded as a form of *idealism*—but see Chapter Three.

external world: aspects of the world that lie beyond sense-perception. According to some philosophical viewpoints, such as *representative realism* (see Chapter Two), various features of the external world may be represented in sense-perception.

geometric-kinematic qualities: see *structural qualities.*

holism: a philosophical position that stresses the importance of the whole, arguing that an analytical study of parts leads to inadequate understanding. Often contrasted with *elementarism* and *atomism,* theories of basic units and indivisible units respectively. In some respects, the world-view that emerges in Part III of the current work can be called a *holistic atomism,* because it includes unfragmentable units that are wholes (namely, the *kosmons* and their *pointworld* states). See Chapter Thirteen.

idealism: a term applied to a variety of philosophies that take mind, thought, consciousness or experience to be fundamental. Idealism provides a *monistic* response to the mind-body problem, explaining matter in terms of mind or experience. The 'idea' of idealism can refer to the whole range of experiential content, including feeling and imagination, and not just the ideas of conceptual thought. In discussions of the philosophy of quantum theory, idealism and positivism are sometimes confused, if mind or experience is understood as merely personal. Idealists, however, can take mind or experience to be an objective, substratal actuality that is no mere creation or projection of personal, conscious minds.

instrumentalism: in the philosophy of science, a form of *anti-realism* according to which scientific theories are simply tools or instruments for making predictions. Scientific theories do not tell us about the workings of the world and have no explanatory power. Opposed to scientific *realism.*

living: adjective used to describe things considered alive, contrasted with things inert or dead—for the biologist, taking an 'external' view, *living* describes things that respire, reproduce, grow, assimilate, excrete, and are sensitive to the environment. In the current work, however, *living* also has a specialised meaning, appropriate to the 'inner', experiential view, denoting the characteristic of *experiencing* or of *being an experience.*

lumen: a term borrowed from scholastic thought, used here to name the intermediary steps that convey information from an object in the external world to the visual sense-organs. In modern science, the *lumen* is considered to be electromagnetic radiation, or particles called *photons.*

lux: the visual experience itself, characterised by brightness, colour, shade. Contrasted with *lumen,* the transmission of signals that stimulate *lux.*

materialism: in philosophical usage, a standpoint that takes matter to be the one and only existence. The materialist hopes to overcome the mind-body problem by interpreting mind in material terms.

matter: (a) in ancient Greek atomism and early scientific philosophy, matter consists of simple, extended bodies in motion through a void (or through a plenum of matter in Descartes' philosophy); (b) in modern physical science, matter has lost its extended solidity, notions of unextended point-particles, forces and fields having become prominent; (c) in the current work, matter has been re-interpreted as the structural facets of an experiential substratum, luminous structures intimately linked with centres-of-experience.

metaphysics: the branch of philosophy concerned with the fundamental nature of things. Metaphysical enquiry has typically looked into the distinction between reality and appearance, the existence and nature of the external world (ontology), the nature of the universe (cosmology), the problems of permanence and change, the plural or singular nature of substance, the relation between mind and body, questions of free will and determinism.

microcosmism: a theory that finds the cosmos at large (the macrocosm) reflected in some or all of its parts (the microcosms). The microcosm is often the human being, considered to reflect the universe in some way. Various types of microcosmism can be distinguished.

mind-body problem: an important subject of debate in philosophy and psychology, concerning the relation between mind, consciousness, or experience and the material/physical world. Also called the *psychophysical problem.* Traditional approaches to the problem are sometimes classified as *dualisms* (interactionism, epiphenomenalism, psychophysical parallelism) and *monisms* (materialism, idealism)—see Chapter Three.

monism: (a) in the philosophy of the mind-body problem, an approach that takes either mind or matter to be fundamental; (b) the view that the underlying reality, substance or substratum is singular (Spinoza's philosophy provides a classic example of monism in this sense).

mysticism: (a) the study of mystical experiences; (b) spiritual systems that incorporate mystical insights, or aim to encourage mystical experiences.

ontology: literally 'the study of being'. Ontology is the branch of metaphysics concerned with existence, reality and appearance, and the nature of the world behind sense-perception.

physical world: (a) in realist philosophy of science (and in the current work), the *external world* described by the physical sciences, a substratum of molecules, atoms, forces, fields, spacetime, and so forth, that supports our experiences; (b) in less metaphysical contexts, the natural world and its objects, open to study by the physical sciences, perhaps contrasted with biological, psychological or spiritual areas of study.

pluralism: in metaphysical discussion, the idea that the underlying substance or world is plural, multiple, as opposed to singular (see *monism).* In Chapter Twelve, we consider the substratum to be plural at an intermediate level (a plurality of wholes), but singular at a deeper level.

positivism: a philosophical standpoint that rejects attempts to go beyond the given of sensory contents and indulge in speculations about underlying existences and causes. Positivism is therefore opposed to metaphysical enquiry, and is closely related to empiricism and anti-realism. There is a belief in the power of science alone to establish knowledge. The positivist influence on the physical sciences and psychology was strongest in the first half of the twentieth century.

rationalism: in epistemology, those philosophical positions that consider innate ideas or reason to be the source of true knowledge. Contrasted with *empiricism* and *constructivism.*

realism: in the philosophy of science, realism is the view that scientific theories tell us something about an external world. Contrasted with *anti-realism* and *instrumentalism.*

reality: (a) often used to suggest an existence beyond, and more real than, our sense-based experiences (dismissed as 'appearance')—see Chapter Five; (b) as used here, *reality* refers to all existence, sense-based and substratal, transient and eternal.

real-time diagrams: name given here to the spacetime diagrams commonly used to illustrate relativistic physics. These diagrams have an algebraically real time-axis, *t,* and therefore do not illustrate directly the absolute Minkowski spacetime, which has an imaginary time-axis, *s.*

reductionism: the tendency, manifested in several areas of thought, including physical science, psychology and psychotherapy, to derive complexities from a small number of explanatory entities or terms.

structural qualities: the qualities of structure (geometric) and motion (kinematic), including shape, relative size, relative position, and changes to these. Often called *primary qualities.*

substance: in philosophy, the term has had various shades of meaning. It may denote the true essence of things, or the substrate supporting transformations, or something with qualities and attributes, or something that can exist independently, without reference to other things.

substratum: the term used here to cover various notions of underlying influences, substances, entities, actualities or existences behind sense-experience, providing the latter with a support, basis, ground, bedrock. Speculations about a substratum have appeared in religious, scientific, psychological and philosophical thought. In philosophy, the substratum is the subject of study of metaphysics, and of ontology in particular. In realist science, the substratum is the *physical world.* In psychology, the substratum may be the unconscious, or a collection of unconscious processes underlying experience. *Substratal:* belonging to the substratum, or contained in the substratum.

NOTES

PART I: THE SCOPE OF EXPERIENCE

Chapter 1: Experience and its Substrata

1 John Dewey, 'The Philosophy of Whitehead', in *The Philosophy of Alfred North Whitehead,* edited by Paul Arthur Schilpp (1951a), p. 645.

2 See Whitehead (1964b), *The Concept of Nature,* Chapter II, especially pp. 30–1.

3 James (1890), *Principles of Psychology,* Vol. 2, p. 450.

4 James (1890), *Principles of Psychology,* Vol. 1, p. 224.

5 C. H. Cooley (1902), *Human Nature and the Social Order,* p. 152.

6 James (1890), *Principles of Psychology,* Vol. 1, p. 371.

7 James (1912), Does 'Consciousness' Exist?, Sect. VIII, *Essays in Radical Empiricism,* p. 37 (reprinted from *Journal of Philosophy and Scientific Methods,* Vol. 1, No. 18, 1 September 1904).

8 Albert Einstein, in *Albert Einstein: Philosopher-Scientist,* p. 4, edited by Paul Arthur Schilpp (1951b).

9 Another instance in the ancient world—on a rather less exalted level than the Platonic Forms—is the *genius* or guiding-spirit of the Romans, which has been called a precursor of the modern notion of 'unconscious mind'—see R. B. Onians (1951), *The Origins of European Thought,* pp. 160–2.

10 See L. L. Whyte (1962), *The Unconscious before Freud.* Also H. F. Ellenberger (1970), *The Discovery of the Unconscious.*

11 Note that *conscious* here means 'revealed or contained in experience', although the word is often used to indicate that a content of experience has been registered, noticed, discriminated. In the first sense, a content is called *conscious* because it is 'in consciousness', is currently a content of one's transient experience. In the second sense, the content is termed *conscious* if it has been discriminated from the background contents. I shall use the terms *conscious* and *unconscious* in the first sense, to differentiate between experiential contents and things not directly in experience. To distinguish between discriminated contents and background contents of experience, we could employ the *figure-ground* terminology of the Gestalt psychologists: the discriminated content, attended to keenly, is the *figure,* whilst the poorly discriminated content is called the *ground.*

12 See L. L. Whyte (1962), pp. 66 ff.

13 David Hume, *Treatise of Human Nature,* 1739, Book I, Part II, Sect. VI *(Of the idea of existence, and of external existence),* edited by L. A. Selby-Bigge (1960), pp. 67–8.

Chapter 2: The Physical World

1 Translated by Stillman Drake (1957), *Discoveries and Opinions of Galileo,* pp. 276–7.

2 See Peter Alexander (1985), *Ideas, Qualities and Corpuscles.*

3 I borrow the terms from Vasco Ronchi's (1970) history of light theories, *The Nature of Light,* p. 61. Ronchi explains that the Latin terms *lumen* and *lux* were translated in Italian mediaeval scientific texts as *lume* and *luce.*

4 *Opticks,* Book One, Part II, Isaac Newton (1931), p. 124, a reprint of the fourth edition of the *Opticks,* 1730.

5 Ronchi (1970), p. 226, notes the confusion generated by the replacement of *lux* and *lumen* by a single word. Light came to mean *lumen,* and *lux* was forgotten, or entered into a confused union with *lumen* in the understandings of Newton's "vulgar people". For instance, the *lumen* stimulating the sensation of green, Newton's "Green-making" light, would become "green" light to later scientists, a physical *lumen* unthinkingly ascribed a green coloration. We shall note Goethe's criticism in Chapter Five.

6 *Opticks,* Book Three, Part I, Query 31, Isaac Newton (1931), p. 400.

7 For example: *Jerusalem,* 54.17., p. 685, in *The Complete Writings of William Blake,* edited by Geoffrey Keynes (1966). All further Blake references are to this edition, with page numbers given in brackets.

8 The term *colour,* as used here, includes black, white and shades of grey.

9 As we shall see, relativistic physics requires that we modify this statement, and clarify what we mean by measurement and observation. The measured dimensions of an object are found to depend, in a regular fashion, on the state of motion of an object relative to the observer.

10 General Scholium, *Philosophiæ Naturalis Principia Mathematica,* in *Sir Isaac Newton's Mathematical Principles of Natural Philosophy and his System of the World,* Florian Cajori (1962), Vol. 2, p. 547.

Chapter 3: The Mind-Body Problem

1 A recent idea derives 'consciousness' from a substrate of quantum-mechanical oscillatory brain-states, so-called "Bose-Einstein condensates" or "pumped phonon systems", which the physicist H. Fröhlich supposed might occur in biological systems: see I. N. Marshall (1989), 'Consciousness and Bose-Einstein condensates', who suggests that the holism of his quantum substrate may be linked with the holographic models of mind or consciousness posited by Karl Pribram and others. We shall discuss the holographic analogy in Chapter Fourteen. Marshall describes his approach to the mind-body problem as a 'neutral monism', hypothesising that mental and bodily realms each derive directly from a common, underlying "quantum realm" (p. 74). Neutral monism, so-conceived, is equivalent to *double-aspect theory*—see Note 2 below.

2 In recent times, a number of responses to the mind-body problem have appeared. These include *Identity Theory* (a form of materialism—mental states are identical with certain physical brain-states) and the *double-aspect theories* (the mental and physical are two properties of one unknowable, underlying substance). *Functionalism* has become a popular approach: the functions or processes of mental activity are important, not the brain matter or computer hardware in which the processes occur. The functionalist may then approach the mind-body problem through identifying mental states with functions supported by physical states. These approaches are not of immediate interest to us here, and the reader is directed to works which introduce the modern theories, such as *Body and Mind* by K. Campbell (1984), and *Matter and Consciousness* by P. M. Churchland (1984).

3 "By the term 'thought', I understand everything which we are aware of as happening within us, in so far as we have awareness of it. Hence, *thinking* is to be identified here not merely with understanding, willing and imagining, but also with sensory awareness." *Principles of Philosophy,* 1644, trans. J. Cottingham, R. Stoothoff and D. Murdoch (1985), *The Philosophical Writings* of Descartes, Vol. 1, p. 195.

4 For an account of Hobbes's materialism and its hostile reception, see S. I. Mintz (1962), *The Hunting of Leviathan.*

5 See Note 2 above.

6 To be distinguished from the usage in empirical philosophy, denoting the view that all knowledge is derived from sense-experience.

7 On the personal and collective unconscious, and the archetypes, see 'Instinct and the Unconscious' in Jung (1969), *The Structure and Dynamics of the Psyche,* pp. 129–38.

Chapter 4: Experiential Intimations

1 *Enneads* 5.8.10., translated by Stephen MacKenna (1969), *Plotinus: The Enneads,* fourth edition, p. 430. All further Plotinus quotations and page numbers refers to this edition, unless otherwise stated.

2 See, for instance, Meg Maxwell and Verena Tschudin (1990) on 'The Taboo', in *Seeing the Invisible,* pp. 16–17, and W. T. Stace (1960), Mysticism and Philosophy, pp. 57–8. Examples include 'The Case of M. C. L.' in *Cosmic Consciousness* by R. M. Bucke (1905), p. 273, and *The Following Feet,* p. 23, Ancilla (1955).

3 William James (1902), *The Varieties of Religious Experience,* p. 381.

4 Studies/anthologies of mystical and religious experience include: *Cosmic Consciousness,* Richard Maurice Bucke (1905); *The Varieties of Religious Experience,* William James (1902); *Mysticism,* Evelyn Underhill (1930); *Mysticism,* F. C. Happold (1970); *Ecstasy,* Marghanita Laski (1961); *The Protestant Mystics,* Anne Fremantle (1961); *The Spiritual Nature of Man*, Alister Hardy (1979); *Seeing the Invisible,* Meg Maxwell and Verena Tschudin (1990).

5 *Enneads* IV.8.1. (p. 357.)

6 *Centuries,* I.1. Quotations from the *Centuries* are taken from Dobell's modernised text of 1908, in *Centuries of Meditations,* Thomas Traherne (1927). The text with original spelling, capitalisation and punctuation is provided by H. M. Margoliouth (1958) in *Centuries, Poems and Thanksgivings,* Vol. 1.

7 *Centuries,* I.3.

8 *Centuries,* III.3.

9 The dramatic unearthing of Traherne's manuscripts continued in the 1960s. In 1964, the *Select Meditations* came to light, and in 1967 a voluminous manuscript was rescued from incineration on a Lancashire rubbish tip. The manuscript was subsequently found to contain an unfinished work by Traherne, the *Commentaries of Heaven,* a work set out in encyclopaedic form. On the discovery of the *Select Meditations,* see James M. Osborn (1964), 'A New Traherne Manuscript'. On the *Commentaries of Heaven,* see Elliot Rose (1982), 'A New Traherne Manuscript' and Hilton Kelliher (1984), 'The Rediscovery of Thomas Traherne'. Some excerpts from the *Commentaries* are given in 'Traherne's Commentaries of Heaven (With Selections from the Manuscript)', by Allan Pritchard (1983). An essay on the new finds, 'Traherne from his Unpublished Manuscripts', is provided by Julia Smith, along with a brief selection of passages, in *Profitable Wonders,* by A. M. Allchin, Anne Ridler and Julia Smith (1989).

10 James (1902), *The Varieties of Religious Experience,* pp. 380–2. A more recent analysis, which has also been widely influential, is that of W. T. Stace (1960) in *Mysticism and Philosophy.* Stace distinguishes between extrovertive and introvertive mysticism, and provides separate lists for each (p. 79 and pp. 110–111). The universal type of mystical experience that we have distinguished here could be equated with Stace's extrovertive category, for both cover experiences in which the multiplicity and structure of the world are apprehended in a completeness and unity. However, Stace regards these experiences as perceptions through the sense-organs, not as direct experiences of the external world: "these external things, although many, were nevertheless perceived—seen by the eyes—as all one; that is, they were perceived as simultaneously many and one." (p. 64.) I do not consider Stace's distinction between the extrovertive and introvertive categories as fully adequate, for some mystics report cosmic multiplicity in *non-sensory* states through an 'inward' contemplation. Stace fails to appreciate distinct categories within trans-sensate ('introvertive') experience, such as the experiences at the levels of *Nous* (multiplicity of intelligible objects) and the One (singular) distinguished by Plotinus.

11 *Cosmic Consciousness,* R. M. Bucke (1905), p. 2. James (1902) quotes the passage in the *Varieties,* p. 398.

12 Bucke's concern with the age at which the experience occurs is tied up with his theory of the evolution of consciousness in the animal kingdom, proceeding from 'simple' to 'self' to 'cosmic' consciousness. He discerned a recapitulation of the three stages in the course of the individual human life, and supposed that the emergence of the third stage was becoming more and more common over the millennia. As a pioneer in the field, working from a limited pool of data, Bucke was handicapped in his study, and we must make allowances for some of his observations. Two of the most glaring deficiencies that may strike the modern reader are the paucity of mystical accounts by women and the description of the level of consciousness to be found in 'primitive' cultures. These deficiencies reflect the social and anthropological awareness of the time and should not blind us to the importance of Bucke's work. In its scientific and critical approach to the subject, the work differs enormously from the turgid spiritualism, theosophy and occult obscurations of the late nineteenth century.

13 Bucke (1905), p. 61.

14 Ibid. p. 61.

15 Ibid. p. 61.

16 Ibid. p. 270.

17 Ibid. p. 271.

18 Ibid. p. 271.

19 Ibid. p. 272.

20 Ancilla (1955), *The Following Feet,* pp. 20–1. The account is quoted in Anne Fremantle's (1961) *The Protestant Mystics.*

21 Quoted from Underhill (1930), p. 252, who provides two references: *Le livre de l'experiènce des vrais fidèles de Ste Angèle de Foligno,* p. 124 (Trad. par M. J. Ferré. Edition critique: texte latin et traduction française. Paris 1927) and *The Book of Divine Consolations of the Blessed Angela of Foligno,* p. 172 (Translated by M. Steegman. With an introduction by Algar Thorold. New Medieval Library. London, 1908).

22 For example, Warner Allen's account in *The Timeless Moment,*(Faber and Faber, 1946), quoted by Happold (1970), pp. 131–3.

23 For example, Ancilla, *The Following Feet,* p. 22.

24 Trans. M. O'C Walshe (1987), *Meister Eckhart,* vol. II, p. 160, Sermon Sixty Eight.

25 Thomas Traherne, *Centuries,* V.6.

26 *A Vision of the Last Judgment, Pp. 69–70.* (p. 605, Keynes.)

27 *Enneads,* V.3.8. (p. 390, MacKenna.)

28 *The Adornment of the Spiritual Marriage,* The Third Book, Chapter I, in *John of Ruysbroeck,* p. 170, translated by C. A. Wynschenk Dom (1916). In the Eternal Now, God "beholds Himself and all things. And this is the Image and the Likeness of God, and our Image and our Likeness; for in it God reflects Himself and all things." (3.III, p. 173.) Reuniting with the Eternal Image, men "behold God and all things, without distinction, in a simple seeing, in the Divine brightness." (3.III, p. 175.)

29 *Living Flame of Love,* Stanza I.12., *The Complete Works of Saint John of the Cross,* Vol. III, p. 23, translated and edited by Edgar Allison Peers (1978).

30 *Jerusalem,* 71.6. (p. 709.)

31 We shall return to the association between space and light in later chapters. Bejewelled locations include the garden at the edge of the sea in the Sumerian Gilgamesh epic, the pure lands of Mahayana Buddhism, and the garden of Eden. The initiatory rites of shamans have involved the ingestion of quartz crystals to confer divine vision. Filled with the solidified light of the crystals—which are thought to have fallen from the sky—the shaman-to-be partakes of the celestial realm of the Supreme Being. See Mircea Eliade (1972), *Shamanism,* pp. 45–8 & pp. 135–9.

32 There is, however, a notable passage in the *Enneads* that may suggest a substratum replete with colours, sounds, tastes, and touch qualities. Plotinus regards the intelligible world as the original of our living, sensory universe, and therefore argues that the intelligible world is itself a living world, a universe of stars, earth, sea, air, animals, plants, brimming with everything that exists and lives. In this intelligible realm of life eternal, "All flows, so to speak, from one fount not to be thought of as some one breath or warmth but rather as one quality englobing and safeguarding all qualities—sweetness with fragrance, wine-quality, and the savours of everything that may be tasted, all colours seen, everything known to touch, all that ear may hear, all melodies, every rhythm." *Enneads* VI.7.12. The meaning of the passage is not clear to me: is Plotinus suggesting that the intelligible substratum has one quality that holds in itself the multiplicity of qualities we find in sensory experience, or is he ascribing the multiplicity of qualities to the substratum itself?

33 For many psychologists, an *attitude* is directed towards its object, the so-called *attitudinal object,* and has three or so aspects: cognitive, emotional, and behavioural. The cognition consists of knowledge of the object, an understanding or belief about it. The affective aspect consists of an emotional response to the object, including body sensations, and is likely to include evaluative feelings, or value-judgements. The behavioural aspect consists of inclinations towards behavioural responses to the object. For instance, suppose that I hold an attitude towards a certain city. Cognitively, I know where it is and its traffic conditions. Emotionally, I might find that I dislike its noise and heat, that I feel physically tight when I think about the city, and that I consider it an unpleasant environment. Behaviourally, I might avoid going to the city, or minimise the time I spend there.

34 *The Art Of Loving,* Erich Fromm (1956).

35 Vladimir Lossky (1968), *The Mystical Theology of the Eastern Church,* p. 234.

36 For example, Plotinus: souls not strong enough to view the radiant light of Being "are dazzled and turn away, unfit to gaze upon that sun, the trouble falling the more heavily on those most remote." *Enneads* V.8.10 (p. 430, MacKenna). Also St John of the Cross, *Dark Night of the Soul,* Book II, Chapter XII, E. Allison Peers (1978), Vol. 1, p. 411. It is a theme central to the death and rebirth process described in Tibetan Buddhist texts,

in which it is supposed that at death the Clear Light of the substratum appears for a while, and that most beings withdraw from the Light to be reborn into various realms, after a transitional, dream-like phase. The withdrawal may be ascribed to karmic tendencies, such as a compulsion towards re-establishing a personal selfhood in the face of a threat to continued personal existence. See, for example, Ken Wilber (1980), *The Atman Project,* Chapter 18, and John Hick (1976), *Death and Eternal Life,* pp. 400–4.

37 The idea is expressed in *Select Meditations* II.92., quoted by Sharon C. Seelig (1979) in 'The Origins of Ecstasy: Traherne's "Select Meditations"'. An intriguing case of two selves is to be found in the Gnostic *Song of the Pearl,* a poetic fable of the second century A.D. that was incorporated into the apocryphal *Acts of Thomas.* The *Song* is notable for its engagingly childlike narrative of exile and return. A little prince is sent by his parents into the dark land of Egypt to rescue a pearl guarded by a terrible serpent in the depths of the sea. The child puts on the garments of the alien land and falls into a deep sleep after eating the heavy local food, but is awakened in time to win the pearl and recover his original clothing, a splendid robe adorned with precious stones and gloriously coloured. The robe constitutes a second self, for the prince discovers it to be a mirror image of himself. United with it, he discerns himself in the robe, and the robe in himself. The divine nature of this other self is unmistakable, for the robe-self is embroidered with the likeness of the King of kings. On the heavenly garment, the divine twin, the transcendental self and the pearl, see the commentary by Hans Jonas (1992) in *The Gnostic Religion,* pp. 122–9. A full translation of the *Song of the Pearl* is given in *New Testament Apocrypha,* Vol. II, pp. 498–504, by E. Hennecke (1965). An abridged version of an earlier translation is given in Happold's (1970) anthology, pp. 197–202.

38 We shall return to the idea of the unmanifest God in a later chapter.

39 *Libellus* XI.ii., 20b–21a, *Corpus Hermeticum,* translated by Walter Scott in *Hermetica* (1924), Vol. I, pp. 221–23. Scott discusses the text and its account of 'self-expansion' in Vol. II, pp. 301–36. The passage is also given in the précis-translations of Frances Yates (1964), in *Giordano Bruno and the Hermetic Tradition,* p. 32. The early Hermetic literature was written in Greek between the first and third centuries A.D., and drew upon a variety of sources, including Platonic, Stoic and Jewish. The writings do not express a homogenous body of thought, but are a varied collection of texts that present contradictory attitudes towards the world, matter and the body, ranging from the world-negating to the world-affirming. *Libellus* XI is an especially positive tract, ending with a powerful assertion of the divine presence in the world: "Everywhere God will come to meet you, everywhere he will appear to you, at places and times at which you look not for it, in your waking hours and in your sleep, when you are journeying by water and by land, in the night-time and in the day-time, when you are speaking and when you are silent; for there is nothing which is not God. And do you say 'God is invisible'? Speak not so. Who is more manifest than God? For this very purpose has he made all things, that through all things you may see him." (Scott, Vol. I, p. 223).

40 From the same era is Plotinus' technique of envisioning the universe to bring forth the divine, described in *Enneads* V.8., 'On the Intellectual Beauty', which we shall note in a later chapter. Visionary cosmologies have commonly been used in oriental meditative practices, often in the form of cosmic mandalas. A sophisticated example from a Mahayana Buddhist text is noted by Thomas Cleary (1989), in the introduction (p. 6) to his translation of *The Gandavyuha Sutra:* each particle of one's body is envisaged as a buddha-land in which all beings in the universe are contained, and thoughts of love towards all these beings are evoked. The meditation is based on the cosmology of the Mahayana *Avatamsaka Sutra.* A Buddhist visionary meditation of the Amida school is

discussed by Joseph Campbell (1984) in *The Masks of God: Oriental Mythology,* Vol. II, pp. 303–20.

41 *Centuries,* I.29.

42 In *Centuries* I, see also I.3, I.15, I.16, I.38.

43 'All Things', *Commentaries of Heaven.* The passage is quoted by Allan Pritchard (1983) in 'Traherne's *Commentaries of Heaven* (With Selections from the Manuscript)', p. 7.

44 Traherne (1675), *Christian Ethicks,* pp. 94–5. A modernised edition of the text is to be found in *The Way to Blessedness,* Margaret Bottrall (1962). An old-spelling text has been prepared by Carol L. Marks and George Robert Guffey (1968), with valuable introductions and commentary. The passage quoted from the 1675 edition is to be found on p. 55 of the Marks and Guffey critical text.

45 *Centuries,* I.69

46 Jung (1967), *Alchemical Studies,* p. 131.

47 Jung (1967), *Alchemical Studies,* p. 182.

48 *Vala, or The Four Zoas,* Night the First, 469–75. (p. 277.)

49 The name *transpersonal psychology* was adopted in the late 1960s as a term for approaches to psychology and therapy that recognise and study the 'farther reaches of human potential', including those facets of experience traditionally labelled spiritual, mystical or religious. On the hazards of personal growth in the transpersonal sphere, see for instance, *What We May Be,* by Pierro Ferrucci (1982), who describes the "pathology of the sublime", and *The Stormy Search for the Self,* by Christina Grof and Stanislav Grof (1991), who discuss "spiritual emergence and spiritual emergency".

50 See *The Image of God in Man,* David Cairns (1953). On St Augustine's trinitarian image of God, its relationship with the Plotinian scheme of reflective emanations, and the history of the divine image in Patristic and later thought, see *The Image of God,* John Edward Sullivan (1963).

51 *Enneads* III.4.3. p. 187.

52 In *Plotinus, The Road to Reality,* pp. 87–8, J. M. Rist (1980) stresses that the contemplation of the Forms is only one function of man, and he interprets the phrase to mean that the soul is "produced and governed" by *Nous,* comprising the intelligible world of objects. The intelligible world pertains to human beings only at the dominant or superior level of their constitution.

53 See James McEvoy's (1982) discussion of medieval microcosm-macrocosm parallels in *The Philosophy of Robert Grosseteste,* Chapter 6, pp. 369–441. On Renaissance concepts, including the centrality of mankind presented in the thought of Marsilio Ficino (1433–99), and the mobility of man up and down the chain of being in Giovanni Pico della Mirandola's (1463–94) thought, see 'The Dignity of Man', *Renaissance Thought and Its Sources,* Chapter 9, pp. 169–81, by Paul Oskar Kristeller (1979), originally delivered as part of the Arensberg Lectures, 1965. A detailed account of Italian humanist thought on the "nature, condition and destiny of man" is given by Charles Trinkaus (1970), *In Our Image and Likeness.*

54 A classification of Western microcosmic theories is provided by Rudolf Allers (1944) in 'Microcosmus, From Anaximandros to Paracelsus'. Allers distinguishes between elementaristic, structural (cosmocentric and anthropocentric), holistic (sociological and aesthetic), symbolistic, psychological and metaphorical microcosmisms. In this classification, man as a partaker in all elements or facets of the creation constitutes *elementaristic* microcosmism. If the order or laws of the cosmos are embodied in man, the microcosmism is *structural.* The *anthropocentric* version refers to the 'cosmos as a

person' idea, the macrocosmic person. *Sociological* microcosmism sees the social or political state as an image of the cosmic order. In *psychological* microcosmism, man mirrors the universe through his *knowledge* of the universe. The microcosmic knowledge may refer to a person's accumulated understandings and information, which describe and encapsulate the world. In modern terms, this microcosm consists of conceptual representations, personal cognitive maps, schemas of the world. In a similar fashion, an encyclopaedia or atlas can be called a microcosm or mirror of the world. If the knowledge is taken to be a direct knowledge of the substratum, say a Platonic *phronesis* or contemplation of the Forms, then the 'psychological' microcosmism approaches the mystical kind of microcosmism that we are primarily interested in here. See Allers, pp. 330–1.

55 In Indian thought, unmitigated expressions of identification are found in the *Upanishads: Tat Tvam Asi*—'Thou art That', the absolute *Brahman* is the soul, the *atman.* Similarly, *Aham Brahma asmi*—'I am Brahma'.

56 *The Sparkling Stone,* Chapter X, in *John of Ruysbroeck,* pp. 201–12, translated by C. A. Wynschenk Dom (1916).

57 *The Book of Mencius (Meng Tzu),* 6A:11, in Wing-Tsit Chan (1969), *A Source Book of Chinese Philosophy,* p. 58. The Confucianism of Mencius has a pronounced mystical orientation. Mencius refers to the all-inclusiveness of the self, the completeness within—see *The Book of Mencius,* VII*a,* 1. Fung Yu-Lan (1983), *A History of Chinese Philosophy,* Vol. 1, p. 129, and also VII*a,* 4. Vol. 1, p. 129.

Chapter 5: Time and Eternity

1 Plato, *Cratylus,* 402A.

2 Heraclitus, Fragment 80.

3 Parmenides, Fragment 8.

4 On classical and Arabic time-atomism, see Richard Sorabji (1983), *Time, Creation and the Continuum.*

5 The association of Eternity with life may be contained in the etymology of the Greek word for eternity, *aion.* It seems that *aion* originally meant *life-span* or *lifetime,* or possibly referred to something like the psyche, the soul, the life-substance of a person. See R. B. Onians (1951), *The Origins of European Thought,* pp. 200 ff.

6 *Enneads* III.7.2. (p. 223.)

7 *Enneads* III.7.11. (p. 234.)

8 *Enneads* III.7.5. (p. 227.)

9 *The Consolation of Philosophy,* V.6.

10 *Consolation,* V.6.

11 On the "all-form" and the "each-forms", see William James (1909), *A Pluralistic Universe,* p. 34.

12 William James (1912), 'Absolutism and Empiricism', pp. 276–7, in *Essays in Radical Empiricism* (reprinted from *Mind,* Vol. IX, No. 34, April, 1884).

13 William James (1909), *A Pluralistic Universe,* p. 252.

14 *The Masks of God,* by Joseph Campbell (1984), contains a wide-ranging presentation of the subject.

15 Trans. M. O'C Walshe (1987), *Meister Eckhart,* Vol. II, p. 83, Sermon Fifty Seven (see also p. 157, Sermon Sixty Eight).

16 Ibid. Vol. II, p. 318, Sermon Ninety Three.
17 *The Marriage of Heaven and Hell,* Plate 14. (p. 154.)
18 *Jerusalem,* 49, 21–22. (p. 679.)
19 *Jerusalem,* 49, 34–37. (p. 680.)
20 E. R. Dodds (1970), *Pagan & Christian in an Age of Anxiety,* Chapter 1.
21 *Revelations* 10.6
22 Traherne (1675), *Christian Ethicks,* p. 525 (Marks and Guffey, p. 263).
23 I. Suttie (1988), *The Origins of Love and Hate,* p. 38.
24 'A Therapist's View of the Good Life: The Fully Functioning Person', in Carl Rogers (1967), *On Becoming a Person,* p. 194.
25 'Some of the Directions Evident in Therapy', 1953, in Rogers (1967), p. 91.
26 Eric Berne (1964), *Games People Play,* Chapter 16.
27 Theories on the relation between self-regard and regard for others are summarised by Ruth C. Wylie (1979), *The Self-Concept,* Vol. 2, pp. 435–9.
28 *The Garden Of Love,* 11–12. (p. 215.)
29 For example., Traherne, *Centuries,* IV.66.
30 Sigmund Freud (1930), *Civilization and Its Discontents,* p. 72. The "oceanic feeling", brought to Freud's attention by Romain Rolland, is "a feeling of an indissoluble bond, of being one with the external world as a whole." (p. 65.) Freud admitted that he had difficulty appraising the oceanic feeling scientifically, for he could not discover the feeling in himself. (p. 65 & p. 72.)
31 Ken Wilber (1980), *The Atman Project,* p. 152.
32 'Psychoanalysis and Zen Buddhism' in *Zen Buddhism and Psychoanalysis,* p. 94, D. T. Suzuki, Erich Fromm, and Richard De Martino (1970). Quoted by Wilber (1980) in *The Atman Project,* p. 155.
33 See Sharon Seelig's (1979) 'The Origins of Ecstasy: Traherne's "Select Meditations"'.
34 *Centuries,* III.8.
35 Patrick Grant (1971). On the various notions of the Fall of Man and Original Sin in the Church Fathers, see John Hick's (1966) *Evil and the Love of God* (on Irenaeus, see pp. 217–21).
36 *Centuries,* III.7
37 On the complexities of 'self-love' in Augustine's thought, see *The Problem of Self-Love in St. Augustine,* Oliver O'Donovan (1980). St Bernard's mystical system described four stages or degrees of love, leading from man's self-love for his own sake to man's self-love for the sake of God—see *The Mystical Theology of St Bernard,* Etienne Gilson (1940). A note on Traherne's debt to St Bernard is provided by N. I. Mater (1985), 'Thomas Traherne and St Bernard of Clairvaux'. In his discussion of self-love in *The Art of Loving* (p. 56), Erich Fromm quotes Eckhart, who refers to the equal love of self and others in one man, Christ, who is both God and man. According to Ficino, our human self-love is a derivative of the self-love that is a primary attribute of God—see *Pagan Mysteries of the Renaissance,* Edgar Wind (1980), pp. 64–5.
38 Traherne discusses the subject at length in the second half of *Centuries,* IV.
39 *Centuries,* IV.55.
40 On the positive role of 'wants' and 'desires' in Traherne's philosophy, see the commentary in Marks and Guffey (1968), p. 371. On 'wants', see also Richard D. Jordan (1972), *The Temple of Eternity,* pp. 81–4. Man takes part in the "circulation of love",

and the act of communicating love to others does not deplete the reservoir, but fills it. Contrast with the depletion of libido in Freud's early 'hydraulic' theory. The idea of needs emerging to replace a satisfied need is reminiscent of Fritz Perls's (1893–1970) figure-ground theory of needs, which was inspired by the Gestalt psychology theory of perception. In Perls's thought, however, needs and their satisfaction were essentially ego-centric, and Perls's version of Gestalt psychotherapy has been criticized for its lack of appreciation of the positive aspects of social dependency and compromise. Traherne, in contrast, recognised the value of needs in a society of beings.

41 Traherne (1675), *Christian Ethicks,* p. 514 (Marks and Guffey, p. 258).

42 Ibid. pp. 518–9 (Marks and Guffey, pp. 260–1).

43 Compare the self-interested natural man of Hobbes, driven by the psychological hedonism of pleasure-aversion and constrained by civil law, with Freud's *id,* the primitive part of the psychological apparatus, which strives to satisfy instinctual needs in accordance with the "pleasure principle" and falls under the control of the *super-ego,* the internalised parental 'law'. Freud, like Hobbes, stirred up religious indignation with his account of human nature.

44 Rousseau, *The Social Contract,* 1762.

45 *Nichomachean Ethics,* Book IX.4 (1166a.1 ff.). Trans. by W. D. Ross (1925), *Ethica Nichomachea* in *The Works of Aristotle.*

46 For Aristotle's discussion of self-love, see the *Ethics,* Book IX.8 (1168a.28–1169b.2).

47 *Letters,* II, 102–4, in *John Keats,* by Robert Gittings (1985), p. 450.

48 Gilbert Murray's 'Excursus on the ritual forms preserved in Greek Tragedy', in *Themis,* pp. 341–63, Jane Ellen Harrison (1912).

49 *Cosmic Consciousness,* Bucke (1905), pp. 268–9.

50 Ibid. p. 269.

51 Ibid. p. 270.

52 Ibid. p. 271.

53 Viktor E. Frankl (1985), *Man's Search For Meaning,* pp. 141–3. In this book, Frankl describes experiences in a concentration camp that led to his views on suffering and meaning.

54 Frankl (1985), Postscript 1984: 'The Case for a Tragic Optimism', pp. 161–79.

55 *Showings,* Julian of Norwich, Chapter Twenty-Seven.

56 On *philosophy of nature* and *natural philosophy,* see 'Nature: Religious and Philosophical Speculations', by Antoine Faivre, in *The Encyclopaedia of Religion,* Volume 10, pp. 328–37, editor-in-chief Mircea Eliade (1987). The article surveys the history of nature philosophy from antiquity to modern times.

57 *Isaiah* 8.14–15; *Isaiah* 28.16; *Psalm* 118.22.

58 *Matthew* 21.42–4; *Mark* 12.10; *Ephesians* 2.19–22; 1 *Peter* 2.4–8.

59 From *The Sparkling Stone,* in *John of Ruysbroeck,* Chapter IV, p. 187, translated by C. A. Wynschenk Dom (1916).

60 See Jung (1968), *Psychology and Alchemy,* Chapter 5, 'The Lapis-Christ Parallel'. The idea of unrecognised treasure rejected as worthless is open to psychological interpretation. There are facets of ourselves that we may find unacceptable and which are liable to be disowned and pushed into the unconscious. The banished contents (which may include primitive and instinctual tendencies, sexuality, aggression, power, self-dislike, spirituality) constitute the 'shadow', the unacknowledged aspects of the personality, which are often projected onto others. The shadow repeatedly leads the individual into

difficult or dangerous situations until it is recognised and receives a greater measure of integration into the conscious personality. According to Jung, the immanence expressed in the earthy symbolism of the *lapis* and the alchemical processes compensated for a spirituality that had become too elevated, rarefied, intellectual.

61 Jung (1968), p. 269.

62 *Ephesians* 2.19–22; 1 *Peter* 2.4–8.

63 On the Indian yogic meaning of the fixation of mercury—the transformation of experience from a transient to a static mode—see Mircea Eliade (1978), *The Forge and the Crucible,* p. 133.

64 Jung (1967), *Alchemical Studies,* pp. 84–7.

65 Ibid. p. 96.

66 Jung (1969), 'On the Nature of the Psyche', *The Structure and Dynamics of the Psyche,* p. 215.

67 See 'On the Nature of the Psyche'. Also 'Synchronicity: An Acausal Connecting Principle' in Jung (1969).

PART II: SPACE, TIME AND MOTION

Chapter 6: The Spatialization of Time

1 William James (1890), *The Principles of Psychology,* Vol. 1, p. 609.

2 Ibid. p. 609.

3 For these and other terms, see Paul Fraisse (1964), *The Psychology of Time,* p. 85. Fraisse provides a psychological discussion of the perceived present, pp. 84–97. See also G. J. Whitrow (1980), *The Natural Philosophy of Time,* pp. 74–7.

4 Compare with James's diagram in *Principles of Psychology,* Vol. 1, p. 257, Fig. 27. James plots the intensity of the brain processes "underlying consciousness" against their temporal order in the moment. "If I recite *a, b, c, d, e, f, g,* at the moment of uttering *d,* neither *a, b, c,* nor *e, f, g,* are out of my consciousness altogether, but both, after their respective fashions, 'mix their dim lights' with the stronger one of the *d,* because their neuroses are both awake in some degree" (p. 257). A *neurosis,* in this context, is a change or excitation of nerve cells that underlies experience, contrasted with the *psychosis,* the psychological experience.

5 On the spacetimes corresponding to various classical and relativistic theories of motion, see *Foundations of Space-Time Theories,* by M. Friedman (1983), and *World Enough and Space-Time* by J. Earman (1989).

6 Scholium on absolute space and time, *Philosophiæ Naturalis Principia Mathematica,* in *Sir Isaac Newton's Mathematical Principles of Natural Philosophy and his System of the World,* revised by Florian Cajori (1962), Vol. 1, p. 6.

7 Cajori (1962), Vol.1, p. 6.

8 'The Four Dimensional World', by M. Schlick (reprinted from Chapter 7 of *The Philosophy of Nature,* 1949) in *Problems of Space and Time,* ed. J. J. C. Smart (1973), p. 293.

9 This version of spacetime is likened by Rudy Rucker (1986) in *The Fourth Dimension,* p. 154, to a block of ice that melts from the bottom up.

10 'Time in Relativity Theory: Arguments for a Philosophy of Becoming', in *The Voices of Time,* pp. 434–54, edited by J. T. Fraser (1981).

11 Hans Reichenbach (1957), *The Philosophy of Space and Time,* pp. 189–90.

12 See G. J. Whitrow (1980), *The Natural Philosophy of Time,* pp. 368–70.

13 Summaries are provided by Max Jammer (1969), *Concepts of Space,* pp. 176–86, and John D. Barrow and Frank J. Tipler (1988), *The Anthropic Cosmological Principle,* pp. 258 ff. The latter book considers the issue in the context of *anthropic* arguments, according to which the basic laws and constants of nature are curiously well-suited for the emergence of life.

14 J. D. Barrow and F. J. Tipler (1988), pp. 266–9

15 See Walter G. Englert (1987), *Epicurus on the Swerve and Voluntary Action.*

16 *The Marriage of Heaven and Hell,* Plate 9, 17. (p. 152.)

17 Milic Capek (1961), *The Philosophical Impact of Contemporary Physics,* p. 160.

18 Capek (1961), p. 163.

19 Kurt Gödel, 'Remark of the Relationship Between Relativity Theory and Idealistic Philosophy', *Albert Einstein: Philosopher-Scientist,* p. 557, edited by Paul Arthur Schilpp (1951b).

20 D. C. Williams (1951), 'The Myth of Passage'.

21 For musings on such awkward possibilities, see *The Fourth Dimension* by Rudy Rucker (1986).

22 Hermann Weyl (1949), *Philosophy of Mathematics and Natural Science,* p. 116.

23 J. W. Dunne (1934), *The Serial Universe.*

24 Adolf Grünbaum (1974), *Philosophical Problems of Space and Time,* Chapter 10: 'Is there a "flow of time" or temporal "becoming"?', p. 314.

25 Karl Popper used the example of a stone dropped onto a water surface to show that there are anisotropic processes which are *not* entropic. In an ideal case, free from dissipative losses, waves radiate outwards from the central disturbance without an increase of entropy. In my kinetic description of the pebble-pond interaction, the process is dissipative and is accompanied by entropy increase—my intention is merely to indicate that process anisotropy can be seen in interactions between a multiplicity of items, without introducing statistical and probabilistic arguments to establish a process anisotropy. For Popper's interest in the arrow of time, which was motivated by a "realist and objectivist" stance (i.e., the arrow of time is not merely 'subjective' personal experience), see *Unended Quest,* Popper (1976), Chapters 30, 35 and 36, first published in 'Autobiography of Karl Popper', *The Philosophy of Karl Popper,* Vol. I, edited by Paul Arthur Schilpp (1974). See also 'Popper's Views on the Arrow of Time' by Adolf Grünbaum in Schilpp (1974), Vol. II, pp. 775–97, and Popper's reply, pp. 1140–4.

26 See, for instance, Grünbaum, in Schilpp (1974), Vol. II, pp. 784–7.

27 The laws describing electromagnetic radiation are time-reversible, and a choice is made to discard the reverse time solution, the *advanced potential.* See G. J. Whitrow (1980), *The Natural Philosophy of Time,* pp. 8 ff.

28 A. Grünbaum (1974), *Philosophical Problems of Space and Time,* p. 325. Grünbaum provides references to his other publications on the "mind-dependent status of temporal becoming" in Appendix 31, p. 832.

29 Ibid. p. 324.

30 Perhaps Blake and Traherne expressed similar ideas. See Blake's *A Vision of the Last Judgement, P.80* (Keynes, p. 606): "Man Passes on, but States remain for Ever; he passes

thro' them like a traveller who may as well suppose that the places he has passed thro' exist no more, as a Man may suppose that the States he has pass'd thro' Exist no more. Every thing is Eternal." Traherne writes of moments that remain, and we who pass on—see the *Select Meditations,* I.95, quoted in *The Temple of Eternity,* p. 15, by R. D. Jordan (1972).

31 For instance, see Abram Hoffer's study of altered 'time perception' (especially pp. 399–400) in *The Future of Time,* edited by Henri Yaker, Humphry Osmond and Frances Cheek (1971).

Chapter 7: The Enigma of Motion

1 *Timaeus,* 37, translated by Desmond Lee (1979), in *Timaeus and Critias,* p. 51.

2 Ibid. 33–4, p. 46.

3 On the idea of an infinite, empty space outside the Aristotelian plenum-universe, an extracosmic void denied by Aristotle but considered by several Stoic and medieval thinkers, see *Much Ado about Nothing,* by Edward Grant (1981), and *Matter, Motion and Space,* by Richard Sorabji (1988).

4 Translated from the Latin. 'Axioms, or Laws of Motion', *Philosophiæ Naturalis Principia Mathematica,* in *Sir Isaac Newton's Mathematical Principles of Natural Philosophy and his System of the World,* Florian Cajori (1962), Vol. 1, p. 13.

5 Cajori (1962), Vol. 1, p. 13.

6 See, for instance, *The Mechanization of the World Picture,* IV: 300–304, pp. 469–74, by E. J. Dijksterhuis (1986).

7 On the various principles of relativity, see A. d'Abro (1950), *The Evolution of Scientific Thought,* pp. 108–15.

8 A complete Venus cycle is plotted in N. F. Michelsen's (1991) *Tables of Planetary Phenomena,* along with numerous other instances.

Chapter 8: In Search of True Rest

1 *De gravitatione,* in *Unpublished Scientific Papers of Isaac Newton,* p. 127, A. R. Hall and M. B. Hall (1962). Newton's comments were aimed at Descartes' understanding of the relativity of motion.

2 Aristotle, *de caelo*. See G. S. Kirk, J. E. Raven & M. Schofield (1983), *The Presocratic Philosophers,* pp. 342–4.

3 On Kepler's solar enthusiasm, see Burtt (1932), pp. 47–8.

4 On the solar theology of the 'Egyptian' Hermetic works, and the religious interest of Giordano Bruno and Tommaso Campanella in heliocentricism, see *Giordano Bruno and the Hermetic Tradition* by Frances A. Yates (1964).

5 For details, see *Much Ado About Nothing,* by Edward Grant (1981), in which the medieval scholastic views on infinite space are also considered.

6 See Grant (1981), Chapter 8. On the contributions of the Italian nature philosophers, see also *Concepts of Space,* pp. 85–91, by Max Jammer (1969).

7 A. O. Lovejoy (1936), *The Great Chain of Being,* p. 52.

8 Lovejoy (1936), p. 63, from Macrobius's Commentary on Cicero's *Dream of Scipio,* a work that was well-known in the middle ages. An accessible account of the Neoplatonic

schemes of procession and reversion is provided by R. T. Wallis (1972) in *Neoplatonism.* On metaphors of mirroring and reflecting in Plotinus, see Rein Ferwerda (1965), *La signification des images et des métaphores dans la pensée de Plotin,* pp. 9–23.

9 On Bruno's application of the principle of plenitude to the universe, see Lovejoy (1936), pp. 116–21. Also, A. Koyré (1957), *From the Closed World to the Infinite Universe,* p. 42, and P. A. Michel (1973), *The Cosmology of Giordano Bruno,* Ch. VI.

10 Michel (1973), pp. 161–2. Also, F. Copleston (1963), *A History of Philosophy, Late Mediaeval and Renaissance Philosophy,* Vol. 3, Part II, p. 68, and Grant (1981), p. 191 & p. 379, Note 57. Grant points out that Bruno's formulation of God as wholly in each part is a traditional way of conceiving the omnipresence of God, as we shall note shortly.

11 General Scholium, *Philosophiæ Naturalis Principia Mathematica,* in *Sir Isaac Newton's Mathematical Principles of Natural Philosophy and his System of the World,* revised by Florian Cajori (1962), Vol. 2, p. 545.

12 On Henry More's criticism of Cartesian relative motion, and his justification of absolute motion in absolute space, see *The Metaphysical Foundations of Modern Science,* by E. A. Burtt (1932), p. 139. Also, Koyré (1957), pp. 142–5. On More and Newton, see Jammer (1969), pp. 40–8 and pp. 110–13, and Koryé (1957), Chapters V & VI.

13 Described by Jammer (1969), but Koyré (1957), p. 261, warns against exaggerating the Kabbalistic influence.

14 The Nullibists are those who accept that there is spirit, but "contend that they are *no where* in the whole World": a spirit is "Nullibi, that is to say Nowhere." Quotations are from Joseph Glanvill's (1682) *Saducismus Triumphatus,* p. 100. The work contains a translation of Chapters XXVII and XXVIII from More's *Enchiridion metaphysicum,* 1671. More names Descartes "the Prince of the Nullibists" (p. 101, Glanvill). On the Nullibists, and More's chapters in *Saducismus Triumphatus,* see Edward Grant (1981), *Much ado about nothing,* p. 223, and Note 238, p. 399.

15 *Enchiridion metaphysicum*, 1671, translated by Burtt (1932), p. 140. Also see translation by Koyré (1957), p. 148.

16 *Enchiridion metaphysicum*, Ch. 8, Par. 14 ff., trans. Burtt (1932), p. 141.

17 *Opera Omnia,* 1675–9, Vol. I, pp. 171 ff., in Burtt (1932), p. 141.

18 *Much Ado About Nothing,* Grant (1981), p. 350, Note 127.

19 Grant (1981), p. 356, Note 33.

20 *Enneads,* IV.2.1. (p. 257.) Plotinus found support for the idea of the soul as both divisible and indivisible, many and one, in Plato's *Timaeus* (see *Enneads,* IV.2.2., p. 259).

21 On Augustine's idea of the soul's full presence in each part of the body, in relation to Neoplatonic sources, see Jean Pépin (1977), *Ex Platonicorvm Persona. Études sur les lectures philosophiques de Saint Augustin,* 'Chapitre VI.—L'influence de Porphyre sur la doctrine de l'ame et la théologie trinitaire d'Augustin', pp. 211–267 (reprinted from *Revue des Études Anciennes,* LXVI, 1964, pp. 53–107).

22 *Opticks,* Queries 28 & 31. See Burtt (1932), pp. 258–61.

23 According to one ancient Greek belief, the shining upper air, the *aither,* was of a fiery nature and divine, the habitation of souls. This radiant sky-*aither* of popular belief may have been a precursor of the Heraclitean logos-fire, and Aristotle's celestial *aither.* See G. S. Kirk, J. E. Raven and M. Schofield (1983), p. 9, pp. 198–9, and p. 204.

24 Max Jammer mentions the English philosopher Robert Grosseteste (*c.*1175–1253) and the Silesian philosopher Witelo (*c.*1230–75), whose theological interest in light provided a stimulus to the science of optics. See Jammer (1969), pp. 36–40. The association of light, space and the 'divine' in Buddhist thought will be noted in Chapter Twelve.

25 Scholium on Absolute Space and Time, *Principia,* in Florian Cajori (1962), Vol. 1, p. 12.

26 Cajori (1962), Vol. 1, p. 10.

27 Cajori (1962), Vol. 1, p. 12.

28 Corollary V, Cajori (1962), Vol. 1, p. 20.

29 Galileo's notion of relativity was a precursor of the classical principle of relativity, presented in Newton's *Principia* and in Huygen's *De Motu Corpum.* It rested, however, on a pre-classical understanding of inertial motion, which included a natural circular motion with the earth's rotation, following Copernicus. The classical principle, in contrast, is based on an inertial motion that is solely uniform and *rectilinear.*

30 See Chapter Two on the shift from the solid atom to the point-particle and field concepts in later classical mechanics.

31 See Jammer (1969), pp. 124–6.

32 *The Leibniz-Clarke Correspondence,* L.V.53, p. 74, edited by H. G. Alexander (1976).

33 Karl Pearson (1949), *The Grammar of Science,* p. 66.

34 See, for example, Jammer (1969), pp. 192–9, and Julian B. Barbour (1989), *The Discovery of Dynamics,* Vol. 1, pp. 2–18.

35 See Lawrence Sklar (1977), *Space, Time and Spacetime,* Chapter III, pp. 161–234, and J. Earman (1989), *World Enough and Space-Time.*

36 The reader may wish to refer to the various absolute-relative distinctions outlined in Chapter Seven.

Chapter 9: Absolute Spacetime

1 The example of the cube is discussed by Edwin F. Taylor and John A. Wheeler (1966) in *Spacetime Physics,* Exercise 50, pp. 96–7, and Answers to Exercises, pp. 23–4.

2 See Einstein's 'Autobiographical Notes', p. 53, in *Albert Einstein: Philosopher-Scientist,* edited by Paul Arthur Schilpp (1951b).

3 See G. J. Whitrow (1980), *The Natural Philosophy of Time,* p. 358.

4 In the relativistic spacetime diagram, the worldline of a light-pulse lies in its own spacetime cross-section of simultaneity. In this sense, the temporal states of the pulse may be described as 'simultaneous' with one another.

5 A. Einstein (1954), *Relativity,* Appendix V, 'Relativity and the Problem of Space', pp. 138–9.

6 R. P. Graves (1885), *Life of Sir William Rowan Hamilton,* Vol. II, The Tetractys, p. 525.

7 H. Minkowski, 'Space and Time' (1908), in A. Einstein, et al. (1952), *The Principle of Relativity,* p. 75.

8 If we suppose that the scope of experience can be enlarged to a universal extent, encompassing all times and places, then all events become experientially simultaneous, a *totum simul,* all things together in one experience, the eternal Now.

9 This time-lag span is additional to the span of the experiential moment ('specious moment') discussed in Chapters One and Six.

10 The example is based on Einstein's well-known illustration of relative simultaneity. In Einstein's example, the events A and B are two strokes of lightning, simultaneous relative to a railway embankment. See Einstein (1954), *Relativity,* pp. 25–7.

11 For a more detailed presentation of the geometry of real-time diagrams to illustrate Lorentz contraction (and also time dilation), see Taylor and Wheeler (1966), Exercise 48, pp. 92–4.
12 K. Gödel, 'A Remark On The Relationship Between Relativity Theory And Idealistic Philosophy', in Schilpp (1951b), p. 558.
13 K. Gödel, in Schilpp (1951b), p. 557.

Chapter 10: The Physics of the Large

1 The example derives from Einstein (1954), *Relativity,* pp. 66–70.
2 See Chapter Eight.
3 A. Einstein (1983), 'Ether and the Theory of Relativity,' in *Sidelights on Relativity,* p. 19.
4 C. G. Jung (1967), *Alchemical Studies,* p. 104. My allusion here is to the tenseless permanence of spacetime, conceived as a bedrock of things in all their states of transformation.
5 Einstein (1983), p. 22.
6 A. Eddington (1987), *Space, Time and Gravitation,* p. 190.
7 Ibid. p. 192.
8 For the version due to Proclus, see the discussion of absolute space in Chapter 6.
9 For details, see C. Lanczos (1970), *Space through the Ages,* Ch. 6.
10 See, for instance, E. H. Taylor and J. A. Wheeler (1966), *Spacetime Physics,* pp. 184 ff.
11 On the globe/chart analogy in the discussion of curved spaces, see J. J. Callahan (1976), 'The Curvature of Space in a Finite Universe'.
12 W. L. Burke (1980), *Spacetime, Geometry, Cosmology,* p. 277.
13 C. W. Misner, K. S. Thorne and J. A. Wheeler, (1973) *Gravitation,* p. 704.
14 J. L. Martin (1988), *General Relativity,* p. 90.
15 E. T. Whittaker (1949), *From Euclid to Eddington,* pp. 39–40.
16 The pitch of a sound depends on the state of motion of the sound-source relative to the observer. The effect is experienced, for instance, when an ambulance passes by.
17 Misner, Thorne and Wheeler (1973), p. 719.
18 See Mircea Eliade (1971), *The Myth of the Eternal Return,* on the periodicity of time in religious world-views, and interpretations of the historical process.
19 There is also a possibility that the general relativistic treatment of cosmology may one day be abandoned, along with the idea of curved spacetime.

PART III: A WORLD OF TOTALITIES

Chapter 11: Relative Spacetime

1 For example, the connection between Einstein's relativistic assumptions and monadological theory was taken seriously by H. Wildon Carr, who developed his own philosophy of monads. See Carr (1922), *A Theory of Monads,* Chapter XV, and Carr (1928), *The Unique Status of Man,* Chapter V.

2 A. Wenzl, 'Einstein's theory of relativity, viewed from the standpoint of critical realism, and its significance for philosophy', in *Albert Einstein: Philosopher-Scientist,* p. 586, edited by Paul Arthur Schilpp (1951b).

3 See quotation in Chapter 9.

4 *Principles of Nature and of Grace, Founded on Reason, 2,* p. 195. Page number references to the *Principles of Nature and Grace* (1714) and the *Monadology* (1714) refer to *Leibniz: Philosophical Writings,* edited by G. H. R. Parkinson (1973).

5 *Principles, 4,* p. 197.

6 *Monadology, 3,* p. 179.

7 *Principles, 3,* p. 196. See also *Monadology, 63,* p. 189.

8 *Monadology, 77,* p. 191

9 *Monadology, 72,* pp. 190–1.

10 *Monadology, 73,* p. 191.

11 The point is made by A. O. Lovejoy (1936) in *The Great Chain of Being,* Ch. IX.

12 See Chapter 8.

13 See Hermann Jacobi's article 'Jainism' in *Encyclopaedia of Religion and Ethics,* Volume XII, p. 469, edited by James Hastings (1964). Also Surendranath Dasgupta (1969), *A History of Indian Philosophy,* Volume 1, p. 190.

14 See *Monadolgy, 16,* p. 181, on the plurality of our experience and the plurality within the monad.

15 *Monadology, 17,* p. 181.

16 *Monadology, 17,* p. 181.

17 *Monadology, 22,* p. 182.

18 Alfred North Whitehead (1927), *Science and the Modern World,* p. 114. For a discussion of Whitehead's rejection of simple location, see 'Space-Time, Simple Location and Prehension' by Evander Bradley McGilvary, in *The Philosophy of Alfred North Whitehead,* edited by Paul Arthur Schilpp (1951a), pp. 229 ff.

19 It has been speculated that an oriental stream of organicism, in the form of Neo-Confucianism, joined or rejoined the occidental stream in Leibniz's philosophical interests, for Leibniz was in communication with Jesuit missionaries in China. Chinese thought shows a very long history of organic philosophy and microcosm-macrocosm analogies. See Joseph Needham (1956), *Science and Civilization in China,* Volume 2, pp. 279–303, pp. 339–45, and pp. 496–505.

20 W. T. Stace (1960), *Mysticism and Philosophy,* pp. 154–61.

21 Ibid. p. 154.

22 Ibid. p. 158.

23 See Note 10 in Chapter Four—Stace places experiences containing multiplicity into his sensory category of mystical experiences, the extrovertive category.

24 See Chapter 4.

25 The Plotinian One will be considered in greater detail in the next chapter.

26 Stace (1960), pp. 160–1.

27 Note that 'matter' in these ancient Indian theories is conceived quite differently from the atomic matter of Democritus and later scientific speculation.

28 Hippolytus, in W. K. C. Guthrie (1962), *A History of Greek Philosophy,* Vol. I, p. 325.

29 Ibid. pp. 326–7.

30 Ibid. p. 327.

31 P. H. Michel (1973), *The Cosmology of Giordano Bruno* Ch. IX.

32 See Nicholas of Cusa's *De Docta Ignorantia,* English translation by Germain Heron (1954), *Of Learned Ignorance,* III.3–4. On creatures as the multiple images of God, see II.3., p. 79. Creatures are not so much mirrors as images, for the mirror suggests a distinct reality that receives an image, whereas a creature has a total dependence on its creator, like an image to its original. "It is like the image of the face in the mirror, provided we suppose that the mirror in itself and of itself is nothing before or after the reflection." (II.2., p. 74.)

33 On the relationships between Conway, More and Helmont, see *Conway Letters,* Chapter Six, Marjorie Hope Nicolson (1930). On Conway's philosophy and Leibniz's monadology, see pp. 452–7. Also 'The Vitalism of Anne Conway: Its Impact on Leibniz's Concept of the Monad', by Carolyn Merchant (1979a).

34 See Carolyn Merchant (1979b), 'The Vitalism of Francis Mercury van Helmont: Its Influence of Leibniz', pp. 172–4.

35 *Cabbalistical Dialogue,* quoted by Merchant (1979b), p. 174.

36 Merchant (1979b), p. 175.

37 Gershom G. Scholem (1954), *Major Trends in Jewish Mysticism, Seventh Lecture.* 'Isaac Luria and his School'.

38 Scholem (1954), p. 265.

39 *Principles of Nature and of Grace,* 14, p. 202.

40 Hans Leisegang (1937), 'La connaissance de Dieu au mirroir de l'âme et de la nature', pp. 147–9.

41 *Timaeus,* 13, pp. 62–4 in *Timaeus and Critias,* Desmond Lee (1977).

42 Thus, in *The Nature of Light* (p. 12), Vasco Ronchi (1970) discerns a *psychology* of perception in Plato's theory of the inner and outer lights, for the theory seems to make little sense as a mere explanation of the *physics* of vision. See also Herbert Grabes (1982), *The Mutable Glass,* pp. 83–5, who describes features of Augustine's theory of vision as they relate to the mirror-metaphor: the ever-changing, passively formed image in the eye is contrasted with the enduring and comprehended image in the soul. Leisegang expands on the mirror-metaphor of the eye, finding early instances in a Platonic dialogue of uncertain authorship, the *First Alcibiades,* and in a work of the alchemist Zosimus. In Leibniz, the mirror-metaphor is applied to the rational soul as a mirror of the universe and God, but as Leisegang points out, others have made God Himself the mirror: God is the mirror in which the soul comes to see and know itself. See Grabes, p. 75. A further mirror-metaphor may be introduced alongside the metaphor of God as mirror: the eyes of others act as mirrors in which one sees oneself or one's eyes. It is a familiar metaphor in love-poetry—the lover is reflected in the eyes of the beloved (see Grabes, pp. 85–8). In the theological and philosophical context, Leisegang (pp. 156–7) mentions the eye of God, which is Eternity, described by the German mystic Jacob Boehme (1575–1624) as a mirror, round like a ball. The human soul is likewise an "eye of fire".

43 Li Zhi Fang and Shu Xian Li (1989), *Creation of the Universe,* p. 17.

44 On the symbolism of the centre, see the works of Mircea Eliade, such as *The Sacred and the Profane* (1959).

45 See C. G. Jung (1970a), *Aion,* pp. 218–21.

46 See E. Grant (1981), *Much Ado About Nothing,* pp. 138–9, and Note 108, pp. 346–7. Also: Edgar Wind (1968), *Pagan Mysteries in the Renaissance,* p. 227; Frances A. Yates (1964), *Giordano Bruno and the Hermetic Tradition,* p. 247; Jorge Luis Borges (1981),

Labyrinths, pp. 224–7, 'The Fearful Sphere of Pascal'. Karsten Harries (1975), in 'The Infinite Sphere: Comments on the History of a Metaphor', focuses on Cusa's transfer of the idea from God to the universe. Dietrich Mahnke (1937) provided a history of the idea in his *Unendliche Sphäre und Allmittelpunkt,* Mahnke (1884–1939) was an important interpreter of Leibniz's monadology.

47 *Thoughts of Pascal,* p. 65, translated and edited by Chas. S. Jerram (1910).

48 Text introduced and edited by Clemens Baeumker (1927) in *Beiträge zur Geschichte der Philosophie des Mittelalters,*pp. 194–214, 'Das pseudo-hermetische "Buch der vierundzwanzig Meister" *(Liber XXIV philosophorum).* Ein Beitrag zur Geschichte des Neupythagoreismus und Neuplatonismus im Mittelalter' (revised, enlarged and amended version of original study, 1913). God is described as an infinite sphere in Definition II (p. 208): "Deus est sphaera infinita, cuius centrum est ubique, circumferentia nusquam."

49 For the text and an introduction, see Marie-Thérèse d'Alverny (1965), *Alain de Lille,* pp. 163–80 & pp. 295–306.

50 See Grant (1981), p. 346, Note 108. In the *Liber XXIV Philosophorum,* it is Definition XVIII (Baeumker, p. 212). Another interesting definition (III) in the *Liber* expresses the 'whole in every part' idea popular in scholastic thought (see Chapter Eight): God is said to be totally present in everything, "Deus est totus in quolibet sui" (Baeumker, p. 208)—see also Harries (1975), p. 10.

51 See Kirk, Raven and Schofield (1983), p. 170.

52 *Enneads* VI.9.8. (p. 622.)

53 R. Kloetzli (1983), *Buddhist Cosmology.*

54 J. G. Neihardt (1979), *Black Elk Speaks,* p. 43.

55 Ibid. p. 43.

56 See *The Sixth Grandfather,* edited by Raymond J. DeMallie (1985), which contains the transcripts of Black Elk's teachings to Neihardt. On p. 97, DeMallie compares the 'centre of the world' passage in *Black Elk Speaks* with the version in the transcript.

57 J. Campbell (1988), *The Power of Myth,* p. 89.

Chapter 12: Flux and the Substratum

1 In *Mysticism and Philosophy,* Stace (1960) notes the possibility of an integration, remarking that it is called *deification* in the Christian tradition, and has also been called *spiritual marriage* or the *unitive life* (p. 61). Some instances of experience that Stace calls extrovertive mysticism may fall into the unitive category—sensory experience fused with the trans-sensate, substratal levels of experience.

2 *Centuries,* III.3.

3 *A Source Book in Chinese Philosophy,* p. 403, trans. Wing-Tsit Chan (1969).

4 Ward (1911), *The Realm of Ends, or Pluralism and Theism,* p. 241.

5 See W. K. C. Guthrie (1978), *A History of Greek Philosophy,* Vol. V, *The Later Plato and the Academy,* pp. 299 ff. Also Richard Sorabji (1983), *Time, Creation and the Continuum,* Ch. 17, 'Plato and Aristotle on the Beginning of Things'. Plotinus, like most later Platonists, interpreted the creation in the *Timaeus* as a *timeless derivation* (e.g., *Enneads,* II.4.5., pp. 107–8). Eckhart expresses timeless derivation thus: "God creates the world and all things in one present now: and the time that passed away a thousand years ago is now as present and as near to God as this very instant." Translated by M. O'C Walshe (1987), *Meister Eckhart,* Vol. II, p. 144, Sermon Sixty Six.

6 See, for instance, A. H. Armstrong (1940), *The Architecture of the Intelligible Universe in the Philosophy of Plotinus,* pp. 17–18.
7 *The Republic,* 508*e,* pp. 308–9, trans. Desmond Lee (1974).
8 *Enneads,* V.5.6. (p. 408.)
9 *Enneads* VI.9.8. (p. 622.)
10 *Enneads* I.3. (pp. 36–40.)
11 *Enneads* VI.7.35. (p. 589.)
12 *Enneads* VI.7.39. (p. 592.)
13 On the One having some kind of knowledge, different from the knowledges at the lower levels, see J. M. Rist (1980), *Plotinus, The Road to Reality,* pp. 38–52. In the Plotinian scheme, self-identifications are usually held to be restricted to the level of *Nous,* although A. H. Armstrong discusses the possibility of a Plotinian "Infinite Self" at the level of the One—see Armstrong (1940), pp. 34–42.
14 *Enneads* VI.7.36. (p. 590.)
15 *Exodus* 20.21.
16 On Nirvana and space, see *Buddhist Thought in India,* pp. 159–66, Edward Conze (1983). Conze notes the parallel with Henry More's space theology.
17 Conze (1983), p. 164.

Chapter 13: Deep Structure

1 Five-dimensional if the embedding dimension of spacetime curvature is ascribed a structural reality.
2 Classic studies of the influence of the telescopic and microscopic discoveries on the literary imagination are to be found in *Science and Imagination* by Marjorie Hope Nicolson (1956).
3 Jonathan Swift, quoted in Nicolson (1956), p. 176: 'On Poetry', from *The Poetical Works of Swift,* edited John Mitford, 1880, II.74. The verse is also quoted by Milic Capek (1961) in *The Philosophical Impact of Contemporary Physics,* pp. 25–6, from Karl Pearson's (1949) *The Grammar of Science,* p. 212. Capek (pp. 21–6) discusses the *relativity of magnitude,* or the "principle of Gulliver", the idea that the world is very similar at different levels of magnitude, and he cites Blaise Pascal, preformationist theory, Fournier d'Albe, Bohr's atomic model, and Whitehead.
4 *Pensées,* Pascal, in *Thoughts of Pascal,* p. 67, translated and edited by Chas. S. Jerram (1910).
5 Ibid. p. 66–7.
6 *Monadology,* 67, in Parkinson (1973), p. 190.
7 For details and references, see the Introduction and Chapter One in *The Physical Effects in the Gravitational Field of Black Holes,* ed. M. A. Markov (1987).
8 V. L. Ginzburg (1985), *Physics and Astrophysics,* pp. 44–5.
9 A pictorial journey from the cosmic to the sub-atomic is provided by Morrison and Morrison (1982), in *Powers of Ten.*
10 See Michael Green, *Superstrings: A Theory of Everything,* pp. 130–1, edited by P. C. W. Davies and J. Brown (1988).
11 See J. D. Barrow and F. J. Tipler (1988), *The Anthropic Cosmological Principle,* p. 275.

12 See Max Jammer (1966), *The Conceptual Development of Quantum Mechanics,* pp. 338–40.
13 Fragment 6.
14 Fragment 10.
15 See 'The Physical Theory of Anaxagoras' by Colin Strang (1963).
16 In *De Docta Ignorantia,* Cusa explains: "To say that 'everything is in everything' is the same as saying that God, by the intermediary of the universe, is in all things and that the universe, by the intermediary of all things, is in God." Trans. Germain Heron (1954), *Of Learned Ignorance,* II.5., p. 84.
17 Compare with Whitehead's rejection of "the fallacy of simple locality", noted in Chapter Eleven.
18 For introductory accounts of symmetry in modern physics, see Heinz Pagels (1985), *Perfect Symmetry,* and Paul Davies (1986), *The Forces of Nature.*

Chapter 14: Minute Particulars

1 Note the account of the seaside vision in *Seeing the Invisible,* pp. 49–51 (AHRC reference no. 2366), edited by M. Maxwell and V. Tschudin (1990). The child thinks of stars, but the adult can make the link with atoms.
2 *Enneads* III.7.3. (p. 224.) In A. H. Armstrong's translation, the last part reads: "... not now some things, and then again others, but a partless completion, as if they were all together in a point, and had not yet begun to go out and flow into lines...." Armstrong (1967), *Plotinus,* Vol. III, pp. 303–4.
3 *Phaedrus* 247 ff.
4 *Enneads,* V.8.4. 'On the Intellectual Beauty'. (p. 425, MacKenna.)
5 A. H. Armstrong (1984), *Plotinus,* Vol. V, pp. 248–9, Note 1.
6 *Enneads,* V.8.9. (p. 430.) See Chapter Four, Note 38.
7 See E. R. Dodds (1933), *Proclus, The Elements of Theology,* pp. 257–60. Dodds (p. xxii) notes that the principle "all things are in all things, but in each according to its proper nature" was first systematically applied by Iamblichus (*c.*270–*c.*330), but may have had Neopythagorean precedents. On the employment of the principle in Neoplatonic thought, see p. 254, Note to Prop. 103.
8 Traherne (1675), *Christian Ethicks,* 'To the Reader' (Marks and Guffey, p. 5).
9 In discussing the greatness of the soul in the *Christian Ethicks,* Traherne quotes the Hermetic passage on reflecting the universe in the mind, in *Libellus* XI, from which we quoted in Chapter Four. On Traherne's relationship with the Hermetica, see Carol L. Marks (1966a), 'Thomas Traherne and Hermes Trismegistus'.
10 See Sharon Seelig's (1979) 'The Origins of Ecstasy: Traherne's "Select Meditations"'. The *Select Meditations* clearly belong to a period following Traherne's adult mystical apprehensions, but they seem to represent a stage of interpretation prior to the maturity of thought found in the *Centuries.*
11 *Centuries* II.81. References for all further quotations from the *Centuries* are given in the main text, prefixed by the letter 'C'.
12 *Christian Ethicks,* p. 133 (Marks and Guffey, p. 73).
13 Marjorie Hope Nicolson (1960): on More and the infinite, see pp. 158–165; on Traherne and the infinite, see pp. 196–204. Nicolson describes the microcosmic aspects of seventeenth-century literature in Chapters One and Five. A discussion of John Donne's

microcosmism, including the use of the lovers' eyes mirror-metaphor, is provided by Toshihiko Kawasaki in 'Donne's Microcosm', *Seventeenth Century Imagery,* pp. 25–43, edited by Earl Miner (1971). On More's changing attitudes to infinity and the plurality of worlds, see Grant (1981), *Much Ado About Nothing,* p. 399, Note 236: More initially rejected infinite space, then accepted it along with an infinity of worlds, but finally dropped the infinity of the worlds. On the eternal and infinite in Traherne, see 'Thomas Traherne and the Infinite: The Ethical Compromise', Rosalie L. Colie (1957), pp. 69–82, and *The Temple of Eternity: Thomas Traherne's Philosophy of Time,* by Richard Douglas Jordan (1972).

14 Traherne's opposition to identifying infinite space with God was expressed in private, in his Commonplace Book. For details, see Carol L. Marks (1966b), 'Thomas Traherne and Cambridge Platonism', pp. 529–531.

15 Marks (1966b), p. 530.

16 On the concentration of God's presence at a point in Jewish thought, see G. G. Scholem (1961), *Major Trends in Jewish Mysticism,* p. 260.

17 *Meditations on the Six Days of the Creation,* 1717, London, p. 87, reprinted in G. R. Guffey (1966). The infinite presence of God at every place is also expressed in *Thanksgivings for God's Attributes,* lines 102–7, in Margoliouth (1958), Vol. II, p. 315. It follows that God's infinity "resideth in every Centre, therefore in my Soul", for God's presence is wholly in a person as "the Sun in a Mirrour" (lines 127–32, p. 315). Traherne aspires to be "A constant Mirror of Eternitie" (line 96, *Thoughts. IV,* Margoliouth (1958), Vol. II, p. 182). On God's full presence everywhere, and therefore in every centre, see also *Centuries,* II.82.

18 See Chapter Eight.

19 *Enchiridion metaphysicum,* 1671, translation in Joseph Glanvill's (1682) *Saducismus Triumphatus,* p. 99.

20 For a discussion, see Grant's (1981) *Much Ado about Nothing,* pp. 223–5.

21 See Burtt (1932), *The Metaphysical Foundations of Modern Science,* pp. 129 ff.

22 The debate may strike the modern reader as vaguely similar in form to the divergent interpretations of quantum theory concerning wavefunctions extended over space, faster-than-light signalling and holistic connections. In both cases, a whole-in-the-part interpretation has been invoked to explain the interconnections between separated parts. The rise of the mechanical science and the focus on purely material interactions made the whole-in-the-part idea irrelevant for a long time, but the closer study of nature has revealed connections between parts that do not fit easily into conventional notions of physical interaction, as we shall see in Chapter Fifteen.

23 *Enchiridion metaphysicum,* 1671, in Glanvill (1682), p. 130. See also Grant (1981), p. 225.

24 *The Immortality of the Soul,* 1663, quoted by Grant (1981), p. 225.

25 *The Preparative,* line 15, in Margoliouth (1958), Vol. II, p. 20. On the soul and the infinite sphere, see also Traherne's poem *My Spirit,* pp. 50–6, and Margoliouth's note for line 94, p. 350: Traherne seems unsure whether it is a sphere he apprehends. In the *Thanksgivings for God's Attributes,* lines 223–5, Traherne uses the sphere metaphor to describe God's eternal nature—it is like a sphere "whose Centre is everywhere, circumference no where" (Margoliouth, Vol. II, p. 318).

26 On seventeenth-century meditational aspiration for the image of God within, see Louis L. Martz (1964), *The Paradise Within,* in which the poetry of Vaughan and Milton is also considered. A discussion of Traherne's meditations in the context of seventeenth-

century meditational literature is provided by R. D. Jordan (1985): 'Thomas Traherne and the Art of Meditation'. In this paper, Jordan (p. 398) provides an illuminating quotation from Traherne's *Select Meditations,* I.81: "When I retire first I seem to com in my Selfe to a centre, in that centre I find Eternitie, and all its Riches. By leavi[ng] things as they Stand without I find them within in a richer Manner. They are all in Thee, & Thou art there: O my God flie unto Thee." Note that Traherne's meditation does not take him to an experience completely unrelated to sensory experience, but reveals the familiar things in "a richer Manner". His account of inward vision supports the idea of a resemblance between sensory and substratal objects, as considered in Chapters Three and Four. These 'interior' objects should not be confused with personal object-representations of the sort discussed in psychoanalytic object-relations theories or in cognitive theories of schemas. Traherne's objects belong to the world outside the person, and are not objects introjected from sense-experience into the personal unconscious. Thus, it seems that the mystic can find the 'outer' by looking to the 'inner'.

27 It is possible that Traherne's distinctive notion of 'sole heirdom', which we came across in Chapter Four, stems from the type of substratal organisation of experience that we have considered in Chapter 11 and the present chapter, namely the existence of a plurality of distinct Totalities, each of which is a whole experience structured from a central vantage-point, yet containing all other perspectives. In a section entitled 'Apprehension' in his *Commentaries of Heaven,* Traherne relates that "We never Apprehend y[e] World aright till we see it as a Sphere or Univers of Glory in w[ch] ourselves are y[e] only Centres." This quotation is from 'Traherne's *Commentaries of Heaven* (With Selections from the Manuscript)', Allan Pritchard (1983), p. 2. A further relevant passage is given by Pritchard (p. 28), in the section entitled 'Ages': "... I have found Man to be a Centre in Worlds of felicitie, and myself a Sphere of infinit Centres."

28 We can share in Allan Pritchard's regret that Traherne's alphabetical *Commentaries of Heaven* finished at the letter 'B' and the 'Sand' entry therefore remained unwritten. See Pritchard (1983), p. 12. Entries relevant to the theme of smallness include 'Acuteness', 'Atom' and 'Ant'. Other entries of interest to our current discussion might include 'All Things', 'All in All', and 'Alone'—we shall have to wait until an edition of the *Commentaries* becomes available.

29 *Christian Ethicks,* p. 347 (Marks and Guffey, p .181).

30 *Christian Ethicks,* p. 349 (Marks and Guffey, p. 181).

31 Traherne also applies the expression "infinitely infinite" to infinite space that is made even more infinite by the eternal space of moments—see C.V.6.

32 The soul, in its loving, is compared to a mirror, reflecting the love of God in the way a mirror reflects the light of the sun. But Traherne adds that the soul also "shineth of itself" and is therefore more a fountain than a mirror—see Centuries IV.84–5. Traherne makes use of another mirror-analogy in his writings, that of self and world reflected in a pool of water. The outstanding classical literary instance of the water-mirror is, of course, the pool in which Narcissus saw his alluring image. A number of scholars have attempted to link literary uses of mirrors with a 'mirror-stage' in the development of the self, postulated by the French psychoanalyst Jacques Lacan. See 'The Self-Mirroring Mind in Milton and Traherne', by Alvin Snider (1986), which also contains a brief account of seventeenth-century mirror-metaphors. Edward Peter Nolan (1990), in the appendix to *Now Through A Glass Darkly,* pp. 273–95, surveys several modern theories that dwell on mirrors, including Lacan's developmental theory and Umberto Eco's semiotic musings.

33 Marks (1966b).

34 Sterry (1683), *The Rise, Race, and Royalty of the Kingdom of God in the Soul of Man,* p. 24. The passage is quoted in part by Marks (1966b), p. 529. Sterry links the title of the work with *Matthew* 18.3, "Except ye be converted, and become as little Children, ye cannot enter into the Kingdom of Heaven". The 'Rise' to the Kingdom corresponds to conversion, the 'Race' to becoming as a little child, a "regenerate person", and 'Royalty' to entry to the Kingdom. Sterry (p. 1) says that "diminutives are signs of affection, delight and dependence".

35 *Rise, Race, and Royalty,* pp. 268–9. Quoted by Marks (1966b), p. 534. Also on the 'point': "As every drop of Milk is Milk: so every thing, the smallest Point in the Person of *Christ* is Beauty. This Finite world cannot satisfie our desires, because they are infinite." *(Race, Rise and Royalty,* p. 210). The light multiplies itself infinitely within itself (p. 211). Glass, mirror, eye and crystal imagery for the divine knowing is much used by Sterry. In *The Appearance of God to Man in the Gospel,* 1710, Sterry describes Roman galleries covered with mirror-like polished stones, in which the occupants could see themselves and their companions entirely reflected. He uses the story to suggest the manner in which all things in heaven are observed, in a "Looking-Glass of Eternal Truth and Love". In the "Sunshine of the Godhead", every heap of dust sparkles "as a heap of Diamonds, as a knot of Angels, yea a Constellation..." (quoted from the selection of passages in Vivian de Sola Pinto (1934), *Peter Sterry,* p. 195). On Heavenly things: "They are to you, and you to them, as clear and shining Glasses, in which you mutually see the Faces of each other, and your selves as reflections of each others Beauties." *(Rise, Race and Royalty,* p. 201). See also p. 305: "Thus we see our selves continually in Him; he seeth Himself continually in us; Eye to Eye, each a Living Glass of glorious Love to the other."

36 *Rise, Race, and Royalty,* p. 240—compare the description of stars-within-stars with the Plotinian account of the Intellectual Beauty, quoted above. Another passage by Sterry reverberates with the Plotinian account: "All things here are *transparent;* each particular, each part is seen distinctly in the whole, and the whole compleatly in each part." Sterry (1675), *A Discourse of the Freedom of the Will,* p. 28. In the *Discourse,* Sterry has further to say on the pure vision in which all things are a treasure. He quotes St Paul *(Titus,* I.15) on all things being pure to the pure (p. 28), and explains that:

> Nothing is *mean and vile,* seen in a right and universal Light. Every degree of Being to the least, the narrowest and obscurest Point, hath Being it self in its amplitude and *majesty* in it, without which it could not be. Every thing that is in any kind or degree, hath the *Throne* of Being set up in it, with God the supream King, and Fountain of Beings, sitting upon it, and filling it with the train of his Glories. Thus look upon each Being, and you will see it as a *spacious Palace,* a sacred Temple, or a new and distinct Heaven.

Sterry (1675), *Discourse,* p. 30, (quoted by Pinto (1934), pp. 151–2). The passage is part of an extended discussion of divine knowledge and the whole in the part: Sterry explains how "in the face of each material, individual object, shineth the *whole nature* of things" (pp. 28–30 in the *Discourse).* As well as citing the purity of the vision, God's omnipresence and the imprint of the divine image, Sterry calls upon a microcosmism in which each nature partakes of the things above and below. Compare Sterry's references to the purity of the vision with Traherne's account of the vision from the Throne, in which all is found to be well.

37 "The entire unity of this high and Heavenly Person standeth compleat in every branch, and point of all the vast variety at once; as the *Soul* is said to be all in the whole Body, and all in every part of it." *Rise, Race, and Royalty,* p. 225.

38 *Rise, Race, and Royalty,* p. 3. Euthydemus and his elder brother, Dionysodorus, figure as sophists in Plato's dialogue *Euthydemus.* Sterry's quotation, which is reminiscent of Anaxagoras' philosophy, may refer to a notion ascribed to Euthydemus presented in another Platonic dialogue, the *Cratylus:* "all things equally belong to all men at the same moment and always." Sterry makes a further reference to the 'all in all' of Paul's *Letter to the Ephesians:* "God also *fills All in All,* Ephes.1.23. So He descends into the *Lowest Relations,* the narrowest Compass, and becomes every where the most *Particular Cause* of every Thing." (*Rise, Race, and Royalty,* p. 161).

39 Leone Ebreo, or Leon the Jew, name of Judah Abrabanel (*c.*1460–*c.*1520), author of *The Dialogues of Love.*

40 Vivian de Sola Pinto (1934), *Peter Sterry,* p. 75 & p. 89.

41 *Rise, Race, and Royalty,* p. 247.

42 See 'A New Traherne Manuscript', J. M. Osborn (1964), and 'The Essential Traherne', an essay by Anne Ridler in *Profitable Wonders,* A. M. Allchin, A. Ridler and J. Smith (1989), p. 11. The author of the unsigned preface to Traherne's *A Serious and Pathetical Contemplation* relates that Traherne was so full of his notions of Felicity and the restoration of the Divine Image that "those that would converse with him, were forced to endure some discourse upon these subjects, whether they had any sense of Religion, or not." The preface is given in Margoliouth (1958), Vol. 1, pp. xxxi–xxxii.

43 See Marks (1966b), p. 534. *Rise, Race and Royalty* was published eleven years after Sterry's death in 1672, and nine years after Traherne's death in 1674. Sterry's *A Discourse of the Freedom of the Will* appeared in 1675. Traherne's works were published posthumously, with the exception of the *Roman Forgeries,* in 1673. Traherne's *Christian Ethicks,* appeared in 1675, *A Serious and Pathetical Contemplation* (containing *The Thanksgivings)* in 1699, and the *Meditations on the Six Days of the Creation* in 1717.

44 See Chapter Five, on the *lapis* trodden underfoot. Here the religious aspect of the veneration of the small shows clearly. Ruusbroec refers to Christ's humbling of himself, and taking on the form of a servant. In the New Testament, it is the gentle, the meek, the child, the diminutive, who will inherit the Kingdom.

45 In Grosseteste's account of the Creation, light expands from a primordial point into a sphere. See James McEvoy (1982), *The Philosophy of Robert Grosseteste,* pp. 151–8.

46 McEvoy (1982), pp. 52–8.

47 McEvoy (1982), pp. 369 ff, and R. W. Southern (1986), *Robert Grosseteste: The Growth of an English Mind in Medieval Europe,* pp. 211–25.

48 See Southern (1986), pp. 216–17, on Grosseteste's *Dictum* 60, "Omnis creatura speculum est...". Southern explains that he translates *atomus* as a 'speck of dust' to avoid unwanted connotations, following Fr. Servus Gieben (1964), who edited the text in 'Traces of God in Nature according to Robert Grosseteste.' In Grosseteste's thought, Gieben finds a "general Augustinian trend" of trinitarian exemplarism, but also notes his familiarity with the first proposition of the *Liber XXIV philosophorum.*

49 Paraphrased by Southern (1986), p. 217.

50 *Jerusalem,* 31.45. (p. 657).

51 *Auguries of Innocence,* 1–4. (p. 431). Compare with Traherne, *Centuries* I.19.: "Your understanding comprehends the World like the dust of a balance, measures Heaven with a span, and esteems a thousand yeers but as one Day." See *Isaiah* 40.12 and *Psalm* 90.4.

On the creation as a tiny object in the palm of the hand, note the vision of Julian of Norwich, of "something small, no bigger than a hazelnut...." See *Showings,* Julian of Norwich, The Fifth Chapter (long text), p. 183, translated and introduced by Edmund Colledge and James Walsh (1978). Julian supposes that we search for rest or well-being in this little thing, interpreted as the creation in flux, but do not find it there, for true rest is to be found only in God.

52 *Jerusalem* 41.15–18. (p. 668.)

53 *Jerusalem* 38.55 to 39.3. (pp. 665–6.)

54 *Milton,* Book The First, 28.29–41. (p. 515.)

55 *Milton,* 29.15–26. (pp. 516–17.)

56 Letter to Thomas Butts, 22 November 1802, 87–88. (p. 818.)

57 *Jerusalem* 31.6–7. (p. 656.)

58 *Jerusalem,* 31.20. (p. 657.)

59 *Milton,* 28.35. (p. 515.)

60 Marjorie Hope Nicolson (1966), in *Newton Demands the Muse,* mentions the light particles in a chapter on Blake's reaction to Newton. Donald Ault (1974), in *Visionary Physics,* pp. 141–7, provides a discussion. Ault interprets Blake's description of 'particles of light' as a visionary response to Newton's corpuscular theory of light and to eighteenth-century theories of vision. I would stress that Blake's criticism is a broad one, aimed at the mechanical conception of matter in general, including both the material corpuscles of bodies and the material light particles involved in sensory vision. The latter are a special type of matter, particles of *lumen,* whilst Blake's light particles are particles of *lux,* luminous particles of matter revealed in the vision of the Imagination. Each gem or sand when falsely understood becomes the inert matter described by the mechanists: "The Atoms of Democritus / And Newton's Particles of light / Are sands upon the Red sea shore, / Where Israel's tents do shine so bright." From *Mock on, Mock on Voltaire, Rousseau,* 9–12. (Keynes, p. 418.)

61 *A Descriptive Catalogue.* (Keynes, p. 576.)

62 For alchemical and Gnostic ideas linking the point, the *prima materia,* the *lapis,* the 'soul-spark' *(scintila),* and the macrocosmic man, see: Jung (1970b), *Mysterium Coniunctionis,* pp. 42–56; Jung (1970a), *Aion,* pp. 196–202 and pp. 218–21; Jung (1969), *The Structure and Dynamics of the Psyche,* pp. 190–9.

63 Sterry (1675), *A Discourse of the Freedom of the Will,* p. 28.

64 Ibid. pp. 29–30. In discussing the spirituality of matter, Sterry goes on to praise a Neoplatonic understanding of the subject that he ascribes to Henry More. However, we have seen that More's later conceptions of matter and spirit were essentially dualistic, and that More was certainly not inclined towards the 'Holenmerian' position.

65 Material relating to the experience at Felpham occurs in *Milton,* 20.56–61, 21.1–14. (p. 503.)

66 Letter to Thomas Butts, 2 October 1800. (p. 804.)

67 *Jerusalem,* 91.29–30. (p. 738.) Also *A Vision of the Last Judgement, Pp.76–77.* (p. 607.) See the discussion of self-and-others in Chapter Four. On the idea of the cosmic Christ, Jung (1970a) comments (p. 221): "we can see how Christ was assimilated to symbols that also meant the kingdom of God, for instance the grain of mustard seed, the hidden treasure, and the pearl of great price. He and his kingdom have the same meaning. Objections have always been made to this dissolution of his personality, but what has not been realised is that it represents at the same time an assimilation and integration of Christ into the human psyche". For the kingdom of heaven likened to the mustard seed,

which grows into "the greatest among herbs", see *Matthew* 13.31–2 (and note the coriander seed of Philo, which can be divided infinitely, yet grows as a complete seed when sown). A similar process took place in Buddhist thought, in those developments that shifted attention away from the historical figure, Siddhartha Gautama. These included the doctrines of many buddhas throughout the universe, the buddha-nature inherent in all beings, the three bodies *(trikaya)* of the buddha, and the cosmic, primordial Buddha *(adi-buddha)*.

68 *Jerusalem,* 98.39. (p. 746.) Also note Blake's description of a scene in his painting *The Last Judgement:* "A Female descends to meet her Lover or Husband, representative of that Love, call'd Friendship, which Looks for no other heaven than their Beloved & in him sees all reflected in a Glass of Eternal Diamond." *A Vision of the Last Judgement, Pp.82–84.* (p. 610.)

69 *Jerusalem,* 31.19–20. (p. 657.)

70 *Jerusalem,* 55.60–64. (p. 687.)

71 *A Vision of the Last Judgement, Pp.82–84.* (p. 611.)

72 Mahayana concepts have been linked with physical theories in the past, and the concept of interpenetration has aroused special interest. Fritjof Capra compared interpenetration with the *bootstrap hypothesis* proposed in the early 1960s by the American theoretical physicist Geoffrey Chew. According to the bootstrap hypothesis, the elementary particles called hadrons are not elementary—they are composites of other hadrons held together by hadron force-carriers. The theory eliminates the conventional concept of the particle, and replaces it with a thoroughgoing force-picture. The philosophical implications are examined in a paper by G. Gale, to which Capra makes reference. In the meantime, the quark model has become the widely accepted theory of hadrons. For Capra's comparison of Buddhist interpenetration with the bootstrap hypothesis, see Capra (1983), *The Tao of Physics.*

73 'The Practice of Universal Good', Cleary (1986), *The Flower Ornament Scripture,* p. 267.

74 On the meditational use of visionary cosmologies, see Chapter Four, Note 40. Also Kloetzli (1983), pp. 155–7.

75 'The Formation of the Worlds', Cleary (1985), p. 200.

76 'The Flower Bank World', Cleary (1985), pp. 242–3 & p. 248.

77 The huge numbers in the *Avatamsaka Sutra* may be connected with a Western estimate of the number of particles in the universe—an ancient Greek estimate of the number of grains of sand that would fill the spherical shell of the earth's orbit in the heliocentric system of Aristarchus. The calculation was attempted by the Greek mathematician and engineer Archimedes (*c.*287–212 B.C.), in a work entitled *The Sand-Reckoner,* for the purpose of exhibiting the capabilities of his mathematical notation for extremely large numbers. For details of the notation and the calculation, see Heath (1912), pp. 221–32, and Dijksterhuis (1956), pp. 360–73. Archimedes arrived at a maximum figure of 10,000,000,000 *stades* (a Greek unit of length) for the diameter of the 'universe', the earth's orbital shell, and went on to estimate that the shell could contain no more than 10^{51} grains of sand, and the shell of fixed stars no more than 10^{63} grains. The calculation is described by Kloetzli (1983), in *Buddhist Cosmology* (pp. 115–19), who connects the results with the numerical attributes of the *asankhyeya* cosmology, the "cosmology of innumerables" that we noted in Chapter Eleven. The connection may suggest a Greek influence on the Buddhist cosmologies, at least as far as the treatment of cosmic numbers goes. Kloetzli (p. 117) refers to a Mr. Joinville, *Asiatick Researches,* 7 (1801), who relates that an 'innumerable', the *asankhyeya,* is 10^{63}, which is the number calculated by

Archimedes. The figures 10,000 and $10{,}000^3$ are also significant in certain Buddhist cosmologies (see Kloetzli, pp. 56–7, on the Pali world-system, and Buddhaghosa's three fields of the Buddha). Now, it is interesting that the diameter of the 'universe' in the *Sand-Reckoner* (the diameter of the sphere of the earth's orbit) is calculated to be 10,000,000,000 *stades* by Archimedes, which is the starting number in 'The Incalculable' chapter of the *Avatamsaka Sutra,* ten to the power ten, or 10^{10}. It is conceivable that the calculations of Archimedes inspired the cosmic numbers on which the *asankhyeya* and *Avatamsaka* cosmologies drew, but we can only guess at the significance of the further treatment of the number 10^{10}. The repeated squaring, beginning with the square of 10^{10}, might simply be a device for creating huge numbers to overwhelm the reader with unimaginable magnitudes. There is also the possibility that the squaring constitutes a numerical transformation of the *asankhyeya* cosmology into the interpenetrating cosmology of the *Avatamsaka Sutra,* a cosmology of innumerable innumerables. It is a possibility, if only a rather speculative one, because the mathematical operation of squaring is equivalent to the multiplication that occurs in the interpenetrative mirroring of the universe in all of its parts. The reasoning might proceed thus: a universe containing 10^{10} atoms is reflected in each of its 10^{10} atoms to give a total of $10^{10} \times 10^{10}$ micro-atoms, which is 10^{10} squared. Further inter-reflections, atoms within micro-atoms, are enumerated by taking a square for each descending level of interpenetration. There is a suggestion of such interpenetrative multiplication in several descriptions in the Sutra, in which world-systems are reduced to atoms, and each atom associated with as many worlds as there are atoms, through a spacing procedure. Besides the passages in 'The Incalculable', see also Book Thirty-Five, 'The Qualities of the Buddha's Embellishments and Lights', Cleary (1986), pp. 262–3, and Book Twenty-Seven, 'The Ten Concentrations', p. 135. Related passages occur in Book Seventeen 'The Merit of The Initial Determination for Enlightenment', Cleary (1985), pp. 405–24. A very similar procedure is to be found in the *Lotus Sutra*—see Note 79.

78 Cleary (1986), p. 203.

79 Kloetzli (pp. 118–19) quotes a similar passage in the *Lotus Sutra.* In the sixteenth chapter, 'Revelation of the Eternal Life of the Tathagata', vast numbers of aeons are generated in order to emphasise the eternity of the life of the Buddha, which is a central theme in the second half of the Sutra. In earlier Buddhist thought, it had been supposed that the Buddha disappeared entirely from existence at his death, his life-flame completely extinguished at the *parinirvana.* In the *Lotus Sutra,* however, it is maintained that the earlier teaching was merely an expedient, a skilful means of encouraging others to work towards liberation, and that the Buddha really continues to work for the enlightenment of beings. It is open to interpretation whether the Sutra means the life of the Buddha to be extremely long but finite, or eternal in the sense of everlasting, or perhaps eternal in the sense of everpresent in an eternal now. The change in interpretation of the Buddha's life-span is presumably related to the development of a cosmic perspective on the nature of the Buddha. The passage enumerating the vast time-periods of the Buddha's activities begins with a reduction of a vast number of *asankhyeya* universes into their constituent atoms. These are spaced eastwards at intervals that cover the same vast number of countries as there were atoms in the original world-system. This multiplies the number of atoms in a manner similar to the squaring operation discussed before, in Note 77. The number of these atoms is said to be smaller than the number of *kalpas* that have elapsed since the Buddha began teaching.

80 Cleary (1986), p. 204.

81 Cleary (1986), pp. 207–8.

82 Cleary (1986), p. 204.

83 On Fa-tsang's mirror demonstration to his students, see Fung Yu-lan (1983), Vol. II, p. 353. In *The Buddhist Teaching of Totality* (p. 24), Garma C. C. Chang (1972) gives a different version: Fa-tsang's mirror-explanation of Hua-yen philosophy is given to the Empress Wu (ruled 684–705). According to the story, a room was lined with mirrors, on the four walls, ceiling, floor, and corners, and a figure of the Buddha and a torch were positioned in its centre. The inter-reflections demonstrated the principles of "one in all" and "all in one". To illustrate how the small contains the large without obstruction, Fa-tsang produced a crystal ball, in which all the mirrors and their reflections were contained. Fa-tsang went on to explain that the unobstructed interpenetration of space is easily demonstrated in this manner, but the unobstructed interpenetration of times is much harder to exhibit.

84 A translation of the *Gandavyuha Sutra* is provided by Cleary (1989). Passages are also to be found in Suzuki (1985), with a useful discussion.

85 On the various interpretations of the *dharmadhatu* in Buddhist thought, and its meaning in Hua-yen Buddhism, see Kang-Nam Or (1979), 'Dharmadhatu, An Introduction to Hua-yen Buddhism'.

86 Temple imagery is not uncommon in seventeenth-century spiritual writing. Sterry's impressive account of "three wonderful" temples, for which he used 1 *Corinthians* 6.19 as a starting-point, occurs in *Rise, Race and Royalty* (pp. 274–6), and leads to a description of eternity: "In the pure, and transparent brightness of this Supream Glory, which is the *first,* and the *last,* are seen all things, that ever passed, or are to pass over the Stage of this Creation from the Beginning to the End with their several Motions, and Changes; yea, Forms far more innumerable, and greater, than ever were, or can be seen in this world...." Sterry stresses that the "distinctions of things" are preserved in the Divine Unity (p. 276). He goes on to describe eternity in words that are reminiscent of Plotinus' point-analogy for eternity, and describes our world "as a small island in the midst of the Ocean of Eternity bounding it on all sides." (pp. 277–8.) The parts of this eternity are full with the whole, for the cosmic Christ has filled "every Form of Things with the Unchangeable Fulness of His own Person", filling "every point of time with Eternity: every spot of Earth with Heaven; every Change on Earth, in time, with the Unchangeableness of Heaven, and Eternity." p. 278. The temple or tower metaphor for eternity is fairly static, although it does at least suggest a directionality. A rather more dynamic image is provided by Sterry in his account of the divine 'chariot', an inter-reflecting, spiritual universe of crystalline luminosity, in which angels, suns and skies are fashioned in a transparent, glass-like gold (Pinto: pp. 154–5 and p. 209, Note 21; on the literary form, see p. 85). At the end of the passage quoted by Pinto, Sterry mentions the vision of God's throne-chariot in *Ezekiel* 1, a passage that formed the basis of early Jewish mystical thought centred on the idea of the throne-chariot or throne-world (the *Merkabah*)—see Scholem (1961), pp. 40–79, and Scholem (1960), *Jewish Gnosticism, Merkabah Mysticism and the Talmudic Tradition.* Sterry may also have drawn on the myth of the chariot journey to supercelestial reality in Plato's *Phaedrus,* an influential dialogue among Neoplatonists and Renaissance Christian Platonists (see Michael J. B. Allen's (1981) introduction in *Marsilio Ficino and the Phaedran Charioteer,* pp. 1–28, and Allen's (1984) *The Platonism of Marsilio Ficino).* Plotinus' Phaedran lines on the vision of the intelligible realm (in *Enneads* V.8, 'On the Intellectual Beauty'—see *The Small is Great* above) may be a source for Sterry's passage, for here Plotinus describes an intelligible universe that is luminous and interpenetrating. It is noteworthy that Sterry's chariot is no mere vehicle on which the soul rises to the vision of truth, like the chariot of the Parmenidean journey or the *Phaedrus* myth, but *is* the intelligible universe itself, and the "spirit of a saint" at one with the cosmic Christ.

87 From 'Hundred Gates to the Sea of Ideas of the Flowery Splendor Scripture' by Fa-tsang, in Chan (1963), *A Source Book in Chinese Philosophy,* p. 421.

88 Odin (1982), *Process Metaphysics and Hua-yen Buddhism,* p. 3.

89 See Odin (1982), pp. 94–5.

90 Odin (1982), p. 4.

91 Cook (1984), 'The Dialogue Between Hua-yen and Process Thought'. Cook refers to the Hua-yen doctrine of causal relations with all places and times as *multi-directional causality.*

92 In addition to Hans Leisegang's paper noted in Chapter Eleven, see *The Mutable Glass* by Herbert Grabes (1982), an updated English version of the German original of 1973, *Speculum, Mirror, und Looking-glass.* Grabes analyses the titles and texts of English works of the Renaissance to reveal the many aspects of mirror-metaphors, and he provides extensive mirror-title listings and bibliographies. In Chinese thought, the mirror has frequently been employed as a metaphor for *mind.* Joseph Needham provides several interesting sidelights on the topic, and notes that the philosopher Chuang Tzu (*c.*369–*c.*286 B.C.) compared the mind to a dustless mirror, an idea employed by later Buddhist teachers—see Needham (1962), *Science and Civilization in China,* Vol. 4, Part I, pp. 90–3. On the Buddhist developments, Needham refers to Paul Demiéville's paper, 'Le miroir spirituel', *Sinologica* I (1984), pp. 112–37, reprinted in Demiéville (1973), *Choix d'études bouddhiques,* pp. 131–56. The discussion opens with the famous mirror-verses of Shen-hsui and Hui-neng in the *Platform Sutra.* Demiéville also takes the opportunity to cite various Western instances of spiritual mirror-analogies and metaphors, including Ruusbroec's reference to the higher part of the soul as a living mirror of God.

93 In fact, the physics of light propagation, involving expanding wave-fronts from point-sources, means that an object emits light from all parts of its surface to each part of any other surface, as long as no obstructions intervene. For instance, the light that is incident on the tiny hole of a pin-hole camera comes from all parts of an object's surface, and therefore a whole image of the object can be recreated on the camera screen from the light that has converged on a point the size of a pin-hole.

94 Grabes (1982), p. 107, and Note 18, p. 342. See also Leisegang (1937), pp. 168–9, who quotes relevant passages from Thomas Aquinas and Martin Luther. In connection with the mirror divided into many smaller mirrors, Leisegang mentions Francis Mercury van Helmont's description of a reflecting ball of mercury that divides into many small, reflecting globules, and links it with Leibniz's reflecting monads (pp. 170–1). Carolyn Merchant (1979b) refers to Leisegang's discussion, in 'The Vitalism of Francis Mercury van Helmont: Its Influence on Leibniz' (p. 179).

95 See *The Holographic Paradigm,* a collection of essays and articles edited by Ken Wilber (1982).

96 From reading Pribram's 'What the fuss is all about', 1978, in Wilber (1982), pp. 27–34, reprinted from *ReVision Journal.*

97 For example, Bohm (1982), *Wholeness and the Implicate Order.*

Chapter 15: The Physics of the Small

1 See Milic Capek (1961), *The Philosophical Impact of Contemporary Physics,* pp. 223 ff.; G. J. Whitrow (1980), *The Natural Philosophy of Time,* pp. 203–5; Richard Sorabji (1983), *Time Creation and the Continuum,* pp. 381–3.

2 The component de Broglie waves are ascribed a velocity *greater* than light, called the *phase velocity.* Note that special relativity is not violated: no signal or energy is propagated by the wave at a velocity greater than *c.*

3 The experimental set-up described here is a simplification of the arrangement required in practice.

4 These are described in some detail by Max Jammer (1974) in his historical investigation of the interpretations of quantum theory, *The Philosophy of Quantum Mechanics* (see Chapter 2: 'Early Semiclassical Interpretations'). Also of interest is Jammer's (1966) *The Conceptual Development of Quantum Mechanics.* Louis de Broglie (1939) refers to his interpretations in 'Wave Mechanics and its Interpretations', 1928, contained in *Matter and Light.* Another early interpretation noted by Jammer was Erwin Madelung's hydrodynamic model of 1926, which utilised similarities between the mathematics of fluid motion and Schrödinger's wave mechanics, and later workers have developed hydrodynamic models.

5 On this problem, and others, see Jammer (1974), pp. 31–3.

6 Quoted from Jammer's translation (1966), p. 330. See also Jammer (1974), p. 76.

7 There are about 6×10^{23} molecules in twenty-two litres of gas under standard conditions of temperature and pressure (Avogadro's Number).

8 For references and details, see P. J. Kennedy, 'Delayed-Choice Experiments', in *Niels Bohr, A Centenary Volume,* pp. 148–152, edited by A. P. French and P. J. Kennedy (1985). See also P. C. W. Davies and J. R. Brown (1985), *The Ghost in the Atom,* pp. 9–11 & pp. 64–7.

9 It has been conjectured that various philosophical influences, additional to positivism and empiricism, paved the way to the nonclassical interpretation of quantum physics. Max Jammer (1966) points to a number of possible influences, including the questioning of the subject-object separation by Sören Kierkegaard and William James (recognition of the participation of the experimental apparatus, and maybe even the experimenter, in the quantum experiment), the pragmatism of C. S. Peirce and James (stress on whether quantum theory *works,* not on the picture of the world it presents), and the indeterminism of Charles Renouvier (1815–1903), Peirce and James (chance enters the quantum process at the wavefunction collapse).

10 John Bell stressed this feature of the orthodox interpretation. See, for example, 'Six possible worlds of quantum mechanics' in *Speakable and unspeakable in quantum mechanics,* Bell (1987).

11 Due to Ghirardi, Rimini and Weber (GRW theory). See, for instance, Bell (1987), Chapter 22.

12 David Bohm, in Davies and Brown (1985), p. 127.

13 Basil Hiley, in Davies and Brown (1985), pp. 138–40.

REFERENCES

ALEXANDER, H. G. ed. (1976) *The Leibniz-Clarke Correspondence.* First published 1956. Manchester: Manchester University Press.

ALEXANDER, P. (1985) *Ideas, Qualities and Corpuscles: Locke and Boyle on the external world.* Cambridge: Cambridge University Press.

ALLCHIN, A. M., RIDLER, A., AND SMITH, J. (1989) *Profitable Wonders, aspects of Thomas Traherne.* Oxford: The Amate Press.

ALLEN, M. J. B. (1981) *Marsilio Ficino and the Phaedran Charioteer.* Berkeley and Los Angeles: University of California Press.

ALLEN, M. J. B. (1984) *The Platonism of Marsilio Ficino, a study of his Phaedrus commentary, its sources and genesis.* Berkeley and Los Angeles: University of California Press.

ALLERS, R. (1944) Microcosmus, from Anaximandros to Paracelsus, *Traditio,* 2, 319–407.

ANCILLA (pseud. of Grace Ashley Wood) (1955) *The Following Feet.* London: Longmans, Green and Co.

ARMSTRONG, A. H. (1940) *The Architecture of the Intelligible Universe in the Philosophy of Plotinus.* Cambridge: Cambridge University Press.

ARMSTRONG, A. H. trans. (1967) *Plotinus.* Vol. III. London: Heinemann.

ARMSTRONG, A. H. trans. (1984) *Plotinus.* Vol. V. London: Heinemann.

AULT, D. D. (1974) *Visionary Physics, Blake's response to Newton.* Chicago: The University Press of Chicago.

BAEUMKER, C. (1927) *Beiträge zur Geschichte der Philosophie des Mittelalters,* Band XXV, Heft 1/2: *Studien und Charakteristiken zur Geschichte der Philosophie, insbesondere des Mittelalters.* Münster: Aschendorf.

BARBOUR, J. B. (1989) *Absolute or Relative Motion?* Vol. 1: The Discovery of Dynamics. Cambridge: Cambridge University Press.

BARROW, J. D. AND TIPLER, F. J. (1988) *The Anthropic Cosmological Principle.* Oxford: Oxford University Press.

BELL, J. S. (1987) *Speakable and unspeakable in quantum mechanics.* Cambridge: Cambridge University Press.

BERNE, E. (1964) *Games People Play, the psychology of human relationships.* New York: Grove Press.

BOHM, D. (1980) *Wholeness and the Implicate Order.* London: Routledge & Kegan Paul.

BORGES, J. L. (1981) *Labyrinths.* Harmondsworth: Penguin.

BOTTRALL, M. (1962) *The Way to Blessedness, Thomas Traherne's Christian Ethicks.* London: Faith Press.

BOWKER, J. (1970) *Problems of Suffering in Religions of the World.* Cambridge: Cambridge University Press.

BUCKE, R. M. (1905) *Cosmic Consciousness, a study in the evolution of the human mind.* First published 1901. Philadelphia: Innes & Sons.

BURKE, W. L. (1980) *Spacetime, Geometry, Cosmology.* Mill Valley, California: University Science Books.

BURTT, E. A. (1932) *The Metaphysical Foundations of Modern Science, a historical and critical essay.* Second edition (first edition 1924). London: Routledge & Kegan Paul.

CAIRNS, D. (1953) *The Image of God in Man.* New York: Philosophical Library.

CAJORI, F. ed. (1962) *Sir Isaac Newton's Mathematical Principles of Natural Philosophy and his System of the World.* Vol. 1: The Motion of Bodies. Vol. 2: The System of the World. Translated into English by Andrew Motte in 1729. Revised by Florian Cajori, 1934. Berkeley and Los Angeles: University of California Press.

CALLAHAN, J. J. (1976) The Curvature of Space in a Finite Universe, *Scientific American,* 235, 2 (August 1976), 90–100.

CAMPBELL, J. (1984) *The Masks of God.* 4 vols. First published 1962. Harmondsworth: Penguin Books.

CAMPBELL, J. (1988) *The Power of Myth,* with Bill Moyers. New York: Doubleday.
CAMPBELL, K. (1984) *Body and Mind.* Second edition. Notre Dame, Indiana: University of Notre Dame Press.
CAPEK, M. (1961) *The Philosophical Impact of Contemporary Physics.* Princeton, New Jersey: Van Nostrand.
CAPRA, F. (1983) *The Tao of Physics, an exploration of the parallels between modern physics and Eastern mysticism.* Second edition. London: Fontana.
CARR, H. W. (1922) *A Theory of Monads, outlines of the philosophy of the principle of relativity.* London: Macmillan.
CARR, H. W. (1928) *The Unique Status of Man.* New York: Macmillan.
CHAN, W. (1969) *A Source Book in Chinese Philosophy.* First published 1963. Princeton, New Jersey: Princeton University Press.
CHANG, G. C. C. (1972) *The Buddhist Teaching of Totality, the philosophy of Hwa yen Buddhism.* London: George Allen & Unwin.
CHURCHLAND, P. M. (1984) *Matter and Consciousness, a contemporary introduction to the philosophy of mind.* Cambridge, Massachusetts: MIT Press.
CLEARY, T. trans. (1985) *The Flower Ornament Scripture, a translation of the Avatamsaka Sutra.* Vol. 1. Boston, Massachusetts: Shambhala.
CLEARY, T. trans. (1986) *The Flower Ornament Scripture, a translation of the Avatamsaka Sutra.* Vol. 2. Boston, Massachusetts: Shambhala.
CLEARY, T. trans. (1989) *Entry into the Realm of Reality: The Text.* Boston, Massachusetts: Shambhala.
COLIE, R. L. (1957) Thomas Traherne and the Infinite: The Ethical Compromise, *Huntingdon Library Quarterly,* 21 (1957–58), 69–82.
COLLEDGE, E. AND WALSH, J. trans. (1978) *Julian of Norwich: Showings.* The Classics of Western Spirituality. New York: Paulist Press.
CONZE, E. (1983) *Buddhist Thought in India, three phases of Buddhist philosophy.* First published 1962. London: George Allen & Unwin.
COOK, F. H. (1984) The Dialogue Between Hua-yen and Process Thought, *The Eastern Buddhist,* New Series, 17, 2, 12–29.
COOLEY, C. H. (1902) *Human Nature and the Social Order.* New York: Charles Scribner's Sons.
COPLESTON, F. (1963) *A History of Philosophy, Late Mediaeval and Renaissance Philosophy.* Vol. 3, Part II. Garden City, New York: Image Books.
COTTINGHAM, J., STOOTHOFF, R., AND MURDOCH, D. trans. (1985) *The Philosophical Writings of Descartes.* 2 vols. Cambridge: Cambridge University Press.
D'ABRO, A. (1950) *The Evolution of Scientific Thought, from Newton to Einstein.* Second edition (first edition 1927). New York: Dover.
D'ALVERNY, M. ed. (1965) *Alain de Lille, textes inédits.* Paris: Vrin.
DASGUPTA, S. (1969) *A History of Indian Philosophy.* First published 1922. Cambridge: Cambridge University Press.
DAVIES, P. C. W. (1986) *The Forces of Nature.* Second edition. Cambridge: Cambridge University Press.
DAVIES, P. C. W. AND BROWN, J. R. eds. (1986) *The Ghost in the Atom, a discussion of the mysteries of quantum physics.* Cambridge: Cambridge University Press.
DAVIES, P. C. W. AND BROWN, J. R. eds. (1988) *Superstrings, A Theory of Everything?* Cambridge: Cambridge University Press.
DE BROGLIE, L. (1939) *Matter and Light.* New York: Norton.
DEMALLIE, R. J. ed. (1985) *The Sixth Grandfather, Black Elk's teachings given to John G. Neihardt.* Lincoln and London: University of Nebraska Press.
DEMIÉVILLE, P. (1973) *Choix d'études bouddhiques.* Leiden: E. J. Brill.
DIJKSTERHUIS, E. J. (1956) *Archimedes.* Trans. C. Dikshoorn. Copenhagen: Ejnar Munksgaard.
DIJKSTERHUIS, E. J. (1986) *The Mechanization of the World Picture, Pythagoras to Newton.* Trans. C. Dikshoorn. First English edition 1961. Princeton, New Jersey: Princeton University Press.
DODDS, E. R. (1933) *Proclus, The Elements of Theology, a revised text with translation, introduction and commentary.* Oxford: Clarendon Press.
DODDS, E. R. (1970) *Pagan and Christian in an Age of Anxiety, some aspects of religious experience from Marcus Aurelius to Constantine.* First published 1965. New York and London: Norton.

DOM, C. A. WYNSCHENK trans. (1916) *John Of Ruysbroeck. The Adornment of the Spiritual Marriage ... The Sparkling Stone .. The Book of Supreme Truth.* Trans. from the Flemish by C. A. Wynschenk Dom. Ed. Evelyn Underhill. London: Dent.

DRAKE, S. trans. (1957) *Discoveries and Opinions of Galileo.* Garden City, New York: Doubleday Anchor.

DUNNE, J. W. (1934) *The Serial Universe.* London: Faber and Faber.

EARMAN, J. (1989) *World Enough and Space-Time, absolute versus relational theories of space and time.* Cambridge, Massachusetts: The MIT Press.

EDDINGTON, A. (1987) *Space, Time and Gravitation: an outline of the general theory of relativity.* First published 1920. Cambridge: Cambridge University Press.

EINSTEIN, A. (1954) *Relativity, the special and the general theory.* Fifteenth edition. Trans. R. W. Lawson. London: Methuen.

EINSTEIN, A. (1983) *Sidelights on Relativity.* First published 1923. New York: Dover.

EINSTEIN, A., LORENTZ, H. A., WEYL, H., AND MINKOWSKI, H. (1952) *The Principle of Relativity.* Trans. W. Perret and G. B. Jeffery. First published 1923. New York: Dover.

ELIADE, M. (1959) *The Sacred and the Profane, the nature of religion.* Trans. from the French by Willard R. Trask. New York: Harcourt, Brace & World.

ELIADE, M. (1971) *The Myth of the Eternal Return, or, Cosmos and History.* Trans. from the French (1949) by Willard R. Trask. Bollingen Series XLVI. Princeton, New Jersey: Princeton University Press.

ELIADE, M. (1972) *Shamanism, archaic techniques of ecstasy.* Trans. from the French (1951) by Willard R. Trask. Bollingen Series LXXVI. Princeton, New Jersey: Princeton University Press.

ELIADE, M. (1978) *The Forge and the Crucible, the origins and structures of alchemy,* Second edition. Trans. from the French (1956) by Stephen Corrin. Chicago and London: The University of Chicago Press.

ELIADE, M. ed. (1987) *The Encyclopedia of Religion.* New York: Macmillan.

ELLENBERGER, H. F. (1970) *The Discovery of the Unconscious.* London: Allen Lane.

ENGLERT, W. G. (1987) *Epicurus on the Swerve and Voluntary Action.* American Classical Studies 16. Atlanta, Georgia: Scholars Press.

FANG, L. Z., AND LI, S. X. (1989) *Creation of the Universe.* Trans. T. Kiang. Singapore: World Scientific Publishing Co.

FERRUCCI, P. (1982) *What We May Be, the visions and techniques of psychosynthesis.* Wellingborough, Northamptonshire: Turnstone Press.

FERWERDA, R. (1965) *La signification des images et des métaphores dans la pensée de Plotin.* Groningen: J. B. Wolters.

FRAISSE, P. (1964) *The Psychology of Time.* Trans. Jennifer Leith. London: Eyre & Spottiswoode.

FRANKL, V. E. (1985) *Man's Search for Meaning.* Revised and updated (first published 1946, Austria). New York: Washington Square Press.

FRASER, J. T. ed. (1981) *The Voices of Time, a cooperative survey of man's views of time as expressed by the sciences and by the humanities.* Second edition (first edition 1966). Amherst: The University of Massachusetts Press.

FREMANTLE, A. (1964) *The Protestant Mystics.* Introduction by W. H. Auden. London: Weidenfeld and Nicolson.

FRENCH, A. P., AND KENNEDY, P. J. eds. (1985) *Niels Bohr, a centenary volume.* Cambridge, Massachusetts: Harvard University Press.

FREUD, S. (1930) *Civilization and Its Discontents,* in *The Standard Edition of the Complete Psychological Works of Sigmund Freud* (1953–1974), Volume XXI (1927–1931), 1961. Ed. James Strachey. London: Hogarth Press.

FRIEDMAN, M. (1983) *Foundations of Space-Time Theories, relativistic physics and philosophy of science.* Princeton, New Jersey: Princeton University Press.

FROMM, E. (1956) *The Art of Loving.* New York: Harper & Row.

GIEBEN, S. (1964) Traces of God in Nature according to Robert Grosseteste. With the Text of the Dictum "Omnis creatura speculum est." *Franciscan Studies,* 24, 144–58.

GILSON, E. (1940) *The Mystical Theology of St Bernard.* Trans. A. H. C. Downes. London: Sheed and Ward.

GINZBURG, V. L. (1985) *Physics and Astrophysics, a selection of key problems.* Trans. O. Glebov. Oxford: Pergamon Press.

GITTINGS, R. (1985) *John Keats.* First published 1968. Harmondsworth: Penguin

GLANVILL, J. (1682) *Saducismus Triumphatus.* Second edition. Microfilm G823, Early English Books 1641–1700, selected from Donald Wing's *Short-Title Catalogue.* Ann Arbor, Michigan: University Microfilms.

GRABES, H. (1982) *The Mutable Glass, mirror-imagery in titles and texts of the Middle Ages and English Renaissance.* Trans. G. Collier. Cambridge: Cambridge University Press.

GRANT, E. (1981) *Much Ado about Nothing, theories of space and vacuum from the Middle Ages to the Scientific Revolution.* Cambridge: Cambridge University Press.

GRANT, P. (1971) Original Sin and the Fall of Man in Thomas Traherne, *ELH,* 38, 40–61.

GRAVES, R. P. (1885) *Life of Sir William Rowan Hamilton.* Dublin: Dublin University Press.

GROF, C., AND GROF, S. (1991) *The Stormy Search for the Self, understanding and living with spiritual emergency.* First published 1990. London: Mandala.

GRÜNBAUM, A. (1974) *Philosophical Problems of Space and Time.* Second edition (first edition 1963). Boston Studies in the Philosophy of Science, Volume XII. Dordrecht, Holland & Boston, U.S.A.: D. Reidel.

GUFFEY, G. R. ed. (1966) *Meditations on the Six days of Creation,* by Thomas Traherne. The Augustan Reprint Society, Publication No. 119. Los Angeles: William Andrews Clark Memorial Library, University of California.

GUTHRIE, W. K. C. (1962) *A History of Greek Philosophy.* Vol. I: The earlier Presocratics and the Pythagoreans. Cambridge: Cambridge University Press.

GUTHRIE, W. K. C. (1978) *A History of Greek Philosophy.* Vol. V: The later Plato and the Academy. Cambridge: Cambridge University Press.

HALL, A. R. AND HALL, M. B. (1962) *Unpublished Scientific Papers of Isaac Newton.* Cambridge: Cambridge University Press.

HAPPOLD, F. C. (1970) *Mysticism. A Study and an Anthology.* Revised edition (first edition 1963). Harmondsworth: Penguin Books.

HARDY, A. (1979) *The Spiritual Nature of Man, a study of contemporary religious experience.* Oxford: Clarendon Press.

HARRIES, K. (1975) The Infinite Sphere: Comments on the History of a Metaphor, *Journal of the History of Philosophy,* 13, 5–15.

HARRISON, J. E. (1912) *Themis, a study of the social origins of Greek religion.* Cambridge: Cambridge University Press.

HASTINGS, J. ed. (1964) *Encyclopaedia of Religion and Ethics.* First impression 1914. Edinburgh: T. & T. Clark.

HEATH, T. L. (1912) *The Works of Archimedes.* New York: Dover.

HENNECKE, E. (1965) *New Testament Apocrypha,* Vol. II. Ed. by W. Schneemelcher; English translation edited by R. McL. Wilson. London: Lutterworth Press.

HERON, G. trans. (1953) *Of Learned Ignorance,* by Nicolas Cusanus. London: Routledge & Kegan Paul.

HICK, J. (1966) *Evil and the Love of God.* London: Macmillan.

HICK, J. (1985) *Death and Eternal Life.* First edition 1976. London: Macmillan

JAMES, W. (1890) *The Principles of Psychology.* 2 vols. London: Macmillan.

JAMES, W. (1902) *The Varieties of Religious Experience, a study in human nature.* London: Longmans, Green, and Co.

JAMES, W. (1909) *A Pluralistic Universe.* London: Longmans, Green, and Co.

JAMES, W. (1912) *Essays in Radical Empiricism.* London: Longmans, Green, and Co.

JAMMER, M. (1957) *Concepts of Force, a study in the foundations of dynamics.* Cambridge, Massachusetts: Harvard University Press.

JAMMER, M. (1966) *The Conceptual Development of Quantum Mechanics.* New York: McGraw-Hill.

JAMMER, M. (1969) *Concepts of Space, the history of theories of space in physics.* Second edition (first edition 1954). Cambridge, Massachusetts: Harvard University Press.

JAMMER, M. (1974) *The Philosophy of Quantum Mechanics, the interpretations of quantum mechanics in historical perspective.* New York: Wiley.

JERRAM, C. S. trans. (1910) *Thoughts of Pascal*. Second edition (first edition 1901). London: Methuen.

JONAS, H. (1992) *The Gnostic Religion: the message of the alien God and the beginnings of Christianity*. Second edition (first edition 1957). London: Routledge.

JORDAN, R. D. (1972) *The Temple of Eternity, Thomas Traherne's philosophy of time*. National University Publications. Port Washington, New York: Kennikat Press.

JUNG, C. G. *The Collected Works of C. G. Jung*. Eds. H. Read, M. Fordham, G. Adler and W. McGuire. Trans. R. F. C. Hull. London: Routledge & Kegan Paul; Princeton University Press.

JUNG, C. G. (1967) *Alchemical Studies*. Vol. 13 of *The Collected Works*.

JUNG, C. G. (1968) *Psychology and Alchemy*. Second edition. Vol. 12 of *The Collected Works*.

JUNG, C. G. (1969) *The Structure and Dynamics of the Psyche*. Second edition. Vol. 8 of *The Collected Works*.

JUNG, C. G. (1970a) *Aion, researches into the phenomenology of the self*. Second edition. Vol. 9, Part II, of *The Collected Works*.

JUNG, C. G. (1970b) *Mysterium Coniunctionis, an enquiry into the separation and synthesis of psychic opposites in alchemy*. Second edition. Vol. 14 of *The Collected Works*.

KELLIHER, H. (1984) The Rediscovery of Thomas Traherne, *Times Literary Supplement*, 14 September 1984, 1038.

KEYNES, G. ed. (1966) *The Complete Writings of William Blake*. London: Oxford University Press.

KIRK, G. S., RAVEN, J. E., AND SCHOFIELD, M. (1983) *The Presocratic Philosophers, a critical history with a selection of texts*. Second edition (first edition 1957). Cambridge: Cambridge University Press.

KLOETZLI, R. (1983) *Buddhist Cosmology, from single world system to pure land: science and theology in the images of motion and light*. Delhi: Motilal Banarsidass.

KORYÉ, A. (1957) *From the Closed World to the Infinite Universe*. Baltimore: The Johns Hopkins Press.

KRISTELLER, P. O. (1979) *Renaissance Thought and Its Sources*. Ed. Michael Mooney. New York: Columbia University Press.

LANCZOS, C. (1970) *Space through the Ages, the evolution of geometrical ideas from Pythagoras to Hilbert and Einstein*. London: Academic Press.

LASKI, M. (1961) *Ecstasy: a study of some secular and religious experiences*. London: Cresset Press.

LEE, D. trans. (1974) *The Republic*. Second edition (first edition 1955). Harmondsworth: Penguin.

LEE, D. trans. (1977) *Timaeus and Critias*. Revised edition (first edition 1965). Harmondsworth: Penguin.

LEISEGANG, H. (1937) La connaissance de Dieu au miroir de l'âme et de la nature, *Revue d'Histoire et de Philosophie religieuses*, 17, 145–71.

LOSSKY, V. (1968) *The Mystical Theology of the Eastern Church*. First published 1944, Paris. Cambridge: James Clarke.

LOVEJOY, A. O. (1936) *The Great Chain of Being, a study in the history of an idea*. Cambridge, Massachusetts: Harvard University Press.

MACKENNA, S. trans. (1969) *Plotinus: The Enneads*. Fourth edition. Revised by B. S. Page. London: Faber and Faber.

MAHNKE, D. (1937) *Unendliche Sphäre und Allmittelpunkt, Beiträge zur Genealogie der mathematischen Mystik*. Max Niemeyer.

MARGOLIOUTH, H. M. ed. (1958) *Centuries, Poems and Thanksgivings*. Vol. 1: Introduction and Centuries; Vol. 2: Poems and Thanksgivings. Oxford: Clarendon Press.

MARKOV, M. A. ed. (1987) *The Physical Effects in the Gravitational Field of Black Holes*. Trans. K. S. Hendzel. Commack, New York: Nova Science Publications.

MARKS, C. L. (1966a) Thomas Traherne and Hermes Trismegistus, *Renaissance News*, 19, 118–31.

MARKS, C. L. (1966b) Thomas Traherne and Cambridge Platonism, *Publications of the Modern Language Association of America*, 81, 521–34.

MARKS, C. L. AND GUFFEY, G. R. eds. (1968) *Christian Ethicks*, by Thomas Traherne, 1675. Ithaca, New York: Cornell University Press.

MARSHALL, I. N. (1989) Consciousness and Bose-Einstein condensates, *New Ideas in Psychology*, 7, 1, 73–83.

MARTIN, J. L. (1988) *General Relativity, a guide to its consequences for gravity and cosmology*. Chichester: Ellis Horwood.

MATER, N. I. (1985) Thomas Traherne and St Bernard of Clairvaux, *Notes and Queries*, 32, 182–4.

MAXWELL, M. AND TSCHUDIN, V. eds. (1990) *Seeing the Invisible, modern religious and other transcendent experiences.* Harmondsworth: Arkana, Penguin.

McEVOY, J. (1982) *The Philosophy of Robert Grosseteste.* Oxford: Clarendon Press.

MERCHANT, C. (1979a) The Vitalism of Anne Conway: Its Impact on Leibniz' Concept of the Monad, *Journal of the History of Philosophy*, 17, 255–69.

MERCHANT, C. (1979b) The Vitalism of Francis Mercury van Helmont: its influence on Leibniz, *Ambix*, 26, 3, 170–83.

MICHEL, P. H. (1973) *The Cosmology of Giordano Bruno.* Trans. from the French (1962) by R. E. W. Maddison. London: Methuen.

MICHELSEN, N. F. (1991) *Tables of Planetary Phenomena.* San Diego, California: ACS.

MINER, E. ed. (1971) *Seventeenth Century Imagery, essays on uses of figurative language from Donne to Farquhar.* Berkeley: University of California Press.

MINTZ, S. I. (1962) *The Hunting of Leviathan.* Cambridge: Cambridge University Press.

MISNER, C. W., THORNE, K. S. AND WHEELER, J. A. (1973) *Gravitation.* San Francisco: W. H. Freeman.

MORRISON, P. AND MORRISON, P. (1982) *Powers of Ten.* Scientific American Books: New York.

NEEDHAM, J. (1956) *Science and Civilization in China.* Vol. 2: History of Scientific Thought. Cambridge: Cambridge University Press.

NEEDHAM, J, (1962) *Science and Civilization in China.* Vol. 4: Physics and Physical Technology. Part I: Physics. Cambridge: Cambridge University Press.

NEIHARDT, J. G. (1979) *Black Elk Speaks.* First edition 1932. Lincoln and London: University of Nebraska Press.

NEWTON, I. (1931) *Opticks, or a treatise of the reflections, refractions, inflections and colours of light.* Reprinted from the fourth edition, 1730. London: G. Bell.

NICOLSON, M. H. (1930) *Conway Letters, the correspondence of Anne, Viscountess Conway, Henry More and their friends, 1642–1684.* New Haven: Yale University Press.

NICOLSON, M. H. (1956) *Science and Imagination.* Ithaca, New York: Cornell University Press.

NICOLSON, M. H. (1960) *The Breaking of the Circle, studies in the effect of the "New Science" upon seventeenth-century poetry.* Revised edition. New York and London: Columbia University Press.

NICOLSON, M. H. (1966) *Newton Demands the Muse, Newton's Opticks and the eighteenth century poets.* First published 1946. Princeton, New Jersey: Princeton University Press.

NOLAN, E. P. (1990) *Now Through A Glass Darkly, specular images of being and knowing from Virgil to Chaucer.* Ann Arbor, Michigan: University of Michigan Press.

O'DONOVAN, O. (1980) *The Problem of Self-Love in St. Augustine.* New Haven and London: Yale University Press.

ODIN, S. (1982) *Process Metaphysics and Hua-yen Buddhism, a critical study of cumulative penetration vs. interpenetration.* Albany: State University of New York Press.

ONIANS, R. B. (1951) *The Origins of European Thought, about the Body, the Mind, the Soul, the World, Time, and Fate.* Cambridge: Cambridge University Press.

OR, KANG-NAM (1979) Dharmadhatu, an introduction to Hua-yen buddhism, *The Eastern Buddhist*, New Series, 12, 2, 72–91.

OSBORN, J. M. (1964) A New Traherne Manuscript, *Times Literary Supplement*, 8 October 1964, 928.

PAGELS, H. (1985) *Perfect Symmetry, the search for the beginning of time.* London: Michael Joseph.

PARKINSON, G. H. R. ed. (1973) *Leibniz: Philosophical Writings.* Trans. M. Morris and G. H. R. Parkinson. First edition 1934. London: Dent.

PEARSON, K. (1949) *The Grammar of Science.* Everyman's Library, No. 939. First published 1892. London: Dent.

PEERS, E. A. trans. (1978) *The Complete Works of Saint John of the Cross, Doctor of the Church.* Translated and edited by E. Allison Peers from the critical edition of P. Silverio de Santa Teresa. First edition 1935. Wheathampstead, Hertfordshire: Anthony Clarke.

PÉPIN, J. (1977) *Ex Platonicorvm Persona. Études sur les lectures philosophiques de Saint Augustin.* Amsterdam: Adolf M. Hakkert.

PINTO, V. de S. (1934) *Peter Sterry, Platonist and Puritan.* Cambridge: Cambridge University Press.

POPPER, K. (1976) *Unended Quest.* London: Fontana/Collins,
PRITCHARD, A. (1983) Traherne's *Commentaries of Heaven* (With Selections from the Manuscript), *University of Toronto Quarterly,* 53, 1, 1–35.
REICHENBACH, H. (1957) *The Philosophy of Space and Time.* Translation of *Philosophie der Raum-Zeit-Lehre,* 1927, by Maria Reichenbach and John Freund. New York: Dover.
RIST, J. M. (1980) *Plotinus, The Road to Reality.* First published 1967. Cambridge: Cambridge University Press.
ROGERS, C. R. (1967) *On Becoming a Person, a therapist's view of psychotherapy.* London: Constable.
RONCHI, V. (1970) *The Nature of Light, an historical survey.* Trans. V. Barocas. First published 1939, Italy. London: Heinemann.
ROSE, E. (1982) A New Traherne Manuscript, *Times Literary Supplement,* 19 March 1982, 324.
ROSS, W. D. trans. (1925) *The Works of Aristotle.* Volume IX: *Ethica Nichomachea.* Oxford: Clarendon Press.
RUCKER, R. (1986) *The Fourth Dimension, and how to get there.* Harmondsworth: Penguin.
SCHILPP, P. A. ed. (1951a) *The Philosophy of Alfred North Whitehead.* Second edition. The Library of Living Philosophers. New York: Tudor Publishing Company.
SCHILPP, P. A. ed. (1951b) *Albert Einstein: Philosopher-Scientist.* Second Edition. The Library of Living Philosophers. New York: Tudor Publishing Company.
SCHILPP, P. A. ed. (1974) *The Philosophy of Karl Popper.* 2 vols. The Library of Living Philosophers. La Salle, Illinois: Open Court.
SCHOLEM, G. G. (1960) *Jewish Gnosticism, Merkabah Mysticism and the Talmudic Tradition.* New York: Jewish Theological Seminary of America.
SCHOLEM, G. G. (1961) *Major Trends in Jewish Mysticism.* Third revised edition (first edition 1946). New York: Schoken Books.
SCOTT, W. (1924) *Hermetica: the ancient Greek and Latin writings which contain religious or philosophic teachings attributed to Hermes Trismegistus.* 3 vols. Oxford: Clarendon Press.
SEELIG, S. C. (1979) The Origins of Ecstasy: Traherne's "Select Meditations", *English Literary Renaissance,* 9, 419–31.
SELBY-BIGGE, L. A. ed. (1960) *A Treatise of Human Nature,* by David Hume, 1739. First edition 1888. Oxford: Clarendon Press.
SKLAR, L. (1977) *Space, Time and Spacetime.* First published 1974. Berkeley: University of California Press.
SMART, J. J. C. ed. (1973) *Problems of Space and Time.* New York: Macmillan.
SNIDER, A. (1986) The Self-Mirroring Mind in Milton and Traherne. *University of Toronto Quarterly,* 55, 4, 313–27.
SORABJI, R. (1983) *Time, Creation and the Continuum.* London: Duckworth.
SORABJI, R. (1988) *Matter, Motion and Space.* London: Duckworth.
SOUTHERN, R. W. (1986) *Robert Grosseteste: the growth of an English mind in medieval Europe.* Oxford: Clarendon Press.
STACE, W. T. (1960) *Mysticism and Philosophy.* London: Macmillan.
STERRY, P. (1675) *A Discourse of the Freedom of the Will.* London. Microfilm S5477, Early English Books 1641–1700, selected from Donald Wing's *Short-Title Catalogue.* Ann Arbor, Michigan: University Microfilms.
STERRY, P. (1683) *The Rise, Race, and Royalty of the Kingdom of God in the Soul of Man.* London. Microfilm S5482, Early English Books 1641–1700, selected from Donald Wing's *Short-Title Catalogue.* Ann Arbor, Michigan: University Microfilms.
STRANG, C. (1963) The Physical Theory of Anaxagoras, *Archiv für Geschichte der Philosophie,* 45, 101–18.
SULLIVAN, J. E. (1963) *The Image of God, the doctrine of St. Augustine and its influence.* Dubuque, Iowa: The Priory Press.
SUTTIE, I. D. (1988) *The Origins of Love and Hate.* First published 1935. London: Free Association Books.
SUZUKI, D. T. (1985) *Essays in Zen Buddhism.* Third Series. First published 1953. London: Rider.
SUZUKI, D. T., FROMM, E., AND DE MARTINO, R. (1970) *Zen Buddhism and Psychoanalysis.* New York: Harper & Row.

TAYLOR, E. F., AND WHEELER, J. A. (1966) *Spacetime Physics.* First published 1963. New York: W. H. Freeman.

TRAHERNE, T. (1675) *Christian Ethicks.* London: Jonathan Edwin. Microfilm T2020, Early English Books 1641–1700, selected from Donald Wing's *Short-Title Catalogue.* Ann Arbor, Michigan: University Microfilms.

TRAHERNE, T. (1927) *Centuries of Meditations.* First published 1908. Edited by B. Dobell. London: P. J. & A.E. Dobell.

TRINKAUS, C. (1970) *In Our Image and Likeness, humanity and divinity in Italian humanist thought.* 2 vols. London: Constable.

UNDERHILL, E. (1930) *Mysticism, a study in the nature and development of man's spiritual consciousness.* Twelfth revised edition (first edition 1911). London: Methuen.

WALLIS, R. T. (1972) *Neoplatonism.* London: Duckworth.

WALSHE, M. O'C. (1987) *Meister Eckhart: Sermons and Treatises.* 3 vols. (vols. I and II first published 1979). Shaftesbury, Dorset: Element.

WARD, J. (1911) *The Realm of Ends, or Pluralism and Theism,* Gifford Lectures, 1907–11. Cambridge: Cambridge University Press.

WESTFALL, R. S. (1971) *Force in Newton's Physics, the science of dynamics in the seventeenth century.* New York: American Elsevier.

WEYL, H. (1949) *Philosophy of Mathematics and Natural Science.* Princeton, New Jersey: Princeton University Press.

WHITEHEAD, A. N. (1927) *Science and the Modern World.* New Impression (first English edition 1926). Cambridge: Cambridge University Press.

WHITEHEAD, A. N. (1964a) *Adventures of Ideas.* First published 1933. Cambridge: Cambridge University Press.

WHITEHEAD, A. N. (1964b) *The Concept of Nature.* First published 1920. Cambridge: Cambridge University Press.

WHITROW, G. J. (1980) *The Natural Philosophy of Time.* Second edition (first edition 1961). Oxford: Clarendon Press.

WHITTAKER, E. T. (1949) *From Euclid to Eddington, a study of the conceptions of the external world.* Cambridge: Cambridge University Press.

WHYTE, L. L. (1962) *The Unconscious before Freud.* Garden City, New York: Doubleday.

WILBER, K. (1980) *The Atman Project, a transpersonal view of human development.* Wheaton, Illinois: Quest.

WILBER, K. ed. (1982) *The Holographic Paradigm and other paradoxes.* Boston, Massachusetts: New Science Library.

WILLIAMS, D. C. (1951) The Myth of Passage, *Journal of Philosophy,* 48, 457–72.

WIND, E. (1980) *Pagan Mysteries of the Renaissance.* Revised edition (first edition 1958). Oxford: Oxford University Press.

WYLIE, R. C. (1979) *The Self-Concept.* Vol. 2: Theory and Research on Selected Topics. Revised edition (first edition 1961). Lincoln and London: University of Nebraska Press.

YAKER, H., OSMOND, H., AND CHEEK, F. eds. (1972) *The Future of Time, man's temporal environment.* London: Hogarth Press.

YATES, F. A. (1964) *Giordano Bruno and the Hermetic Tradition.* London: Routledge & Kegan Paul.

YU-LAN, F. (1983) *A History of Chinese Philosophy.* 2 vols. Trans. Derk Bodde (first English edition 1937). Princeton, New Jersey: Princeton University Press.

INDEX

Page numbers followed by 'g' refer to glossary entries. Numbers followed by 'n' refer to the pages on which endnotes *begin* (number after 'n' indicates the note number).